From Retorts to Lasers

From Retorts to Lasers

The Story of Chemistry
at Berkeley

William L. Jolly

Distributed by the College of Chemistry,
University of California, Berkeley, California 94720

Contents

Foreword

The College of Chemistry has been pleased to assist in the publication of this volume, which is a personal, colorful view of College history, based on archival research, interviews, reminiscences, and opinions of a distinguished and long-time member of our faculty. Professor Jolly has put much effort into this project, and we are grateful to him for it.

From the College viewpoint, the book is not intended to be either a comprehensive or an official history. The views expressed are those of the author only and do not necessarily represent those of the College or of the University of California.

We invite others to write their own recollections, thereby contributing to the store of knowledge about earlier days of the College of Chemistry. The history of this unique and distinguished College should be of interest to alumni and the scholarly community as well.

C. Judson King
Dean, College of Chemistry

Preface

This book, essentially a history of the College of Chemistry in the University of California at Berkeley, is largely made up of a series of biographical vignettes. It was conceived in the summer of 1985, researched and written in spare time during the following eighteen months, and prepared for the printer in the winter of 1986-87. The people whose biographical sketches were included are those whose careers I judged to be interesting and relevant to the development of the College. In the case of faculty members, only those appointed to the College of Chemistry before 1950 were included. The careers of more recent appointees would have been too difficult for me to assess objectively from an historical perspective. Undoubtedly I have left out important people. However, I hope that the stories that have been included provide the essence of the College.

I am much indebted to the helpful personnel of the Bancroft Library and the University Archives, particularly to William M. Roberts and Marie C. Thornton. Many other people, too numerous to mention, have provided information or help in the production of the book. However, I would like especially to thank Dorothy H. Horne, Frances B. Jolly, Jennifer F. Jolly, C. Judson King, Lawrence H. Moe, Dan W. Neumann, and Jane L. Scheiber for their help. I am also grateful to the following for granting permission to reproduce photographs of historical interest: the Bancroft Library and University of California Archives, the California Institute of Technology Archives, Michael Kasha, Ed Kirwan Graphic Arts, Robert M. Latimer, Jeanne Pimentel, and Glenn T. Seaborg. Acknowledgments for permission to reproduce copyrighted written material are given on page 220.

William L. Jolly
Berkeley, California
February, 1987

Introduction

CHAPTER
1

Thermodynamics and Kinetics in the Mountains

After graduating in 1948 from the University of Illinois at Urbana, where I had carried out senior research in synthetic inorganic chemistry with Ludwig (Lou) F. Audrieth, I stayed on for another year to get a Master's degree. At that time, Illinois was probably the best school in the country in inorganic chemistry, and, inasmuch as I had decided to specialize in that field, I felt it would be helpful to study there for another year before going elsewhere to get a Ph.D. It turned out to be a wise decision. During that year I learned a lot of chemistry by taking almost all the courses required of Illinois graduate students in inorganic chemistry, and I lived at the Alpha Chi Sigma fraternity house (a professional fraternity for chemistry students), where I made a number of friends with whom I have maintained contact over the years. I applied for admission to the graduate divisions of Harvard, Cornell, and UC Berkeley. Audrieth must have written glowing letters of recommendation for me, because in the spring of 1949 I was offered teaching assistant positions at all three schools. Audrieth suggested that I go either to Cornell, where he had done his graduate work, or to Harvard, where his friends Eugene Rochow and George Kistiakowsky taught. He did not personally know Wendell M. Latimer at Berkeley, but he did know that Latimer was famous for his thermodynamic studies of inorganic compounds. Well, people sometimes make important decisions for trivial reasons. I decided to go to Berkeley partly because I had used the *Reference Book of Inorganic Chemistry* by Latimer and Hildebrand in my advanced inorganic chemistry course at Illinois, and I figured that whoever could write such a useful book must be pretty knowledgeable in his field. I also pictured California as a romantic, exotic place, with palm trees, beaches, mountains, and so on; so my yearning for adventure settled the matter.

The adventure started when I boarded the California Zephyr in Chicago. I saw mountains and deserts for the first time in my life. On the final day of the trip, as the train entered California and crossed the Sierra Nevada mountain range, I knew I would never again be happy in a flatland like Urbana, Illinois. The train stopped on Saturday afternoon at the end of the line in Oakland. The passengers for San Francisco were then ferried across the Bay, but I didn't go with them because Berkeley is on the east side of the Bay. Unfortunately, dining on the train had been more expensive than I had anticipated, and my last five dollars went to my Pullman porter when he took my bags off the train. So there I was, penniless in Oakland on a day when the banks were all closed. Fortunately, a kind cab driver said he would take me to Berkeley if I would send him the fare later. Such charity would have been a rarity in Chicago. He took me right to the Alpha Chi Sigma house in Berkeley. One of the advantages of being an AXΣ member in those days was that you could easily find a place to sleep on any campus having an AXΣ chapter house. After introducing myself to my Berkeley fraternity brothers and putting my suitcases in my room, I strolled down to a little grocery store on Euclid Avenue about half a block from the campus and asked if they would cash a check for twenty dollars drawn on a bank in a little town in Illinois. The man in charge was at first somewhat reluctant, but when I showed him my letter from the University offering me a job as a teaching assistant with a salary of $1200 per academic year, he cashed the check immediately. That was the second time in one day that I had been trusted and treated kindly by a complete stranger. The remainder of the afternoon I spent walking around Berkeley and the campus. It was incredible. Drivers would stop their cars if you just looked as if you might want to cross the street. There were, indeed, palm trees in California. And there was even a pretty creek flowing through the campus.

In Urbana I had made arrangements with Harold Watson, a fellow AXΣ member whose home was in Sausalito (north of San Francisco, across the Golden Gate), to go on a hiking trip in Yosemite. He and his parents picked me up in their car on Sunday morning, and we drove across the hot San Joaquin Valley to Yosemite Valley. Of course, the wonders of Yosemite Valley and the Sierra high country really impressed this kid from Chicago.

However, I'll also never forget a self-inflicted lesson in physical chemistry that I had after we hiked up to Vogelsang campground, at about 10,000 feet elevation. Harold had recommended that I bring along light-weight food. So I had a package of dried beans, and I proceeded to cook them in a pot of boiling water. Firewood was not too plentiful at that elevation, and it was quite a chore keeping the pot boiling. After an hour and a half, the beans were just as hard as when I started, and I gave up. I was disgusted with myself because I had failed to heed some elementary principles of thermodynamics and kinetics that every freshman chemistry student is taught. First, the boiling point of the water in the pot was considerably less than 100° Centigrade because atmospheric pressure at the elevation of Vogelsang is much lower than it is in a place near sea level, such as Berkeley or Chicago. That's thermodynamics. Second, the rate at which beans are converted to a digestible state increases with increasing temperature, as is the case for practically all chemical reactions. Of course, the cooking temperature was simply the boiling point of water, and because that was much lower at Vogelsang than at lower elevations, the cooking time was greatly increased - perhaps to several hours instead of the usual half-hour. That's kinetics.

However, I didn't starve. There was a High Sierra Camp nearby where I was able to buy some fresh fruit that was probably better for me anyway.

CHAPTER
2

First Impressions of Latimer

When I returned to Berkeley from the mountains, it was registration week for the fall semester. I went to Latimer's office, introduced myself, and said that I would like to do research with him. His response was that, before he would take me on as a student, I must first talk with a number of other faculty members and consider working with them . However, he did indicate that he was interested in having somebody study the thermodynamics of germanium compounds, because he thought it would be nice if one could prepare germanium metal by electrodeposition. Of course I didn't fully appreciate the importance of such research. It had recently been shown that germanium could be used to make transistors, and, anticipating their technological impact, Latimer realized that it would be important to be able to grow crystals of the element. I probably appeared as a rather scatterbrained oaf to him because I paid more attention to what he was doing as he spoke than to what he was saying. You see, Latimer smoked cigarettes almost constantly, and he had the remarkable habit of continually rolling the cigarette back and forth from one side of his mouth to the other, using his tongue as a pusher. In the process, the end of the cigarette in his mouth became all wet and brown, and looked rather disgusting. But it was quite a clever trick, and he knew it.

I didn't have the nerve to say that I didn't want to work with anybody else and that I didn't want to talk to other faculty members, so I thanked him and said that I would do as he had asked. I quickly went around and talked about possible research problems with several instructors and professors, waited a few days, and then went back to Latimer and said that none of the other problems seemed as interesting as the germanium problem and that I hoped he would take me on. He did.

Latimer said that he would find a laboratory place for me in a few days. When he did, it turned out to be a corner in a large laboratory with some students of William D. Gwinn. It then became apparent to me that I was Latimer's only student! At Illinois, even in those days, it was common for a professor to have as many as ten or twenty students working with him, and I was amazed that such a prominent chemist as Latimer did not have a large group of coworkers. I soon learned that this was not unusual; few of the Berkeley faculty members had very many students at any one time.

However, Latimer was an unusual research director: during the entire two and a half years that I spent working for my Ph.D., he never once entered my laboratory. In fact, he never summoned me to his office for any purpose. We made contact only when I would occasionally (perhaps once a week) go to his office to ask for advice, to get a permit slip for alcohol, etc. This minimal research direction had the advantage of allowing me to acquaint myself with a wide variety of physical techniques. In my study of germanium chemistry I made use of electrochemistry, calorimetry, vacuum line manipulation, spectrophotometry, Raman spectrometry, induction heating of Knudsen effusion cells, and various synthetic techniques. I thereby acquired a broader technical experience than most of my peers, who generally were stuck with a particular technique throughout their Ph.D. research. Latimer's type of research direction has a disadvantage, however. A student who is allowed to jump around to whatever aspect of a problem appeals to him at a given moment is not trained to persevere and to complete a thorough study of a particular problem. However, maybe Latimer was keeping his eye on me more closely than I thought. In any event, I have always believed that I chose the best research director in the department.

The main reason Latimer had no students when I arrived in the fall of 1949 was that he had been too busy for individual research during the preceding eight years or so. He was Dean of the College of Chemistry from 1941 to 1949, Chairman of the Department of Chemistry from 1945 to 1949, Director of a Manhattan project on the chemistry of plutonium from 1943 to 1947, and, after 1947, Associate Director of the Radiation Laboratory. Just the month before, he had relinquished his positions as Dean and Chairman to Joel H. Hildebrand. How lucky I was to arrive just as he was catching his breath!

CHAPTER
3

Livermore

In September 1949, the Russians set off their first atom bomb. At that time some U.S. scientists were convinced that a much more powerful bomb, an H-bomb, could be made by either the United States or the Russians. The Russian explosion threatened our atomic deterrent power and caused numerous U.S. leaders to propose that work on an H-bomb be started immediately. David Lilienthal, then chairman of the AEC, and the powerful General Advisory Committee of Atomic Scientists, headed by Robert Oppenheimer, were against this proposal. They offered both moralistic and technological objections. However Commissioner Lewis L. Strauss, who became AEC chairman in 1953, argued that the Russians would most certainly try to make an H-bomb and that, if they succeeded, our stockpile of ordinary atom bombs would have little value. Strauss was supported by Ernest O. Lawrence, head of the UC Radiation Laboratory, and Edward Teller, a theorist who had been studying the H-bomb at Los Alamos during World War II. President Truman gave the go-ahead to the H-bomb program in 1951.

In 1952 the United States exploded its first H-bomb. According to educated guesses published by *Time* magazine, this device contained liquified deuterium and tritium and weighed, with its necessary insulation and cooling equipment, more than 65 tons.[216] Clearly this was not a droppable bomb.

In 1953 the Russians exploded their first H-bomb. According to the educated guessers, this device was much less complex than our first device, and probably involved lithium hydride (or, more precisely, lithium-6 deuteride) as an important constituent. These historical data give some idea of how close the U.S./Russian balance of power was in those days.

In the fall of 1951, about a month or two before I got my Ph.D., Latimer asked if I would like to be an instructor in the chemistry department in 1952. He might as well have asked if I wanted to continue breathing. The next semester was wonderful. I was able to work on whatever I wanted, and my only teaching duties were to hold office hours for students in Latimer's course in inorganic chemistry (Chem 104). Toward the end of that semester, he asked if I would work on a project in Livermore, California, which, he said, involved thermonuclear energy and would be very important for the security of the nation. He wanted me to start that summer. I remember he made it sound very important. Well, I agreed, but with the proviso that I start a couple of months late because I had told Audrieth that I would work with his group in Urbana that summer on an Army hydrazine project that he had organized. So I actually started on the H-bomb project in September of 1952.

There were perhaps two dozen Berkeley chemists who started laboratory work on the project at that time. Ed Orlemann, Don Hanson, Amos Newton, Ken Street, George Barton, Bill Crane, and Pete Stevenson are some of the names that come to mind. Chemists like Latimer, Glenn Seaborg, and Kenneth Pitzer were involved in the administration of the project, but they spent their time in Berkeley and Washington. The rest of us worked at Livermore, about 40 miles from Berkeley.

The commute to Livermore took about an hour and a quarter each way in those days. At first, we had a ride pool. But that was a real drag, and anyway Orlemann couldn't stand the limericks that I kept telling to fight the boredom. So most of us ended up moving out to Livermore. At first, there was no real laboratory there at all. We worked in buildings that had been part of a Navy airfield during the war. Until a new laboratory building was built, we did our work in a one-story wooden office building and an old hangar.

The work was quite exciting. We were trying to do some rather unusual things, and we eventually succeeded. I remember being told now and then, "There's going to be a seminar in such and such a room at such and such a time that you might like to go to." At these seminars I listened without much comprehension to physicists such as Herb York and John Foster talk about the hydrodynamic problems associated with setting off an H-bomb. These sessions were usually attended by an older man with a thick Hungarian accent (a Bela Lugosi with bushy eyebrows) who made wise comments every now and then. You see, I had never before seen or even heard of Edward Teller. Actually Teller wasn't terribly old in those days, but almost all the rest of us were in our twenties, and he seemed old.

Every couple of months or so, there would be a "colloquium" to which the entire scientific staff was invited. At these sessions, Ernest O. Lawrence would bring us up to date on what was happening at the Livermore laboratory and would give us a pep talk. I was reminded of these colloquia in 1983, and again in 1985, when Lawrence's widow told the Regents of the University that the Lawrence Livermore Laboratory shouldn't be named after her husband because "he would be as distressed as I am that his name is now associated, all too frequently, with these horribly destructive devices."[39] What bunk! He was gung-ho on the H-bomb, and the Livermore lab might never have been formed if it hadn't been for his efforts.

One of the most exciting intervals during my tenure at Livermore was a trip in 1954 to Eniwetok atoll in the South Pacific. This trip was in connection with Project Castle, part of the second American H-bomb test program. My job was simply to act as a courier for some air filters which had been flown through the bomb cloud and had collected some of the radioactive debris. However, while at Eniwetok, which was 180 miles from ground zero (Bikini atoll), I got to see a thermonuclear explosion. A number of us were standing around in the early morning darkness, looking in the general direction of Bikini and wondering if the weather was good enough to allow us to detect the light from the explosion. Well, when it happened, it was overwhelming. For a period of several seconds it seemed as if the entire sky became as bright as day. In awe, we went to the mess hall for breakfast. As we were finishing breakfast, two loud shock waves arrived. For the rest of the morning, we were able to watch the cloud expand and eventually even cover Eniwetok.

In 1955, I got a letter from John C. Bailar, of the University of Illinois, inviting me to be an assistant professor in their chemistry department. I called up Pitzer in Berkeley (he was dean of the College of Chemistry) and told him that, although I would like to accept the offer, I would much rather teach at Berkeley. Well, one thing led to another, and soon I was offered an assistant professorship at Berkeley, which I accepted. That one phone call to Pitzer is the only job application I ever made after getting my Ph.D. Such behavior is a far cry from the way assistant professors are hired these days, in which a promising applicant may be asked to give formal talks at half a dozen or more schools, with wining and dining at each.

Anyway, I have never regretted my work at Livermore. In view of the Russian H-bomb developments, it is clear that our work was none too soon. I also matured somewhat in my scientific abilities and became acquainted with some areas of chemistry that were new to me.

Except for the short interlude at Livermore, I have been a member of the chemistry department at Berkeley ever since receiving my Ph.D. there in 1952. I have had a few offers to move elsewhere, but I never considered these seriously because the research and teaching environments elsewhere never looked as good as those at Berkeley. Most other Berkeley faculty members would say the same thing. The reason why it is hard to move

Berkeley chemists has relatively little to do with the facts that Berkeley enjoys a pleasant climate, that Berkeley is located in an attractive area, that it is near a major cultural center, and that there are many opportunities for recreation within a few hours' drive. The reason has much more to do with the attitudes and spirit of the faculty. To some extent it's a question of tradition and a sense of belonging. Anybody with even a passing acquaintance with the Berkeley College of Chemistry realizes that it is rich with history and that many fascinating personalities have been involved in its evolution. In order to understand the traditions that influence the development of the College, it is necessary to look at the past.

The following chapters constitute a history of the College of Chemistry that includes many of my own recollections, interpretations, and opinions. This approach accounts for the presence of the introductory, autobiographical section, which was included, not because my activities have been of any importance *per se*, but rather to provide a context for understanding the following chapters. Most of the remaining story consists of biographical sketches of faculty members who have influenced the growth of the College or who have contributed to its fame. The sketches are presented in chronological order of the dates of appointment to the faculty, thus causing the overall narrative to zigzag through time.

The Pre-Lewis Era

CHAPTER
4

Genesis

In 1868, exciting things were happening in chemistry. Bunsen and Kirchhoff had recently invented spectral analysis, and this new technique was being used to discover elements left and right. Chemists were beginning to understand the meaning of atomic and equivalent weights, thanks to Cannizzaro's famous paper in which he applied Avogadro's hypothesis. Other important discoveries were soon to come. Mendeleev[142] would publish his periodic table the following year. Van't Hoff[226] and Le Bel[116] would describe the tetrahedral carbon atom in 1874. And physical chemistry would be born within a decade or two.[51]

However, almost all chemical discoveries were being made in Europe, and the few American chemists of any importance worked in the eastern states. In wild and woolly California, there was no chemical business other than that which had survived the Gold Rush. Thus there were only a few assayers and some purveyors of soda ash, bone ash, acids and other chemicals related to gold mining.[166] The first transcontinental railway connecting California to the East would not be completed until the following year. San Francisco was a city of wooden sidewalks and frequent fires.

In this frontier with few cultural advantages, the University of California was created. It was understandably difficult to attract well-qualified faculty to teach in such an environment at a university which had no reputation and essentially no facilities.

Robert A. Fisher-[54, 153, 159, 207]

The University was formed by the merger of an existing private liberal arts college, the College of California, and a state-supported Agricultural, Mining and Mechanical Arts College that had been recently created to take advantage of the Morrill Land Grant Act. The new University consisted of several colleges, but did not specifically include a college of chemistry. However, in the fall of 1868, Robert A. Fisher was appointed as the Professor of Chemistry, Mining, and Metallurgy by the Regents. Fisher came highly recommended; he had spent several years as a student and teacher at the Sheffield Scientific School at Yale, had spent two years in the laboratories of Heidelberg, Göttingen, and Paris, and had briefly been a professor of chemistry at

Vassar. His first assignment for the University was to go to Europe to order supplies for the scientific laboratories of the University. He was authorized to purchase equipment valued as follows:[222a]

Physical and mechanical apparatus:	$572
Chemical and metallurgical apparatus:	$5205
Geological, botanical, etc. apparatus:	$1100
Books of reference:	$2400

The University was first opened to students in buildings at Twelfth and Harrison streets in Oakland on September 23, 1869. Fisher gave a course of lectures on chemistry in the evenings, illustrated by experiments. They were open to the public and were well attended. Thus he was a pioneer in University Extension in California.

However, in the October, 1870, meeting of the Regents the professorship of chemistry, mining and metallurgy was discontinued and its duties "devolved upon the professor of agriculture." Fisher learned of this action by reading the daily paper, and was prompted to send a letter to the Regents on Nov. 1, 1870:

Hon. H. H. Haight
Pres't. of the Board of Regents
Dear Sir,

On the morning of the 4th inst., perusing an account, in one of the daily papers, of the Meeting of the Board of Regents of the University held on the 3rd, I noticed the paragraph stating that the Professorship of Chemistry, Mining and Metallurgy had been abolished.

Soon after the above meeting, it was announced that, although retrenchment was the "ostensible" reason, the true reason for abolishing the professorship was because of sufficient evidence that I had prostituted my official position.

. . . I hear through various channels vile slanders against my character, that are assigned as the true cause of the late extraordinary action on the part of the Board. It will be remembered that I was elected to a chair in the University upon the recommendation of ten of the most distinguished professors in the country, who vouched for my character as well as my professional ability. Under these circumstances, I feel it my duty, as well as my right, to request you to bring up the matter for a thorough investigation at the next meeting of the Board.

I hereby pronounce any charges that reflect unfavorably upon my integrity or honor as basely and maliciously false. If it should be the pleasure of the Board, I will be happy to meet them in session, to confront my accusers. I know that a thorough investigation will prove that any rumours that may have been circulated detrimental to my character are without any foundation whatever.

When elected to a chair in the University, I determined to identify myself for life with the institution - to devote my best energies to build up my department, and otherwise assist in making the University eventually an institution realizing all that has been expected of it: that it should be an honour to the state.

I trust that after the desired investigation, the Board of Regents will realize that their action in abolishing the chair over which I presided without assigning any reason therefor has resulted in doing me personally a great injury, and that I have a right to expect that they will adopt such measures as will leave me with the unspotted reputation that was mine before the Professorship was abolished.

I have the honor to remain

Yours respectfully
R. A. Fisher

At the next Board meeting, a motion to reconsider the abolition of the professorship was defeated, but they did adopt a resolution that stated that "nothing in the action of the Board in abolishing the Chair he occupied was intended to reflect upon his character."

Ezra S. Carr-[30, 56, 71, 174]

Ezra Carr was born in Rensselaer County, New York, in 1819, and obtained his B.S. degree at Rensselaer. He also earned a degree in civil engineering and, after working as a civil engineer, obtained an M.D. degree at Castleton Medical College, Vermont, in 1842. From 1842 to 1853, Carr taught chemistry at Castleton. During the next fifteen years, he held a variety of professorial posts in New York, Wisconsin, and Illinois. In 1869 he was appointed Professor of Agriculture, Chemistry, Agricultural and Applied Chemistry, and Horticulture at the University of California. He must have been an exciting teacher. One of his first students was Edmond O'Neill, who later served as Dean of the College of Chemistry from 1901 to 1912. Fifty years later, on the occasion of the dedication of Gilman Hall as a chemistry building, O'Neill recalled going as a boy to the evening lectures of Professor Carr, who presented the elementary principles of chemistry, illustrated with experiments. "Although it was fifty years ago, I remember the lectures and experiments as though they occurred yesterday. It fired my imagination and gave me my first insight into the charm and interest of science."[160]

Carr kept himself very busy giving lectures to the public at various places in the San Francisco Bay Area. Typical topics for his lectures were "Educational Needs of Woman" and "The Influences of Physical Causes on Human Development."[153a]

In 1873, allegedly at the instigation of Professor Carr and his wife, two political groups sent a memorial to the state legislature calling for an increase of "practical" instruction in the College of Agriculture and Mechanics and for the substitution of an elective board for the appointed Regents. However, the legislature refused to enact these changes, and instead adopted a report praising the Regents. The Regents then passed a resolution requesting the resignation of Professor Carr. He refused, asserting that he could not resign "without an apparent abandonment of the cause of industrial education." On August 11, 1874, the Regents voted to dispense with his services "in view of his incompetency and unfitness for the duties of the chair."

After leaving the University, Carr did quite well. With the aid of his wife, Jeannie Carr, who had considerable energy and influence, he achieved the Republican nomination for Superintendent of Public Instruction in 1875. The party planks that year stressed that public education should be kept free of sectarian influence. Former State Superintendent Oscar P. Fitzgerald was nominated by the Democrats, but Carr was elected by a plurality of almost 6000 votes. On taking office, he named his wife as his chief deputy. She took care of his office and was in demand as a lecturer at school affairs and various educational meetings.

As Superintendent of Public Instruction, Carr was an ex officio Regent of the University. However, no further interference with the development of the University has been traced to him. Indeed, he helped select a new president of the University when, in 1875, President Daniel C. Gilman resigned. John LeConte was appointed acting president and then elected president in 1876. In 1879 Carr said that he would not seek reelection to the state Superintendency. On completing his term, he moved from Berkeley to Pasadena, where he died in 1894.

Thus the first two professors of chemistry in the University were dismissed by the Regents soon after their appointments. Unfortunately, in those days there was no Academic Senate Committee on Privilege and Tenure to which professors could appeal!

Willard B. Rising-[93, 225]

In 1872, three significant events occurred. First, Daniel Gilman was inaugurated president of the University. Second, at the bidding of President Gilman, the state legislature created the College of Chemistry. And third, Willard B. Rising arrived on the campus to serve as professor of chemistry.

Rising was born in Mechlenburg, New York, on September 26, 1839. He graduated from Hamilton College in 1864, and two years later was appointed instructor in chemistry at the University of Michigan. In 1869 he was appointed Professor of Natural Sciences in the College of California. That institution soon merged into the University of California, and Rising went to Germany to study under Bunsen at Heidelberg. In 1871 he received his Ph.D. and was named Professor of Chemistry of the University of California, although he did not return to Berkeley until 1872.

Although Willard B. Rising was a diligent and effective administrator, at least some of his students felt that he was not a particularly good chemist or teacher.[101] His nickname among the students was "Bewildered Rising." Rising's principal expertise was, as for most chemists in that era, in the chemical analysis of minerals, drugs, agricultural products, and water. Indeed, in 1885 he was appointed to the post of State Analyst. No money to cover his expenses for assistants was ever provided by the Regents or by the State Board of Health, despite his pleas. Nevertheless, he greatly helped local communities improve the quality of their drinking water, in many cases free of charge. He performed analyses for industry for a fee (that did not go into his pocket) and recruited student help on the basis of "exchanging services for chemicals." In those days local newspapers frequently carried an advertisement containing a statement attesting to the purity of Royal Baking Powder over Rising's signature.[154]

Inasmuch as he was a Professor of Chemistry, the State Analyst, and the Analyst of the State Board of Health, his signature carried considerable weight.

Although Rising was in effect the head of the College of Chemistry from the time of his first arrival in Berkeley, he was not appointed to the Deanship of that College until 1896. In fact, he was not even the first Dean of the College. That office was actually first held by Irving Stringham, who, from 1886 to 1896, held the titles of Professor of Mathematics and Dean of the College of Letters and of the Colleges of Science. Rising's total tenure at Berkeley lasted thirty-six years, during which the number of baccalaureate degrees in chemistry rose from about three per year to about fifteen.

I shall now tell you what I have been able to learn about several faculty members who were appointed during the period when Rising was the effective head of the College of Chemistry. Here and elsewhere in this history, faculty members whose terms of service were shorter than five years are usually ignored.

John Maxson Stillman,[99a, 209, 246] appointed in 1876, was born in New York in 1852. His early years were spent in Sacramento, and later he moved to San Francisco. In 1874 he graduated from the University of California; after two years of study at Würzburg and Strassburg, he returned as instructor in chemistry. He left Berkeley in 1882 to take a job as Chief Chemist and Superintendent for the Boston and American Sugar Refining Company, which paid him more than the $150 per month he made as instructor. The University conferred its first Ph.D. degree on Stillman in 1885, while he was working for the sugar company. He did not write a formal dissertation; the degree was awarded for his exemplary record as a student and for his publication, while on the Berkeley faculty, of nine papers on the composition of certain resins and the ethereal oil of the California bay tree.[208a]

In 1891 Stillman resigned from his position at the sugar company to become the first executive head of the Chemistry Department at the newly founded Leland Stanford Junior University. He held that position until 1917, when he retired.

Stillman was much interested in the history of chemistry. He wrote short articles on early chemists such as Paracelsus, and finally, in 1923, finished a book, *The Story of Early Chemistry.*[208b] He died that year.

Edward Booth[155] graduated from the University in 1877 and was appointed instructor in 1878. After two years, he left to spend nineteen years as a journalist for the *San Francisco Daily*

Report. He returned as instructor in 1899, was later made assistant professor, and continued at that rank until his death in 1917. According to the *Oakland Tribune* obituary, he was financially independent of his University income. He carried out studies with radium, corresponded with Mme. Curie and Sir William Ramsay, wrote a text, *Outlines of Quantitative Analysis*, and did some government testing work during World War I.

Edmond C. O'Neill, who joined the staff in 1879, was so important to the College that I have devoted the entire next chapter to him.

John Hatfield Gray, Jr. graduated from the University in 1887, served as instructor from 1890 to 1892, and again from 1896 to 1900. One of his duties was Assistant to the State Analyst (Rising); prior to 1909, he was Chemist for the Board of Public Works.

William John Sharwood[188] was born in 1867 and attended the Normal School of Science and Royal School of Mines of London from 1884 to 1887. In his final year he obtained the Associateship in Mining and was awarded the De la Beche Medal. He then worked as an assayer at various gold mines and mills in Tuolumne County, California, until, in 1892, he was appointed Instructor in the Chemistry Department. He wrote at least two books, including one on qualitative analysis and one on methods of fire analysis. In 1898 he left Berkeley to join the Montana Mining Company in Maryville, Montana. He returned to UC Berkeley for one term in 1904 and received his Ph.D. for a thesis on "A Study of the Double Cyanides of Zinc with Potassium and with Sodium." He then became Chemist and Assistant Metallurgist at the Homestake Mining Company in Lead, South Dakota, where he remained for at least fifteen years. He has not been heard from since.

Walter Charles Blasdale[60] was born in Jericho, New York, in 1871. He matriculated at the University of California in 1888, received his B.S. in 1892, his M.S. in 1896, and his Ph.D. in 1900. He was appointed instructor in 1895 and continued on the staff until his retirement in 1941.

Blasdale was probably more interested in botany than in chemistry. His first paper, "Studies in the Life History of a Puccinia Found on the Leaves of Oenothera Ovata," was prepared while still an undergraduate. For his Ph.D., he studied the chemistry of a botanical specimen. Later, he extensively studied the primrose in his garden and greenhouse; this work culminated in a major publication, *The Cultivated Species of Primula*, UC Press, 1948.

During the year 1904-05, Blasdale studied with the famous van't Hoff in Berlin. Subsequently he published a number of papers on the phase diagrams of mixtures of salts and water. This work led to publication of "Equilibria in Saturated Salt Solutions" in the ACS Chemical Monograph Series.

Blasdale was a partner in one of the many research collaborations between the Department of Chemistry and other departments in which the analytical expertise of the Chemistry Department was exploited. In 1907, samples of a gem mineral found in San Benito County were given to George D. Louderback of the Geology Department for identification. Louderback soon determined that these were samples of a hitherto unknown gem stone, to which he gave the name benitoite. For chemical analysis, he prevailed upon Blasdale, who found that the composition corresponded closely to the formula $BaTiSi_3O_9$.[139] X-ray diffraction studies, performed later by other workers, showed that this mineral is one of very few compounds known to contain the cyclic trisilicate ion, $Si_3O_9^{6-}$.[231] Benitoite crystals are usually blue and are often as striking and flawless as the finest sapphires. In 1985 the California legislature designated benitoite as the official state gem.[44]

Blasdale died in 1960. If one counts his last years as an Emeritus Professor, he had a seventy-two-year association with the University, perhaps the longest on record.

. . . .

A few words about the physical facilities and general atmosphere during the early years of the College are appropriate.

South Hall, the first building of the Berkeley campus, was built in 1873. More than half of it consisted of chemical laboratories which served the College of Chemistry for almost two decades. This building was constructed of quality materials; it survived the earthquake of 1906 and now houses the School of Library and Information Studies. The interior furnishings were built of California laurel; the laboratory desks were of black walnut, and the hoods were of plate glass. When completed, the laboratory was physically superior to any in America and was probably unexcelled by any in the world.[160] Of course, superior facilities do not guarantee superior activities. In those days the University was not first-rate. It genuflected academically to older eastern schools as they in turn deferred to those of Europe. Some idea of the relaxed character of the campus in the nineteenth century can be gathered from remarks of O'Neill, who, when describing those days, said,[160] "With the smallness of the classes and the lack of distracting avocations and activities, now unhappily so prevalent, we could devote ourselves to study and reflection and discussion in a leisurely way which now no longer is possible. The closeness of association of professor and student, so often referred to by the old graduates, was the rule. The small college in the midst of uninhabited fields of Berkeley had a charm that can never come again."

Stillman painted a less romantic picture:[208]

"The career of the chemist in those days offered few inducements and little of promise. The Pacific Coast in particular still lingered in the epoch of exploitation of its rich natural resources in gold and silver, grain, cattle, and timber. The occupation of chemist meant to the general public little more than that of assayer of gold and silver, or pharmacist. Outside of mining, the chemical industries were few and were conducted primitively and on traditionally established lines. Indeed, the chemical industries of the whole United States were largely contented to depend upon the scientific and technical achievements of Europe.

"Those were years of sacrifice and of many trials for the little band of teachers with advanced concepts of university education and for their relatively few but very earnest supporters in California. Isolated by distance from sympathetic co-workers in the Eastern States, struggling against public apathy, and battling against attempts to obstruct their aims or to divert from the young University its needed financial support, their disappointments were frequent and their discouragements many."

The public apathy could not have been too rampant, because in 1890 a beautiful large brick building containing a lecture hall, numerous laboratories for instruction and research, and faculty offices (some furnished with fireplaces) was erected for use by the College of Chemistry. This building, later known as the "Old Chemistry Building," remained in use until 1963, when it began to be torn down in preparation for the building of Hildebrand Hall. Of all the buildings which have been built exclusively for the College of Chemistry, the Old Chemistry Building was the only one noteworthy for architectural niceties. Fortunately, its cupola was saved from destruction and now sits atop Giauque Laboratory. Hildebrand Hall has a certain flair and architectural inventiveness, but all of our other buildings have been dull or even ugly. For example, there is no angle from which Latimer Hall can be viewed to hide its factory-like appearance, the worst view being that from the west.

Fortunately the chemists who have worked in a particular building remember the pleasures of their work there more clearly than the architectural flaws of the building. Therefore I suspect that many of the chemists who worked in the wooden "Rat House," probably the least comely of the College structures, recall it with affection because of the exciting work they performed there.

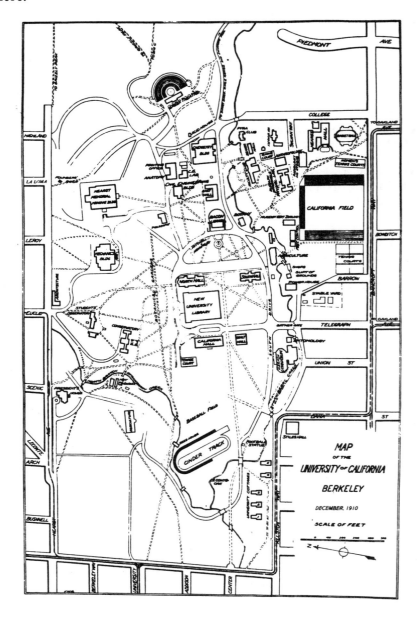

CHAPTER
5

Edmond (Eddie) O'Neill

O'Neill was born in Nashville, Tennessee, on December 13, 1858. The Irish in him was rather dilute because his paternal ancestors moved from Ireland to France in 1660. His father was a Breton, his mother a German. In 1830 they landed in New Orleans and settled in Tennessee, later moving to California.[21] After his early schooling in San Francisco, Eddie enrolled in the University of California in 1875, specializing in chemistry and agriculture. Upon graduating in 1879, he was appointed instructor in analytical chemistry. Except for the period 1884-1887, during which he was a graduate student in Strassburg, Heidelberg, Berlin, and Paris, O'Neill spent the rest of his professional life in the College of Chemistry at Berkeley. He taught practically every kind of chemistry: freshman, analytical, organic, inorganic, technological, and physiological. Physiological chemistry (biochemistry) was his favorite field of study and led him to study the fatty acids of the seeds of the California bay laurel and the terpenes of the Monterey cypress. But he had little time for research. He was frequently called upon to analyze products, both natural and manufactured, and to serve as a chemical expert in legal cases. He helped solve the water supply problems of many communities, pointed out the need for legislation restricting hydraulic mining, helped in the adjustment of damages to property owners resulting from injury by smelter fumes, and helped determine the causes of, and remedies for, explosions in mines. He gave sympathetic attention and advice to many private citizens who forwarded to his office requests for information on almost every conceivable subject.[161, 162]

During the 1880s, the water provided to Oakland by the Contra Costa Water Company was putrid and cloudy. A young doctor named George C. Pardee (son of a former mayor of Oakland) was appointed to the Oakland Board of Health in 1889 and made Chairman of the Committee on Water.[10] The following excerpts from an 1890 letter from Pardee to O'Neill give some idea of the political shenanigans associated with a relatively simple water analysis.[164]

My dear Piggy:-

Yours, with results, duly received. Thanks. I was anxious to have the figures last Thursday night because I thought I might have particular use for them at the meeting of the Board of Health - accounts of which you have seen in the papers. But, luckily, I did not have to produce them, and they are still where they can be brought into action when required.

You don't quite grasp the situation, dear boy. I don't think the Water Co. has "taken you in." But I know how desperate these fellows are, and that they will not hesitate to twist and turn any innocent thing either you or Rising may say into something very different from what you did say. You know how little the Water Co. hesitated to give Rising a dose in the Tribune, in the shape of an "interview" and followed it up with a little editorial abuse. I suppose, of course, you understand that it <u>was</u> the Water Co. who caused that "interview" to be published, and that the Tribune is ready to repeat the dose if the Co. thinks it advisable to try the thing again. I take it for granted, also, that you are aware of the fact that when you are with Pierce [Superintendent of the Water Co.] you are with a man who is very bitter, who has not hesitated to lie - through his paper - about the water and those who are engaged in this water controversy; a man who is pleasant to you, as he is even to me, because he is trying to make something out of you; a man who, as I told you in my last letter - which read again - is already lying about you, Rising and myself. Now of course I do not, for a moment, believe that either you or Rising has said or even thought that this water is good; yet this man Pierce tells people that both of you say that the water <u>is</u> good and has always been good; that you are working for the Co. and are about to give the Co. a report saying that the water is good and that the present straining apparatus is better than any filter that they can use. . . .

You must be very careful in telling these fellows even the truth about the water. It will not do for you even to say "the water is not what it was last summer." For that will be twisted into the assertion that the water is good. Nor can you allow yourself to say to them, "the present straining apparatus is better than the old one." For that will, and undoubtedly has been, twisted into the assertion that it is better than any filter they could put in. . . .

Thirteen years later, Pardee was elected governor of California, and many years later he became president of the East Bay Utility District, an organization responsible for the water supplies of Oakland, Berkeley, and other East Bay cities.

Here is a letter O'Neill received from an Oakland firm soon after the earthquake of 1906.[52]

Dear Sir:-

A short time ago we noticed an extract from an article by you in a local paper regarding the deciphering of burned manuscripts.

In consequence of the disastrous fire in San Francisco we find ourselves with several of our important records utterly illegible and we are writing to ask you whether you could suggest the name of one of your students who would be willing to assist us in rereading the presently illegible writing on them.

We could of course obtain the necessary chemicals ourselves but we assume that the successful use of them depends largely upon the solution being of a certain strength, and it would probably involve considerable experimenting before we got the proper degree of strength.

Thanking you in anticipation for your kind assistance in the matter, we remain,

Very truly yours,
FAIRBANKS, MORSE & CO.

Aside from O'Neill's teaching duties and professional consulting activities, he was closely associated with the student life of the University. He was a member of all the student honor societies, was chairman of the Faculty Committee on Athletics, and helped to organize the Alumni Association, of which he served as president. O'Neill was also one of the founders of the Faculty Club and was its president for ten years.

In 1901 O'Neill issued a call to chemists in the San Francisco Bay Area to organize themselves into a local section of the American Chemical Society. Nearly forty chemists responded to attend the first meeting of what was to become the California Section of that society. O'Neill was named first chairman of the Section.[149] The German tradition of Gemütlichkeit prevailed at the early meetings, and the charter members did not take themselves too seriously. Talks, mainly of a nontheoretical nature, were followed by informal discussions in a friendly beer session called the Nachsitzung. Beside O'Neill, the names of J. M. Stillman, Harry E. Miller, Jacques Loeb, S. W. Young, Arthur

Lachman, and E. C. Franklin repeatedly appear in the minutes of the early meetings. In April, 1906, the Section received its first national recognition when famed Ira Remsen, national ACS president, visited the Section and spoke on the difficulties confronting research scholars. Within the month San Francisco lay in ashes, but in December of that year a small group gathered at the Odeon Cafe to show that the California Section was still extant.

In 1901 O'Neill took over as dean of the College from Rising. Around 1911 he played an important role in getting G. N. Lewis to come from M.I.T. to Berkeley. He recommended Lewis to President Wheeler, and after Wheeler's official invitation, he personally encouraged Lewis to come. When Lewis made a preliminary visit to Berkeley in December of 1911, O'Neill organized an unofficial committee for his entertainment, consisting of himself, Felix Lengfeld, Ralph Gould, and Arthur Lachman - all jolly good fellows well chosen to welcome a newcomer to a frontier. The entertainment consisted of taking Lewis to San Francisco's notorious Barbary Coast. Although Lewis's New England and Nebraska upbringing clashed with this introduction to San Francisco, it is said that he soon entered into the spirit of the outing with gusto.[101]

When Lewis took over as dean in 1912, O'Neill was made Director of the Chemical Laboratories, a position he held until his retirement in 1925. During World War I, a number of the chemistry faculty, including Lewis, left to do war work in Europe or Washington, D.C., and in Lewis's absence, O'Neill was temporarily appointed Dean.

Albert G. Loomis, a graduate student from 1916 to 1919, recalled that most of the graduate students remained behind. "I would have gone if that was what they wanted. All of the teaching assistants, including Latimer and myself, registered with the draft board, but following Professor Bray's insistence, we were told to continue teaching chemistry." In spite of the war, there was a large influx of new students in beginning chemistry. O'Neill decided that the teaching assistants should help bear the load of the war effort. As Loomis told it, "He decided that we'd all have to teach eight hours a day, five days a week, at the same salary we'd been making before the war - $50 a month. We all held a meeting, the teaching assistants and assistant professor Eastman, and decided that we should make $100 a month, the same as a second lieutenant, while Eastman wanted $150, the same as a first lieutenant. I was elected to present our demands to O'Neill, and I did. Well, I could tell he was mad, but he just said, 'Mr. Loomis, I don't think we have the money to meet these demands, but I'll consider them, and speak to you again.' We told him that if he didn't raise our salaries in a week, we'd go on strike, and we knew that we could go to the Hercules powder company at $300 a month.

"Well, the first thing O'Neill did was to send a telegram to Bray in Washington. 'Send me some new assistants, so I can fire this bunch of jackasses.' But he couldn't do it. Bray wired back that there wasn't a teaching assistant to be found in the country during the war. So O'Neill was stuck. After a week was up, he called me back into his office. He smiled and said, 'Mr. Loomis, I've been thinking over your requests, and have decided that they are justified. I said that there was no money, but I have found it.' Well, he didn't have much of a choice. Then he clenched his teeth and said, 'Now get to it.'"[16]

O'Neill's last years were spent quietly at home, bulb-growing in his garden. His health failed, and in 1933 he was confined to bed. In the commencement exercises of 1933, the Regents showed their appreciation of O'Neill by conferring upon him the honorary degree of Doctor of Laws, characterizing him as "fertile in imagination, rich in human experience, full of keen wit and wisdom, kindly and tolerant toward all." For the first time in the history of the University, the degree was conferred *extra muros*; immediately after the commencement ceremony, President Robert Gordon Sproul proceeded to O'Neill's bedside and personally conferred the degree. Newspapers showed a picture of O'Neill smiling proudly, with Sproul standing beside his bed. In October of that year, O'Neill died.[21, 162]

In accord with O'Neill's will, the Regents were entrusted with his residual estate, worth $56,633, the income from which was to be paid to his wife.[180] After her death, the first $100 of monthly earnings was to be paid to his niece, Edith Armes, so long as she lived and remained unmarried, and the balance of the income was to be used:

(1) to purchase and install a pipe organ at the Berkeley campus,
(2) to maintain and repair the pipe organ,
(3) to employ an organist, either regularly or occasionally, and
(4) in due course, to purchase, acquire, construct or install another or new organ or organs to replace the first organ.

His wife died in 1941, and his niece died in 1980. However, it wasn't until 1958 that the University had a building - Hertz Hall - that could house an organ. At that time a massive organ with 3,247 pipes was built at a cost of $71,360 by Walter Holtkamp. Professor Lawrence Moe has served as University Organist since then, without extra compensation. In the meantime, the worth of O'Neill's estate has multiplied at a rate beyond the needs of the original endowment.[145] In 1966, the terms of the endowment were modified by court order[180] so that surplus income could be used for "any and all other purposes related to the Edmond O'Neill organ and the work of the University organist," including:

a) professional recordings by the University organist,
b) concerts by the University organist,
c) publication of scholarly works about the organ and of organ literature written, edited or approved by the University organist,
d) research grants and leave of absence grants to enable the University organist to study projects involving the organ and organ literature,
e) purchase of organ books for the music library at the Berkeley campus;
f) commissions for composers of organ music, and
g) the purchase and maintenance of other organs and organ equipment for the Berkeley campus.

At the end of 1985, the market value of the O'Neill fund was more than $700,000,[97] and the organ collection had grown to thirteen pipe organs. Among these musical treasures are a 1783 chamber organ built by Ibe Peters Iben of Emden, Germany, for a Netherlands castle, a circa 1750 Italian organ constructed for a church near Verona, and a lap-size reproduction of an organ popular in Europe in the twelfth, thirteenth and fourteenth centuries for minstrel and dancing music. Moe's aim has been to acquire a wide variety of styles. The collection is the only one in the world that has so many kinds of high quality pipe organs.[85]

CHAPTER 6

Frederick G. Cottrell

Frederick Cottrell was one of the most distinguished graduates of the College of Chemistry.[18, 25, 35] He was born in Oakland in 1877 and attended Oakland High School. Before graduating from high school, he entered the University in 1893 by examination and graduated from the College of Chemistry in 1896. Cottrell possessed a rare combination of traits: an analytical mind, manipulative dexterity, unbounded energy, great imagination, and a sympathetic nature. He would typically arrive at the University at seven in the morning and would work at high pressure all day. Often, after returning to his Oakland home, he would walk the four miles back to Berkeley to finish an experiment, and would either walk back or work all night until his eight o'clock lecture. At the beginning of his third and last undergraduate year, Professor Rising wrote him:[183a]

I wish to say to you that I consider your attainments in chemistry and your faithful devotion to the science worthy of some special recognition. I have accordingly, with the consent of the President of the University, designated you Assistant to the Professor of Chemistry. While this is merely a name and carries with it few duties and few privileges, nevertheless it is meant to be an honorable title and is only given after mature deliberation. I shall be able to give you certain privileges in the laboratory which otherwise would hardly be possible.

The University Register for that year lists Cottrell's name with that title.

When Cottrell graduated, he was awarded the prized Le Conte Fellowship and carried out a year of graduate work. The next year he was again awarded the Le Conte Fellowship, but he resigned to become a teacher of chemistry at Oakland High (from which he had not graduated) at $1200 per year. He chose this more lucrative position so that he could save enough money to allow him to do graduate work in Germany under one of the top chemists of the day. By 1900 he had sufficient funds, and in June of that year he set off for Europe. After touring England, Paris, and southern Germany, he went to Berlin and worked with van't Hoff. However, the research problem he was given, involving the application of the phase rule to geological phenomena, seemed pedestrian and too close to work he had done in Berkeley. So in March of 1901 he moved to Leipzig and started work with Ostwald on a theoretical study of the effect of the counterflow of an electrolyte on the migration of ions through a diaphragm in an electrolytic cell. As usual, Cottrell worked like a dog. After a few months, he had accomplished enough to present a paper at the August meeting of the British Association for the Advancement of Science in Glasgow. He made this trip during the summer recess, during which he also travelled around England. His final oral examination for the Ph.D. was held in July of 1902. His examiners, Ostwald, Boltzmann and Zirkel, passed him *summa cum laude*. Imagine completing the work for a Ph.D. in less than a year and a half at one of the top universities in the world!

O'Neill and Rising had kept in touch with Cottrell while he was in Leipzig. President Wheeler was searching the world for the best possible man to fill a newly created post in physical chemistry. He had not been highly impressed by Cottrell because he didn't seem to have "staying power." That is, he felt that Cottrell "danced around from one topic to another." However, when Wheeler learned from Rising and O'Neill that Cottrell was about to receive a German Ph.D., he was convinced that Cottrell was the man for the job. In May of 1902, Cottrell accepted Wheeler's formal offer of appointment as an instructor at a starting salary of $1000 a year.

In 1904, he installed the first liquid air plant on the Pacific Coast.[34] The apparatus consisted of a Hampson liquefier, manufactured by the Brin's Oxygen Company, London, together with low and high pressure air purifiers from the same firm, and a four-stage air compressor designed and built by the Rix Compressed Air and Drill Company of San Francisco. This rudimental plant was the start of the low temperature laboratory that later was to be developed and used by thermodynamicists such as Gibson, Latimer, and Giauque. Cottrell recognized the possibility of producing very cheap industrial oxygen by the liquefaction and distillation of air. However, he was unable to carry these studies very far because, in 1905, an even more important project - one that was to change his life and lead to one of the most unusual corporations that the world has ever seen - made heavy demands on his time.

In Pinole, about twelve miles north of Berkeley on San Pablo Bay, Du Pont had a sulfuric acid plant using the new catalytic "contact" process. The Du Pont people asked Cottrell if he could help with the problem of precipitating the acid mists which form when sulfur trioxide vapor is bubbled through water or dilute sulfuric acid. Cottrell found that an electrical method, similar to one unsuccessfully tried by Sir Oliver Lodge in 1884, could be used for precipitating the mists. The method devised by Cottrell consists of producing a corona discharge at a wire electrode in a stream of the mist or cloudy gas. The suspended particles become electrically charged and are attracted to, and deposited on, large electrode surfaces of opposite polarity.

Before the full development of this technique, it became apparent that considerable money would be needed to purchase some special equipment. Eddie O'Neill put Cottrell in contact with a consulting chemist named H. E. Miller, who provided initial funding and technical help. When more money was required, Miller interested E. S. Heller, a wealthy San Francisco attorney, in the project. (Heller's son, Edward, was a regent during the '40s and '50s.) These four men - Cottrell, O'Neill, Miller, and Heller - formed a corporation, the Western Precipitation Company. With this financial backing, Cottrell was soon able to demonstate that every bit of the sulfuric acid in a gas current representing about 3 tons per day of sulfuric acid could be collected with a power consumption of less than one-third kilowatt. But before the people at Pinole could be convinced of the effectiveness of the method, a Cottrell precipitator was actually first used in a commercial application at the Selby lead smelter in Vallejo Junction, a few miles further north. One of the Selby stacks ordinarily gave off copious white fumes from the refinery where acid was used to dissolve the silver out of the gold-silver alloy extracted from the lead. When the fumes were passed through Cottrell's device, hardly anything came out of the stack and it looked as if that part of the smelter operation had been shut down.

In 1906 Cottrell was promoted to assistant professor of physical chemistry. Some idea of his work schedule can be gained from a letter he sent to O'Neill in 1908:[33]

Dear Sir:-

In response to your request for a definite statement of the disposition of my time as regards the relations of my University duties to other matters for the present semester, would say:-

(1) My regularly scheduled hours are as follows:

Lectures in Physical Chemistry	Tu Th 8:00
Lectures in Electrochemistry	Tu Th 10; Sat. 8:00
Office hours	Tu Th 11:00

Chemistry Department meetings   Wed. 4:00
University and Faculty meetings Fri. 11:00
The laboratory work which I have this term will all be
of the nature of special problems with individuals, the times
for consultation and supervision of work being arranged
with the student as occasion demands.

(2) The only matter outside of University work proper
which I expect to make any regular demands on my time
during the present term is the supervision of the experiments
on the suppression of fumes from the Selby Smelter at
Vallejo Junction, on account of which I sought and received
a leave of absence for the whole of last semester. The men
upon the grounds now have the work so well in hand that an
occasional trip to the works on my part is sufficient, while
the train service is such that I can make a trip to the works
any day that it is necessary without interfering with the
above schedule of hours.

Very truly yours,
F. G. Cottrell

The Cottrell precipitator was found to be widely applicable,
not only for the precipitation of sulfuric acid mists and smelter
fumes, but also for the precipitation of cement dusts, the removal
of water from oil, the saving of metal in blast furnaces and
roasters, the improvement of paint manufacturing, the prevention
of explosions in flour mills, the removal of smoke from the
atmosphere, and for eliminating fumes and dusts wherever they
are a hazard to life and an economic waste. Nowadays the
precipitator is even found in many homes for the removal of
pollen and dust from the air.

When it became apparent to Cottrell that the patents on the
precipitator were likely to provide a significant income, he
convinced his associates that they should donate the patents to
existing institutions so that they could use the proceeds to support
future research. After futile attempts to find an organization
willing to undertake such a program, he resolved with the help of
the secretary of the Smithsonian Institution to form his own
institution to carry out this scientific philanthropy. Thus in 1912
the Research Corporation came into being.[181] It was a true
innovation: a non-profit corporation for utilizing the proceeds of
the Cottrell patents for the further advancement of science and
technology. It was not for a decade or so that the patents yielded
enough money to allow the award of research grants. However
the first grant to a university, $5000 for support of cryogenic
work at Harvard, was made in 1920. In 1923 a $5000 grant was

made to the Smithsonian Institution to help the early experiments of "the father of rocketry," Robert H. Goddard. In 1931, Cottrell was enthused by the work of Ernest O. Lawrence and saw to it that the Research Corporation contributed $5500 to help acquire the giant magnet that was used in the construction of the first big cyclotron. In 1965, Neil Bartlett (then at the University of British Columbia) received a grant to support his studies of the reactions of the noble gases. Over the years, the Corporation has given many millions of dollars to help young investigators in their research. Obviously, Cottrell and his fellow stockholders in the original Western Precipitation Company gave up large personal fortunes when they formed the Research Corporation.

About the same time as the formation of the Research Corporation, Joseph A. Holmes, director of the U.S. Bureau of Mines, invited Cottrell to set up a San Francisco office and laboratory of the Bureau. Cottrell accepted, and at the end of the spring semester in 1911, he resigned from the University and took up his new work as physical chemist for the Bureau of Mines. He served successively thereafter as chief chemist, chief metallurgist, assistant director, and finally as director beginning in 1920. During his years with the Bureau of Mines he developed and administered the process of separating helium from natural gas. He resigned from the Bureau on January 1, 1921, to become chairman of the division of Chemistry and Chemical Technology of the National Research Council. From 1922 to 1927 Cottrell served as director of the Fixed Nitrogen Research Laboratory of the U.S. Department of Agriculture. One of his assistants in that laboratory was young Paul H. Emmett, who eventually had an illustrious career in heterogeneous catalysis. Emmett enjoyed a happy and productive eleven years in that laboratory because of Cottrell's policy of letting his key people plan and pursue their goals with little interference.[48] After the laboratory was reorganized in 1927, Cottrell remained as a Division chief of the Bureau of Soils in the Department of Agriculture. After resigning from that post in 1930, he continued as consultant to the Bureau for another decade.

Although Cottrell's formal connection with the University was severed when he resigned in 1911, he always maintained close relations with, and was a loyal supporter of, the Chemistry Department. For several years he played an important role in the recruiting of faculty. In fact, Lewis, while he was being recruited, was so impressed by Cottrell that he suggested (and Wheeler concurred) that Cottrell remain associated with the department as a "non-resident professor."[235]

Nitrogen fixation was one of Cottrell's major interests during the Second World War. He collaborated with Farrington Daniels of the University of Wisconsin and with the Food Machinery Corporation of California on a nitric oxide process of fertilization. During the same years, he advised on projects involving the industrial use of domestic manganese resources, the production of magnesium, and the manufacture of high-temperature ceramics.

During his life many scientists looked upon Cottrell as an inventor rather than as a scientist. It was not until 1939 that he was elected to the National Academy of Sciences, and then as a member of the Engineering Division rather than the Chemistry Division to which he more properly belonged.

In November, 1948, Frederick Cottrell attended a business meeting of the National Academy on the campus of the University of California. He was seated between his friends, Joel Hildebrand and Farrington Daniels, when he suddenly died. After removal of the body, the meeting was continued.

CHAPTER 7

Illustrious Visitors

During the first few years of this century, President Benjamin Ide Wheeler and Professor Jacques Loeb of the Department of Physiology, with help from Dean Rising, spent considerable effort attracting famous European scientists to visit Berkeley and to give lectures. Loeb was German by birth, had been educated on the Continent, and had many contacts with European scientists. He was well known because of his research on the fertilization of sea-urchin eggs; he had obtained evidence that a purely chemical treatment could trigger the development of an infertile egg. Of course, the fact that honoraria of $750 to $1000 and all local expenses were paid by the University helped considerably in attracting luminaries to the Wild West.

The first celebrity to come was Wilhelm Ostwald, the German chemist who organized physical chemistry into an almost independent branch of chemistry and won the 1909 Nobel Prize for his work in catalysis, chemical equilibria and reaction rates. He was probably the last great chemist not to believe in atoms; he sought the explanation for all phenomena in terms of energy. He wrote books on the philosophy of science, and his interest in painting led him to an investigation of the theory of color. Several of the major figures in the Berkeley College of Chemistry (Cottrell, Lewis, and Bray) studied at Leipzig in Ostwald's laboratory.

In the Fall of 1903, Professor Ostwald made a rather extensive tour of America, including an approximately two-week visit to the San Francisco Bay Area. During this visit, Loeb served as his constant escort. Ostwald noted that the admiration which Loeb expressed to him appeared to be "a little pathological." Some idea of the whirlwind nature of the visit can be obtained from the following description of his stay in the Bay Area.

He arrived at noon on the train in San Francisco and was taken by Loeb to his Berkeley home, where he met Loeb's family and had lunch. The following quoted section, and later similar sections, are my translations from Ostwald's autobiography.[163]

"That evening marked the beginning of countless festivities arranged for me. The California State University at Berkeley was still rather young, and a visit by a professor from the famous old Leipzig University was considered a distinct honor. Because the visit was arranged by Loeb, it contributed to his reputation, as he constantly reminded me with thanks. Similar feelings were felt by the few members of the scientific community in San Francisco, who naturally felt closely associated with the University." That evening Ostwald and Loeb were entertained by a Dr. Herzfeld of San Francisco, who hosted a lavish dinner with all kinds of exotic sea food, including a Japanese flounder, the portions of which were wrapped in paper envelopes and cooked in hot butter.

The next day was spent touring Berkeley in a carriage, lunching with President Wheeler, touring the campus, giving a talk and listening to talks at a large formal meeting with the students of the University, and attending a festive dinner at the Loebs'. At this dinner, Ostwald was amused when, "with the American penchant for superlatives, they designated me as the 'greatest living chemist,'" and the evening's speeches continued in this flattering mood.

The next day was spent discussing and examining painting in San Francisco and having lunch at the Bohemian Club. The evening was spent at a banquet organized by the newly-formed local section of the American Chemical Society. Ostwald was impressed by the large turnout - sixty people.

The following day was much like that of a typical modern tourist in the Bay Area. He was taken to Golden Gate Park, the Cliff House, the top of Mount Tamalpais (via railroad), and a grove of giant redwoods (probably what is now Muir Woods). The next three days were spent visiting the Lick observatory, Stanford University, and the Pacific coast.

"After returning to Berkeley, I was invited to a 'smoker' at the Faculty Club of the University. This was a social gathering with beer, bread, and butter - an improvement over German drinking sessions because of the absence of ceremony and because people move around much more and are not confined to one place.

"However, this time all kinds of officials came to speak. After everyone had warmed up, I gave a talk and was made a member of the Faculty Club. I gave thanks and then assumed that we could relax. However, President Wheeler soon stood up with heavy artillery. In my honor he gave a gracious speech, rich in jests and flattery, in which the 4000 miles that I had travelled in their behalf [the round trip from Chicago] were mentioned. With earnestness and solemnity, he presented me with a parchment diploma certifying my unanimous election as an honorary member of the California State University at Berkeley. This and my thankful response were received with jubilation, and the evening passed with great merriment.

[The following day,] "the professor of chemical technology, Christy [actually Christy was a professor of mining and metallurgy at that time], who was one of the first Americans to employ the new theory of ions in his lectures and writing and with whom I had often corresponded, asked me to give his students a special short lecture. He had proposed as a theme a report on my technical studies of painting, which I had mentioned in my 'Malerbriefen' and in some papers. I gladly granted his wish." This session was followed by a University meeting and an evening at the University Club in San Francisco.

On one of his free evenings, Ostwald was taken to Chinatown, where he attended a Chinese funeral, visited an opium den, and looked in on a Chinese theater where a month-long play was in progress.

"The Berkeley days concluded with a visit to the home of Mrs. [Phoebe Apperson] Hearst, a very rich widow of about 60, the 'Alma Mater' of the University, as she was called in respectful jest, because she continually gave large sums of money for the further development of the University. The Hearst name is well known in Europe because of the political influence of her son, the press magnate.

"The invitation was to the 'Hacienda,' a summer house (or, better, palace) about three train-hours from San Francisco in a beautiful location [near Pleasanton]. That time of year was the dry season in California; there was no rain and all the grass was dried out, so that the ground had a uniformly yellow-brown color. When we were picked up in a magnificent carriage from the train station, which was not far from the Hacienda, we saw in the hills the Hacienda grounds, lying green as an emerald in the yellow-brown of the surroundings. We also saw, in the valley, the source of this beauty, namely the pump-house where water was drawn from a deep well by a steam engine. We entered through a heavenly garden with fabulously beautiful flowers under palms and were received at a magnificent mission-style house. Loeb and I, as guests of honor, were assigned to the rooms which Mrs. Hearst's son occupied when he stayed at the Hacienda. They were furnished in lavish magnificence completely with Chinese and Japanese valuables that now I would be able to appreciate much more than I could then.

"Dressed in evening jacket and white tie, we went to dinner, where I found a collection of my recently-acquired friends. Loeb had been asked whom I had especially enjoyed, and they had been invited. Mrs. Hearst proved to be a pleasant-appearing woman of somewhat more than average size, with friendly and kind facial expression. She asked about my impressions of the University and engaged me in conversation about possible improvements. The service and food surpassed in splendor everything that I had so far experienced; I even saw and ate the Japanese fish in paper again. The conversation was lively and free from stiffness. Fortunately I didn't have to hear or give any speeches. Coffee was taken in a large, richly decorated hall which contained, among other things, an organ. Mrs. Hearst persuaded me to try it, but I disappointed her and the others because they expected my musical performances to be as good as my chemical performances."

After another day visiting the vicinity of the Hacienda,* he returned to Berkeley and then took the train back to Chicago.

It is significant that, in his account of his visit to the Bay Area, Ostwald did not mention the name of any member of the College of Chemistry. One might have expected him to mention his former student Cottrell, who was then on the staff at Berkeley. But perhaps instructors were beneath Ostwald's dignity, or perhaps Cottrell did not attend any of the Ostwald functions because, at that time, he was preoccupied with his father's fatal illness.[25]

In the summer of 1904, Professor Svante Arrhenius of Stockholm, a very good friend of Ostwald, visited Berkeley and gave a series of lectures.[7, 49, 232] Just the year before, Arrhenius had won the Nobel Prize in Chemistry for his work on the electrolytic theory of dissociation. However, he was a man of wide interests, and his lectures covered a wide territory. He spoke on the fundamental theories of chemistry, including molecular structure, valency, the kinetic theory of gases, solutions, and electrolytic theory. These lectures were published in 1907 in a book, "Theories of Chemistry," in the preface to which Arrhenius wished to recall "many pleasant memories to my Californian friends and colleagues, who gave me such a cordial and unforgettable reception in their beautiful country."[8] At the time of his visit he was also interested in the chemistry of living matter, and he gave a second series of lectures which were

---

*   The Hearst "Hacienda" property was purchased in 1924 by a group of businessmen who converted it into the Castlewood Country Club. Except for the period 1940-1952, when it was operated as the Old Hearst Ranch, the property has been in operation as a private club. In 1969, the magnificent old Hacienda burned to the ground. A modern Castlewood Clubhouse now stands in its place.[28]

designed to illustrate the application of physical chemistry to explaining the reactions of toxins and antitoxins. These lectures were also published in 1907, under the title "Immunochemistry."[9]

During this same summer, the Dutch botanist and geneticist, Hugo De Vries, also visited Berkeley and lectured.[224] It had been hoped that yet another celebrity, Sir William Ramsay of London, would be present. Rising had made Ramsay's acquaintance when he visited London in 1902, and in 1903 invited him to teach a course in the 1904 summer session.[184, 224] Indeed, Ramsay accepted the invitation but then reneged on the agreement in the spring of 1904, blaming the pressure of work.[175, 176, 236, 237] In 1904, Ramsay was awarded the Nobel Prize for discovery of the inert gases. Wheeler invited him to deliver the Hitchcock Lecture (an endowed University lectureship) in 1913, but again Ramsay was unable to accept the invitation.[86]

CHAPTER
8

George A. Hulett

Immediately after Cottrell resigned from the University, President Wheeler started the machinery for finding a replacement. A recruitment committee was appointed, and the unanimous choice was Professor George A. Hulett of Princeton University. Hulett was a forty-three-year-old physical chemist whose fields of study included surface tension and solubility, the nature of precipitates, and standard cells. He had obtained his undergraduate education at Princeton, his Ph.D. at Leipzig, and, after thirteen years of teaching at the University of Michigan and six years at Princeton, had achieved a full professorship and considerable prominence.[29] The situation as it stood in the early part of August, 1911, is indicated in the following correspondence. On August 4th Wheeler sent a telegram to Hulett:[233]

To Professor G. A. Hulett
I offer you appointment as professor of physical chemistry at salary of $4000 with allowance of $300 for removal expenses and earnestly hope you may accept.
Benjamin I. Wheeler

On August 9th Hulett, who was vacationing in Ontario, replied as follows.[87]

My Dear Dr. Wheeler:
Your telegram of Aug. 4th has only just reached me as I am up here on a canoeing and fishing outing, but I am sending you a telegram at once and this letter.
Some time in April I had a note from Professor O'Neill inquiring as to whether I would consider a position there at the Univ. of California, and if so that he and Professor Cottrell would write me in detail about the position. I replied in the affirmative and Professor O'Neill wrote me that he expected to be East and would see me but later wrote me that you expected to see me yourself. I saw Professor Cottrell while he was East and got some general information about the conditions there, but the only definite communication was your telegram and I should like to have some further information from you before making a decision. I

understood from Professor Cottrell that the facilities for work there have been ample. I understood him to say that he had been having some $1500 a year for his work aside from glass and chemicals. The work in Physical Chemistry and Electrochemistry, which is coming so rapidly into prominence, would require all of this and more and need additional teaching face [force?] when established. Is the impression as to facilities I have gained Prof. Cottrell correct? How is the Department of Chemistry to be administered and what plans are there for its development? In comparing the teaching force and students it seems to me that the staff there is at a disadvantage compared to other Universities. At all events comparatively few publications have appeared from Berkeley. It is of considerable moment for me to hear that a really strong department of Chemistry is to be developed there for my experience at Michigan and Princeton has shown me very decidedly the importance of being in a progressive department for the good of my own work and has convinced me that only such a department does justice to the student body and the community. I hope that you will inform me fully about these points and any others that may occur to you for if I join your faculty I wish to feel that my ideas and interests are in accord with your policy for the development of the Chemistry Department.

                                    Very sincerely yours
                                    G. A. Hulett

    Soon thereafter Hulett received a letter sent on August 3rd by O'Neill, stating,[157] "The class of students we have are most excellent, sincere, and with the right spirit. Cottrell probably has told you of the enthusiasm he has evoked in numbers of them in problems in which he is interested. We are excellently equipped in the way of apparatus and material. We have all the money we need for new equipment, and there is no supervision as to what we want to spend our money for. We have simply to ask to get whatever we desire. Our University is a growing one, and President Wheeler stands for high ideals in men and in their privileges." This letter was followed by another telegram from Wheeler:[234]

To Professor G. A. Hulett,
    Letter of August ninth received. Professor O'Neill's letter of August third states situation correctly. I myself earnestly desire the inspiriting and upbuilding of pure

science work within department. I shall encourage research.
Professor Cottrell's statement to you correct. New laboratory
of best equipment to be built at earliest opportunity. You
will be left entire freedom in the conduct of your work,
reasonable co-operation with other branches only being
expected. Relations within department harmonious and
cordial. I am sure you would find position agreeable and
advantageous to yourself. Should hope you could come this
year. Your welcome will be most cordial.

                    Benjamin Ide Wheeler

   In further correspondence, Hulett told Wheeler that he was
somewhat concerned about his salary.[88] He had promises that his
Princeton salary would likely go to $5000 or more, and he had an
offer of a position in the Bureau of Mines at a salary of $4500,
with assurance of regular increases. He also questioned the plan
of filling the vacancy created by Cottrell's resignation without
also adding other first class men. On September 19th he declined
the invitation to join the faculty,[89] whereupon Wheeler and
O'Neill immediately began to entice Gilbert N. Lewis of MIT. In
1912, Hulett accepted an appointment as Chief Chemist in the
Bureau of Mines.

The Berkeley campus of 1874. The two prominent buildings are North Hall on the right and South Hall on the left.

Ezra S. Carr, ca 1873.

Willard B. Rising, ca 1880.

Edmond O'Neill, 1879.

Edmond O'Neill, 1910.

The Old Chemistry Building, as seen from the west, 1905.

Willard B. Rising lecturing in the Old Chemistry Building, ca 1899.

Willard B. Rising lecturing to section 2 of the general chemistry class, September 1899.

Rising's comfortable office in the Old Chemistry Building, 1894.

A group of professors in the botanical gardens of the University, 1904. The men in the foreground are, from left to right: Professor E. J. Wickson, superintendent of the university extension work in agriculture, the authority on California fruits; Dr. Jacques Loeb, of the University of California, physiologist; Professor Eugene W. Hilgard, director of the agricultural college of the university; Professor Hugo de Vries, of Amsterdam, the foremost living botanist; and the portly Professor Svante August Arrhenius, of Stockholm, the famous physicist and chemist.

Cottrell's laboratory in the Old Chemistry Building, ca 1905.

The O'Neill Memorial Organ in Hertz Hall, with Lawrence H. Moe at the keyboard, ca 1960.

Gilbert N. Lewis, 1910.

Theodore Roosevelt and Benjamin I. Wheeler on the Berkeley campus, Charter Day, Mar. 23, 1911.

College of Chemistry personnel on the south side of Chemistry Annex, May 14, 1917. Left to right, front row (seated): Axel R. Olson, Thomas B. Brighton, Orville E. Cushman, and Guy W. Clark. Back row (standing and seated): William C. Bray, William L. Argo, Gilbert N. Lewis, Constance Gray, Parry Borgstrom, George S. Parks, Merle Randall, Charles S. Bisson, Asa L. Caulkins, Svend Holmstrup (shopman), and William J. Cummings (glassblower).

A Cal Tech outing in 1917. From left to right: David A. Smith, Arthur A. Noyes, Gilbert N. Lewis (on running board), (?), Mrs. Gilbert N. Lewis, James E. Bell, (?).

G. Ernest Gibson with students in the Freshman Chemistry Laboratory, ca 1953.

Wendell M. Latimer, ca 1915.

Joel H. Hildebrand, 1946.

College of Chemistry Staff Members in Front of Newly Constructed Gilman Hall (Fall of 1917). Front row (left to right): M. J. Fisher (bookkeeper), Esther Branch, Esther Kittredge, Constance Gray, Gilbert N. Lewis, William L. Argo, Edmond O'Neill, T. Dale Stewart, C. Walter Porter, G. Ernest Gibson, Merle Randall, William C. Bray, Walter C. Blasdale, and Ermon D. Eastman. Ascending stairs (left to right): Charles S. Bisson, Wendell M. Latimer, William J. Cummings (glassblower), Carl Iddings, Reginald B. Rule, J. T. Rattray (woodworker), Charles C. Scalione, Hal D. Draper, William G. Horsch, William H. Hampton, Willard G. Babcock, John M. McGee, George S. Parks, Parry Borgstrom, Albert G. Loomis, George A. Linhart, William D. Ramage, and Harry N. Cooper. Seated (left to right): Axel R. Olson and Angier H. Foster.

Third annual banquet of the Sigma chapter of the Alpha Chi Sigma fraternity, January, 1916. Near side of table, from right: (?), Reginald B. Rule, Carl Idding, "Bob" Donaldson, P. Dieckmann, (?), Charles C. Scalione, William G. Horsch, Parry Borgstrom, (?), Worth H. Rodebush, Ewing C. Scott. Continuing to the left from Scott: William H. Hampton, Bill Foshar, "Art" McCullom. Continuing to the right from McCullom: (?), H. Slater, (?), (?), Jesse W. Barnes, T. Dale Stewart, (?), (?), Horace Skinner, (?) (?). Far side of table, from right: Ellefson, Donald Keyes, Ross McCullom, Harold Marsh, Angier H. Foster, Walter C. Blasdale, (?), Thomas B. Brighton, Joel H. Hildebrand, Merle Randall, (?), Arthur Mohr, Erle Brock. Standing behind right side of table, from left to right: Robert Dunham, Bill Nutting, (?), (?).

The Lewis Era

CHAPTER
9

Gilbert Newton Lewis

The first American Lewis of record was George Lewis, who came from East Greenwich in Kent to the Plymouth Colony in 1632.[136] He was one of the founders of the town of Barnstable, the first English settlement on Cape Cod. The census of 1790 listed no fewer than 34 Lewises as heads of households in Barnstable, probably all descendants of George, including a Jabez Lewis, for whom a direct lineage with Gilbert Newton Lewis is known.

Gilbert Lewis, the second of three children, was born in Weymouth, Massachusetts on October 23, 1875. At the age of nine his parents moved to Lincoln, Nebraska, where his father was a lawyer and broker. Up to the age of fourteen he was educated entirely by his parents. His mother taught him to read at the age of three, and soon he was reading everything that he could get his hands on. His father taught him arithmetic and mathematics, which Gilbert enjoyed very much.[62]

In 1889 Lewis was admitted to the preparatory school of the University of Nebraska. In 1893 he transferred to Harvard College, where his main field of study was chemistry. However, he had broad interests, and he was particularly impressed by a course in political economy under Professor Taussig which gave him a life-long interest in that subject.

After graduating from Harvard in 1896, he spent a year teaching at the Phillips Academy at Andover and then returned to Harvard for graduate work and received the M.A. degree in 1898 and the Ph.D. in 1899. His thesis work involved the thermodynamics of zinc and cadmium amalgams and was performed under the supervision of the famous T. W. Richards, who won the Nobel Prize in 1914 for his accurate atomic weight determinations. In this early work, Lewis showed a thorough grasp of the power of the thermodynamic method in chemistry which was to influence much of his later work.

After remaining at Harvard for one year as an instructor, he spent the first semester of a traveling fellowship in 1900 with Wilhelm Ostwald at Leipzig. It is interesting that this visit preceded a similar visit by Frederick Cottrell by only a few months. The second semester was spent with Nernst at Göttingen.

The following three years Lewis spent at Harvard as an instructor, and then he did something for which I have never heard an adequate explanation. He spent the next year as Superintendent of Weights and Measures in the Philippine Islands, and as a chemist in the Bureau of Science at Manila. I suppose he did this partly for the fun of it. He was a young man, eager to enjoy life, and the perquisites of the Manila job may have tempted him more than any position that was open to him in the States. While in Manila, he did acquire a habit for Philippine cigars that held him captive for the rest of his life. And he was able to continue his researches: at least three papers resulted from that sojourn in the Philippines.

The Manila escapade may be related to the fact that Lewis was not completely satisfied with his experiences at Harvard. Years later he described those experiences in harsh terms:[124]

"I went from the Middle-west to study at Harvard, believing that at that time it represented the highest scientific ideals. But now I very much doubt whether either the physics or the chemistry department at that time furnished real incentive to research. In 1897 I wrote a paper on the thermodynamics of the hohlraum which was read by several members of the chemistry and physics departments. They agreed unanimously that the work was not worth doing, especially as I postulated a pressure of light, of which they all denied the existence. They advised me strongly not to spend time on such fruitless investigations, all being entirely unaware of the similar and more successful work that Wien was then doing. A few years later I had very much the same ideas of atomic and molecular structure as I now hold, and I had a much greater desire to expound them, but I could not find a soul sufficiently interested to hear the theory. There was a great deal of research work being done at the university, but, as I see it now, the spirit of research was dead.

"Fortunately both departments at Harvard have improved greatly since that time, but I give these examples to illustrate how provincial science may become even in one of our largest universities. It is not the small institutions which gives me concern; it is the great number of large universities in which the scientific departments have become atrophied, and yet which show a great deal of self-complacency regarding the work which they are doing. This is largely due to inbreeding and lack of contact with the outside."

In 1905 he joined the Research Laboratory of Physical Chemistry at MIT, under the direction of Arthur Amos Noyes. The situation at MIT was nicely described by John Servos in a review article on Lewis:[200]

"When Lewis arrived at 'Boston Tech' (MIT then occupied its original site in Back Bay) he found what was lacking at Harvard - a band of talented, young physical chemists who exhibited not only the form, but also the spirit of research. Among those working with him that first year at MIT were Charles A. Kraus, later to become professor of chemistry at Brown University, Edward W. Washburn, who went on to a professorship at the University of Illinois, Richard C. Tolman, who would work with Lewis again at Berkeley and who ended his distinguished career at Caltech, and William C. Bray, whose future would be linked with Lewis' at the University of California. Kraus, who had just turned 30, was the oldest in the group; every one of these chemists was later elected to membership in the National Academy. It was a remarkable concentration of talent for any American university of that period, and it was all the more remarkable that it existed at MIT, a school that had not yet awarded its first Ph.D.

"Their presence in Back Bay was due largely to the efforts of one scientist, Arthur Amos Noyes. Noyes, then approaching the age of 40, had been among the first and most talented of Ostwald's American students. He had obtained his doctorate at Leipzig in 1890, and then had returned to his undergraduate alma mater, MIT, as an instructor. . . . He was not as skillful an experimentalist as Richards, nor did he display the creative instincts of his teachers, Ostwald and Nernst, but he had a clear head, a sound knowledge of thermodynamics, and the ability to identify important questions."

During his seven years at MIT, Lewis engaged in intense scientific activity, both experimental and theoretical. The results appeared in over thirty papers, ranging from discussions of relativity theory to precise determinations of the electrode potentials of elements. Lewis rose through the ranks to full professorship and achieved a reputation as the brightest American chemist in his age group.

CHAPTER
10

Lewis's First Years at Berkeley

In view of his reputation in 1911, it was no wonder that Lewis came to the attention of President Wheeler, who at that time was looking for someone to renovate the Chemistry Department. Wheeler invited Lewis to Berkeley to look over the situation and to make recommendations. Lewis arrived on Dec. 1, 1911, and very soon formulated a plan. He sent the following letter to Wheeler on December 9.[123]

My dear President Wheeler:

As a result of my study of the conditions in the Chemical Department I should like to make the following recommendations:

It seems desirable that work should be begun as soon as possible upon a permanent building to house all of the advanced work in Chemistry and to constitute a wing of the ultimate Chemistry Laboratory. There is a plan in the Architect's office of such a building which would, in outline, represent the demands of the Department. The details of construction must be considered with great care and it is probable that the final specifications could not be prepared before next Fall. After that time, however, the work of construction should proceed with all possible speed. [A "wing" of the Chemistry Laboratory was never built; an entirely separate building, Gilman Hall, was built in 1918.]

During the time of construction of this permanent building, the work of instruction would be seriously hampered and no quarters could be provided for the new members of the instructing staff without extension of the present laboratory facilities. I therefore recommend the erection, at once, of a cheap, temporary building of wood, with two stories, each 1500 square feet in area and a basement of 900 square feet. This would provide for the laboratory courses in Physical Chemistry, special rooms for research, private rooms for new Instructors, and a machine shop. The space now occupied by Physical Chemistry in the old building, about 1600 square feet, would thus be set free for a much needed extension of the Freshmen Laboratories. I should estimate that the total cost of this temporary structure, including the cost of Chemical tables, plumbing, concrete piers etc., would not exceed $7000 at the most. About $2000 would be needed to equip the new addition to the Freshmen Laboratory in the old building. Plans can be made for the temporary building immediately, and the structure could be finished in ample time for the beginning of the next academic year.

The new temporary structure should be built near the old laboratory, preferably in the small plot of land between the old laboratory and the road. [This "temporary" structure was built; it was first called the Chemistry Annex and eventually became known as the "Rat House."]

In the reorganization of the Department, I recommend that the new Professor of Chemistry [Lewis] be made Chairman of the Department of Chemistry, and that a Secretary of the Department be chosen from among the instructing staff to attend to the routine and detailed work of the departmental committee. I should further recommend that the present Professor of Inorganic Chemistry [O'Neill] be made Director of the Chemical Laboratories with a salary of $4000. The duties of the Director would be to order supplies and to attend in general to the business administration of the laboratory, pursuant to such policies as might be determined in the Department Committee.

The Salary budget of the Chemical Department for the present year is, I believe $28,735, which includes a provision of $4000 for a Professor of Chemistry, $2000 for an Assistant Professor, both unfilled during the present year. It also includes $1035, paid from the Carnegie Foundation to Mrs. Sarah F. L. Rising, and a provision of $1000 for Laboratory Assistance. I suggest the following additions to this budget for the coming year:

Additional to Chairman of Department	$1000
Additional to Director of Laboratories	400
Additional to Asst. Prof. of Physical Chemistry	200
Assistant Professor of Inorganic Chemistry	2200
Instructor	1200
Instructor	1200
Instructor	1200
Assistant	900
Assistant	600
Bookkeeper	1000
Assistant to Chairman of Department	900
Teaching Fellowship	600

Teaching Fellowship	600
Mechanic	1300
Glass Blower	1200

	$14500

I believe that the two new Assistant Professors should receive at the out-set $2200 and that this should be raised by $100 annually until the salary is $2500. The bookkeeper, or clerk, should be a man who is able to serve also as Stenographer. The Teaching Fellowships would provide for men studying for a higher degree and the amount of laboratory instruction demanded of them should be strictly limited. Moreover, the University should provide at least one unrestricted Fellowship of not less than $500 each year in the Chemical Department. The Glass Blower would be in demand by other Departments of the University and his whole salary would not necessarily come from the Chemical budget.

This large increase in the salary budget should suffice to put the work of instruction and the organization of research on a satisfactory foundation, but when the new building is constructed and it becomes possible to increase the number of laboratory courses and especially to develop the work in Technical Chemistry, considerable further increase will be required.

The annual appropriation for apparatus and supplies must likewise be increased. In particular, I estimate that an additional sum of about $7000 should be spent during the next two years for permanent apparatus to be used in research and in the equipment of a Machine Shop.

I believe that such a reorganization of the Department of Chemistry, as I have here suggested, would make this Department strong and efficient in instruction and research and that with the right men, whom I feel sure could be secured, this laboratory would assume high rank and reputation among the best Chemical Laboratories of the world. If the program which I have outlined is acceptable to the President and the Regents of the University, I, for my part, will take great pleasure in associating myself with this University, for which I see so large a future; and I shall do all that is possible to make this Department of Chemistry a great asset to the University of California.

Yours very respectfully,
Gilbert N. Lewis

No one knows whether Lewis actually expected Wheeler and the Regents to accept his rather drastic recommendations. Perhaps Wheeler had already told him that drastic measures were needed and expected. Perhaps Lewis was taking advantage of the fact that the job he was being offered had recently been turned down by Hulett. In any case, Lewis's demands were met almost to the letter, and he spent the next eight months at MIT contracting for new faculty and staff members and making sure that the Chemistry Annex was built on time so that it would be ready for the new faculty when they arrived.

When Lewis arrived in the fall of 1912, the faculty on hand were Edmond O'Neill, Edward Booth, Walter Blasdale, William Morgan, and Henry Biddle.

O'Neill was, as always, an affable gentleman who had no reason to resist any of the changes proposed by Lewis. In fact, he was very cooperative and helped Lewis in the routine running of the department.

Edward Booth was a quiet, gentle, old man who caused no trouble. He was able to help out in the freshman laboratories.

Walter Blasdale was a fairly good chemist who served faithfully, as we have already pointed out, for many years.

William C. Morgan, on the other hand, was a problem. Since 1903 he had been in charge of the freshman chemistry course at Berkeley. He tried to get Lewis to agree that he would not be interfered with in organizing and teaching the freshman course. Lewis, of course, would not agree to that, because the changes that he wanted to bring about had to start right in the first year of the curriculum.[40, 150] Morgan was not research-oriented and would not have enjoyed the scientifically competitive atmosphere that was to begin when Lewis arrived. Hence he started to look for a job elsewhere. Wheeler put him on sabbatical leave in 1912.[235] Because Lewis wanted the freshman chemistry lectures to start out on a first class basis, he convinced Wheeler to hire Professor Harry W. Morse, of Harvard, as a temporary lecturer for freshman chemistry in the 1912-13 term.[122] As it turned out, Morgan went to Reed College in Portland, Oregon, as chairman of the Chemistry Department, and, in 1913, the position of freshman lecturer at Berkeley was permanently filled by the appointment of Joel Hildebrand of the University of Pennsylvania.

Morgan stayed at Reed for seven years and was then appointed head of the Chemistry Department at the newly formed southern campus of the University of California (UCLA). Glenn Seaborg, who did his undergraduate work at UCLA, took freshman chemistry from Morgan.[151] He remembered him as a formidable man, about six feet four inches tall. On the first day of class, Morgan strode into the lecture room with a glower and said dramatically, "Look at the person on your right," then, "Look at the person on your left," and then he waited. Finally he announced, "One of you three will not be here at Thanksgiving time." An impressive, if uncomfortable, introduction to chemistry.

Henry C. Biddle also was a source of trouble to Lewis. Biddle had received his Ph.D. in organic chemistry at Chicago and had joined the Berkeley department in 1901. In 1914 he began a great deal of consulting work, with the aid of graduate students, for the California Ink Company. Biddle received a very substantial remuneration for this work.[101] Lewis was strongly opposed to private consulting within the department, so, in 1917, he convinced Biddle to resign.[150] Biddle then continued private consulting independently until 1926, when he was appointed to the UC College of Pharmacy, where he remained until 1932.[13]

Lewis brought with him from MIT the following colleagues: William Bray (as an assistant professor), Merle Randall (as his personal research assistant), and Richard Tolman (as an assistant professor). The next year saw the arrival of Hildebrand as an assistant professor and Gibson as an instructor. Lewis then proceeded to inbreed the department. For the next thirty years or so, practically all the tenure staff appointees were men with Berkeley Ph.D.'s.

Lewis and Langmuir

Soon after Lewis's arrival at Berkeley, he began to discuss his ideas about the nature of chemical bonds with his colleagues in research conferences. His development of the concept of the electron-pair bond was undoubtedly influenced by earlier proposals of electron sharing in chemical bonds, both in the literature and from his associates in the chemistry department. This study led to the publication in 1916 of his classic paper entitled "The Atom and the Molecule," in which he described the electron-pair bond and "the rule of eight." A few years later, Lewis was irritated when Irving Langmuir, of the General Electric Research Laboratory, elaborated on the ideas expressed in this article in a series of articles and talks. Whereas Lewis had been content to prepare a single brief and polished statement of his ideas with a few key illustrations, Langmuir covered every detail and preached from every pulpit.[91, 100] Lewis was not at ease when speaking in public and rarely accepted invitations to give popular scientific talks. On the other hand, Langmuir was an enthusiastic and dramatic lecturer.

Lewis's book, *Valence and the Structure of Atoms and Molecules*, was published in 1923.[128] The dedication reads, "To my colleagues and students of the University of California, without whose help this book would not have been written. In our many years of discussion of the problems of atomic and molecular structure, some of the ideas here presented have sprung from the group rather than from an individual; so that in a sense I am acting only as editor for this group." In spite of this generous testimony, it is clear that Lewis recognized and cherished his place in history. In Chapter 2 he wrote, "In the year 1902 (while I was attempting to explain to an elementary class in chemistry some of the ideas involved in the periodic law) becoming interested in the new theory of the electron, and combining this idea with those which are implied in the periodic classification, I formed an idea of the inner structure of the atom which, although it contained certain crudities, I have ever since regarded as representing essentially the arrangement of electrons in the atom." He illustrated these remarks with a copy of his 1902 memorandum, reproduced on the next page. After Edwin B. Wilson of Harvard had read Lewis's book, he sent him a letter,[242] saying,

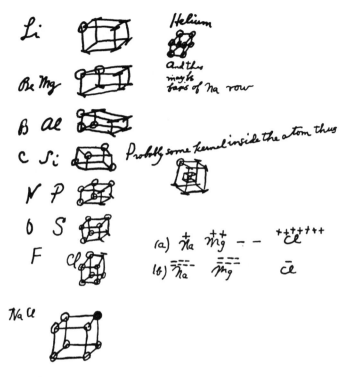

Lewis's 1902 memorandum, reproduced in his Valence
and the Structure of Atoms and Molecules.

You are getting old and beginning to talk about what you did in 1902, and show your baby photographs and other reproductions facsimile of immature days. That is a sign that you are getting old but apart from the years I can't see that your mind is getting any less able to work although I presume that you may feel that it is.

Undoubtedly Lewis's main reason for writing the book was to establish clear priority over Langmuir.[210] In Chapter 6 he wrote, "In my original paper I contented myself with a brief description of the main results of the theory, intending at a later time to present in a more detailed manner the various facts of chemistry which made necessary these radical departures from the older valence theory. This plan, however, was interrupted by the exigencies of war, and in the meantime the task was performed, with far greater success than I could have achieved, by Dr. Irving Langmuir in a brilliant series of some twelve articles, and in a large number of lectures given in this country and abroad. It is largely through these papers and addresses that the theory has received the wide attention of scientists.

"It has been a cause of much satisfaction to me to find that in the course of this series of applications of the new theory, conducted with the greatest acumen, Dr. Langmuir has not been obliged to change the theory which I advanced. Here and there he has been tempted to regard certain rules or tendencies as more universal in their scope than I considered them in my paper, or than I now consider them, but these questions we shall have a later opportunity to discuss. The theory has been designated in some quarters as the Lewis-Langmuir theory, which would imply some sort of collaboration. As a matter of fact Dr. Langmuir's work has been entirely independent, and such additions as he has made to what was stated or implied in my paper should be credited to him alone."

This latter paragraph is a masterpiece of understated vitriol. He was not always so tactful. In a 1926 letter to W. A. Noyes, he objected to Noyes' reference to a structural formula of $HClO_4$ as the "Lewis-Langmuir" formula:[127]

This formula . . . should be called the formula of Lewis, Langmuir and W. A. Noyes, and so on, adding the name of every author who quotes it hereafter. Or perhaps it would be simpler to call it the formula of Lewis, and not mention the names of all the others who have quoted it.

Perhaps I am inclined to be too caustic in this matter, but I really do feel that while people were justified in being carried away a bit by Langmuir's personal charm and enthusiasm some years ago, to persist, especially as they do in England, in speaking of the Langmuir theory of valence is inexcusable. If anyone feels the contrary I would like to ask him to mention any one original principle of Langmuir's regarding valence which has proved tenable.

CHAPTER
12
A Way with Words

Lewis did not enjoy speaking in public; he avoided lecturing except when he could read from notes. However, he was very effective with the written word. By the use of metaphor, he brought vigorous life to subjects that ordinarily are discussed in a dull, lifeless fashion. Probably the most often quoted of his writings is the following passage from the preface to *Thermodynamics and the Free Energy of Chemical Substances*, written with Merle Randall:[129]

"There are ancient cathedrals which, apart from their consecrated purpose, inspire solemnity and awe. Even the curious visitor speaks of serious things, with hushed voice, and as each whisper reverberates through the vaulted nave, the returning echo seems to bear a message of mystery. The labor of generations of architects and artisans has been forgotten, the scaffolding erected for their toil has long since been removed, their mistakes have been erased, or have become hidden by the dust of centuries. Seeing only the perfection of the completed whole, we are impressed as by some superhuman agency. But sometimes we enter such an edifice that is still partly under construction; then the sound of hammers, the reek of tobacco, the trivial jests bandied from workman to workman, enable us to realize that these great structures are but the result of giving to ordinary human effort a direction and purpose.

"Science has its cathedrals, built by the efforts of a few architects and of many workers."

At the end of his 1923 book *Valence*, Lewis wrote a short section on The Future of Quantum Theory that began thus:[128]

"In that old American institution, the circus, the end of the performance finds the majority of spectators satiated with thrills and ready to return to more quiet pursuits. But there are always some who not only remain in their seats but make further payment to witness the even more blood-curdling feats of the supplementary performance.

"Our own show is now over, and I trust that the majority of readers who have had the patience to reach this point will now leave the tent; for what I am about to say is no longer chemistry, nor is it physics, nor perhaps is it sense. But since we have been obliged here and there to take cognizance of the entering wedge of scientific bolshevism, which we call quantum theory, or the theory of discontinuity in nature, I cannot refrain from attempting to forecast some of the logical consequences which must follow from the new facts that have been discovered and the interpretation which they have been given."

He concluded this section with "Some of these abstractions may have to be abandoned as the conventional ether was abandoned after the acceptance of relativity. Others may have to be modified, and my chief purpose in writing the present section is not so much to predict just how the modifications are to occur as it is to emphasize the necessity of maintaining an openness of mind; so that, when the solution of these problems, which now seem so baffling, is ultimately offered, its acceptance will not be retarded by the conventions and the inadequate mental abstractions of the past."

From 1925 to 1930, Lewis was preoccupied with a concept he referred to as "the symmetry of time." He, of course, was familiar with Einstein's theory of relativity and, like Einstein, was adept at illustrating difficult concepts with language that could be grasped by laymen. A letter of 1930, written to a Mr. Fischer, illustrates this ability:[120]

My dear Mr. Fischer:

A clock is not a measure of time alone, but of time and space. If a man fastens one end of a tape measure to a fixed object, and then wanders off, on reading the tape he can measure the distance that he has gone. Somebody else starting at the same point and going over a different path will find a different reading on his tape when he joins the first. A clock is a good deal like such a tape measure.

Yours very sincerely,

G. N. Lewis

At this point I cannot resist quoting Woody Allen. "Time," he said, "is nature's way of making sure everything doesn't happen all at once."[199]

Lewis's Modus Operandi

Lewis's head was in the clouds most of the time. He refused to be burdened by the administrative duties of the Dean of the College of Chemistry. Glenn Seaborg wrote, "To a large extent he ran the College from his laboratory. I recall that his efficient secretary, Mabel Kittredge, would come into our laboratory, stand poised with her notebook until she commanded his attention, describe clearly and briefly the matter that required his attention or decision. Lewis would either give his answer immediately or ask her to come back in a little while, after he had given the matter some more thought. This system worked very well in those days but might not be adequate today and certainly could only function then with a man of Lewis' ability."[194]

Lewis's relaxed approach to administration occasionally caused mistakes to be made. For example, in 1922, Linus Pauling applied to Berkeley for his graduate work. Lewis was slow about giving him an offer, and so Pauling went to Cal Tech. When Lewis realized he had missed a prize, he delegated the selection of graduate students to Latimer, who was much more interested in personnel and organizational matters.[198]

Berkeley also just missed getting Pauling as a faculty member. This loss was not due to any negligence on the part of Lewis, but rather to machinations on the part of Arthur A. Noyes, the head of Chemistry at Cal Tech and Lewis's former associate at MIT. Pauling himself told the story:[165] "When I was approaching the completion of my work for the Ph.D. degree there were many National Research Council Fellows in Pasadena, and I applied for a National Research Council Fellowship, saying in my application that I would go to Berkeley and work with Gilbert Newton Lewis. There was a rule that a National Research Council Fellow had to leave the institution from which he had received his doctorate. Noyes had in fact been largely responsible for setting up these research fellowships of the National Research Council, and he, of course, had determined what the rules would be. When I prepared to go to Berkeley, after having received the NRC fellowship, Noyes said 'You have done a large amount of x-ray work that you haven't yet written up for publication. That work could most conveniently be done here in Pasadena, so why don't you just stay here and complete writing the papers?' I had not been thinking much about the future, about where I would get a job after the completion of my fellowship. After I had held the fellowship for about four months, Noyes said to me 'There are some new fellowships, the first of which were given this year. They are called the John Simon Guggenheim Memorial Fellowships. You ought to go to Europe, which is the center of scientific work now, so why don't you apply for a Guggenheim Fellowship for the coming year?' I applied for the fellowship, and again my wife and I packed up to go to Berkeley. Noyes then told me that the Guggenheim fellowships are not decided on until the end of April, but he said 'You are sure to get a Guggenheim Fellowship, so I'll give you enough money to pay the fare to Europe and to support you from the end of March until the beginning of the Guggenheim Fellowship. It really isn't worth while for you to move to Berkeley and then make another move to Europe.' I agreed, and resigned from my National Research Council Fellowship; the Secretary of the Fellowship Board sent me a very disapproving letter. My wife and I went to Munich. After a couple of months, when our funds were getting low, Noyes wrote that I had received a Guggenheim Fellowship, and after a year I received word that I had been appointed as Assistant Professor of Theoretical Chemistry in Pasadena. It wasn't until about twenty years later that I realized that Noyes was afraid that I would become a member of the staff at Berkeley if I took up my fellowship in Berkeley, and that he had made his arrangements to keep me from having the experience of being in that interesting Department of Chemistry. In fact, Gilbert Newton Lewis had made a visit to Pasadena a few months earlier, about the time that I got my doctorate. Many years later I learned that he had come to offer me an appointment, but that Noyes had talked him out of it."

Lewis was an unusual professor. He never taught any undergraduate courses and did relatively little laboratory work himself. But he had a succession of top-notch assistants (we would now call them post-docs) who helped him carry out the experimental work that he dreamt up. These assistants included Randall, Ronald T. Macdonald, Philip Schutz, Seaborg, and David Lipkin. He also frequently assigned junior faculty members (and who were they to argue?), such as Samuel Ruben and Melvin Calvin, to help him with his experimentation.

Lewis had lots of ideas, but he had trouble distinguishing those that were difficult to implement from those that were relatively easy. Examples of unsuccessful projects were an attempt to diffract neutrons with paraffin lenses (with Schutz), an attempt to separate praseodymium from neodymium in a long column by exchange between the aqueous ions and their hydroxide precipitates (with Seaborg), and an attempt to show that there was a neutron component in cosmic rays (with Ruben). However, many of his research projects were very successful and important; in later chapters, we'll refer to some of them.

Lewis's teaching was limited to presiding over the weekly research conferences of the entire department. These conferences consisted of two talks. The first was a review by a graduate student of a published paper. The second talk was given either by a faculty member, a postdoctoral student, or an advanced graduate student discussing his research when it was almost ready for publication.

Lewis's influence at these conferences was impressive, and all who attended found them to be memorable experiences. The rather small seminar room in which they were held had a blackboard on the front wall. In front of this blackboard was a large table around which the faculty sat. Lewis always sat in the first chair on the left-hand side of the speaker. The graduate students sat in chairs arranged on three sides of the table, on raised tiers, forming a kind of amphitheater. Lewis's upper left-hand pocket started out full of cigars, and he lit one after the other until the end of the seminar. After lighting the first cigar, he waited until the room was more or less full, and then invariably said, "Shall we begin?" That meant that the graduate student should get up and give his talk.[151]

It was a rare seminar that did not elicit some stimulating question or comment from Lewis's far-ranging knowledge and interest. Lewis had the ability to find the salient points in almost any area related to chemistry and picked out the areas that needed further exploration in the discussion period. Anyone was free to ask questions or to speak his piece. However, the comment had better not be foolish. Lewis did not suffer fools gladly.

Hildebrand liked to tell the story of one of the first research conferences he attended, in which Lewis, who took a boyish delight in shocking conservative prejudice, made a deliberately challenging statement.[79] A graduate student interrupted him with, "No, that isn't so!" Hildebrand was aghast at his temerity - such a remark at the University of Pennnsylvania (from which Hildebrand hailed) would have landed the upstart out on his ear; but Lewis turned to him with interest, saying, "No? Why not?" A lively, logical discussion followed. On another occasion, when a student made a similar remark during a research conference, Lewis said, "That was an impertinent remark, but it was also pertinent."[82]

Seaborg remembers that when he gave his first talk as a graduate student he studied it until he was absolutely sure there was no aspect of it that he did not understand. He gave what he thought was a good talk and then turned to Lewis, as was the custom, for the inevitable question. Despite all of Seaborg's preparation, Lewis asked a penetrating question for which Seaborg couldn't think of an answer.[151]

Lewis kept the faculty on their toes, too. He questioned them just as he did the students and wasn't very patient with them if they couldn't answer the questions. However, Gerald Branch was able to hold his own with Lewis, and therefore Lewis held him in the greatest respect. In fact, Branch and Lewis occasionally had friendly arguments about molecular structure that the students greatly enjoyed.

After Lewis died in 1946, there was no longer one person in charge of the research conferences. Because of the influx of returning GIs to the campus, the College underwent an enormous expansion and the research conference had to be held in a much larger hall, less cozy than the old room. However, the new conference retained some of the flavor of the old. Students would talk about articles from the literature or about their own work, and the discussion would include both faculty and students in the audience.

Even into the early 1950s, Latimer regularly attended the research conferences. He usually dozed off about half-way through each talk. But then during the discussion period he would surprise everyone by making a very cogent remark or asking a penetrating question. In those days, however, Pitzer was the best performer during the discussion periods. It appeared that there was never a topic on which he was unable to make a helpful comment. I think Charles Tobias tried to copy him, and he did rather well. Students would often ask one another, "Who is this fellow Tobias who asks so many questions?"

In those days, most people were not afraid to enter into the research conference discussions. Graduate students sometimes made some very useful comments. Once, when Andrew Streitwieser was an assistant professor, he gave a lecture in which he made the statement that such and such a structure was not likely because it involved an oxygen atom with four bonds, and, he said, there is no known compound in which oxygen is quadrivalent. At that point Ronald Henry, a first-year graduate student of Richard Powell, said: "Oh yes there is: beryllium basic acetate!" And he was right; in fact, there are now other examples he could cite.

After about 1962, the College became so big that it was impossible to schedule all the graduate students to talk at the weekly College research conferences. Eventually all sorts of separate, regularly scheduled seminars were organized on topics as specialized as Theoretical Chemistry and Surface Chemistry. Since then there has never been one regularly scheduled seminar which all College or Department members were expected to attend.

Lewis the Man

When Lewis took over in 1912, he was quite considerate of the older men on the staff, such as O'Neill and Blasdale. O'Neill, who had been dean, was made the Director of the Chemical Laboratories. Blasdale was allowed to continue with his research in botany. When Blasdale eventually lost interest in chemical research, he offered to resign. However, Lewis had no intention of letting him resign; he recognized that Blasdale was a good teacher, that he was faithful, and that he had served the University for many years. If he preferred botanical investigations to chemistry, that was his own private business. All Lewis expected of him was that he do *something*.[101]

In 1920, Arthur Lachman, an earlier graduate of the University, was out of work and asked Lewis for a job. Lachman said that Lewis "was kind enough to say that he would like to have me in the Department, but he simply could not afford to do so. His budget was already strained. He had prior commitments to a large number of young men whom he had placed on his staff, and his first obligation was toward them. . . . Lewis then made me an extraordinary offer. He said that he would give me a laboratory, that I could have free access to all of the supplies in the Department, and that he would have me appointed as 'Research Associate,' an honorific title carrying no salary."[101] Lachman accepted and, a few years later, developed a gasoline refining process that made him fairly wealthy.[244] Remembering Lewis's kindness, he contributed a sizable amount of money to a trust fund which eventually became known as the Gilman Hall Fund. In 1937 this fund was established on a legal basis. The Declaration of Trust reads, in part, as follows.[65]

The undersigned, Gilbert Newton Lewis, Joel Henry Hildebrand and William Crowell Bray, members of the faculty of the Department of Chemistry of the University of California at Berkeley, California, hereby declare that they presently hold in trust upon the terms and conditions, and for the uses and purposes hereinafter set forth, the sum of $3332.71. The trust hereby declared is, and shall be, known as [the] Gilman Hall Fund. . . . The Fund has been created through the kindness of friends of said Department of

Chemistry and consists of money contributed by them. . . .
The object of the Fund is, and shall be, to provide money
for whatever use or uses shall . . . be for the best interests of
said Department of Chemistry or any work conducted
therein or for whatever use or uses shall be deemed to be for
the advancement of the science of chemistry . . .

For many years the Gilman Hall Fund provided loans to
students or even to new faculty members who were in financial
straits. In recent years the balance of the Fund has been around
$6000, and the interest is used to pay for awards at commence-
ment time.

Biographical memoirs usually omit reference to the lesser
qualities of an individual. Although I never met Lewis and have
obtained most of my information about him from such sources
and from his own writings, I am convinced that he was no saint.
Although he could show sympathy and concern for others, he also
could occasionally show characteristics of arrogance, pomposity,
and pique. Surely his refusal to teach courses was a kind of
arrogance that might have been acceptable in the nineteenth
century, especially in Europe, but which must have caused some
ill will in a society that prided itself on its democracy. It is true
that he presided over the research conference, but even there he
was rather pompous - he was always in full control, always in the
same seat, and derisive of stupid remarks. Once, in the research
conference, he made a very disparaging remark to Bray, to the
effect of "Why are you wasting your time on that?" However, to
his credit, he later went to Bray's office and apologized.[138]

At academic senate meetings he was a fearsome opponent of
anybody who disagreed with him. Soon after the resignation of
President Wheeler in 1919, faculty discussions in the senate were
marked by frayed tempers.[55] Prominent in these discussions were
a quartet of faculty members whose names began with L: A. C.
Lawson, A. O. Leuschner, G. N. Lewis, and G. D. Louderback.
The contemporary quip was that the University was going to L.

At the Faculty Club, Lewis's associates were aware of his thin
skin. Arthur Lachman told this story: "One day at the bridge
table, an opponent was severely critical of some of Lewis's
remarks. Finally, Gilbert quietly laid down his cards and said:
'Mac, you are a fine fellow, and I like you very much. But I
shall never play cards with you again.' And he did not."[101]

I believe that the bitter grudge he held against Langmuir for
many years is an example of Pride overcoming Reason. Langmuir
surely cannot be faulted. In all his writings on chemical bonding,

he acknowledged his indebtedness to Lewis's seminal paper of 1916. In a long letter of 1920, Langmuir wrote to Lewis,[103]

In all of my publications on this subject I have endeavored in every reasonable way to be what I have considered scrupulously fair. In every paper I have placed in as conspicuous a place as possible a statement to the effect that my work has consisted in a development and an extension of your theory. In many cases I have repeatedly referred to your paper in the course of one of mine. In all the personal letters I have written in connection with this work I have gone out of my way to be fair in giving you credit. As one illustration I enclose that first page of a letter which I wrote recently to Sommerfeld, and I assure you that this is typical of all of my letters of this kind. I am really at a loss to know what more I can do. For the reasons I have already give [sic] and will give, I cannot honestly say that the theory that I am using is Lewis' theory of valence. In order to explain without needless repetition I must refer frequently to my own papers rather than to yours, but in doing so I do not mean to claim priority. . . .

Consider the letter sent by Lewis in a fit of pique to Dean W. M. Hart in the spring of 1924:[119]

My dear Dean Hart:

I enclose herewith a letter which I have just sent to Campbell resigning my position as Dean of the College of Chemistry, and recommending the appointment of Professor Porter to that position.

It may be well for me to review very briefly the circumstances which have in part led me to this decision. During the academic year 1921-22 I received a salary of $7000 as professor, and $500 as dean. The Budget Committee that year decided to recommend some increases in professors' salaries, and they proposed that my salary be raised from $7000 to $8000. When this was done, however, my salary of $500 as dean was dropped, while the salary of other corresponding deans in the University was increased by $500 each, so that my total salary was just what it would have been presumably if the Budget Committee had not made the recommendation to which I have referred.

I felt then, and have since felt, that this action was unpleasantly evasive in character, and that it cast, although perhaps not intentionally, a slur upon the college which we have taken such pains to build up, and which we regard as one of the real assets of the University. . . .

Yours very sincerely,
Gilbert N. Lewis

Of course, his resignation was not accepted, and he probably did not expect it to be. However, it showed that G. N. Lewis was not to be trifled with.

A similar situation arose in 1934, when Lewis resigned from the National Academy of Sciences. Lewis never made it clear why he resigned. Ken Pitzer says it was rumored that he resigned because they didn't elect Ernest Gibson to membership. Edwin B. Wilson, of Harvard, wrote to Lewis as follows:[243]

Some people around here who have heard of the resignation attribute it to the fact that Giauque was not nominated this year in the section of chemistry. They are more apt to assign petty reasons than large ones. If you are going to stick by your resignation I wish there was some way that you could let all your colleagues in the Academy know why you resigned.

Wilson went on to guess that he resigned because of politicization of the Academy and because the Academy was exerting no scientific leadership. In 1985, I asked Lewis's sons if they knew of any reason for the resignation. They did not, but the younger son, Edward (Ted) Lewis of Rice University, suggested that his father may have been dissatisfied with the election policies of the Academy and may have felt that the Academy was a kind of "old boy" club.[117] In any event, the resignation appears to have been an act of pique and was especially unfortunate in view of the lack of a known motive.

Lewis's Self-Esteem and the Nobel Prize

Many words have been written about G. N. Lewis and the importance of his work; however it is more interesting to see how he himself looked upon his career. First consider the following quotation from a letter[125] he wrote to the publishers of his book, *The Anatomy of Science*,[130] who had requested some biographical information to use in their advertising.

Most of my life has been spent in the typical painstaking work of modern science, both experimental and theoretical, but I have never enjoyed being a mere specialist, and have occasionally found myself wandering away from an allotted task, as, for example, when I went to the Philippines to spend a year as Superintendent of Weights and Measures, or, during the war, when I left the chemical work of the army and entered instead into the problems of the organization of actual warfare. So also I have allowed my mind to wander in many fields. When the principle of relativity was in its infancy I was the first to present a paper on this subject before the American Physical Society, where it was received with anything but enthusiasm. Since then much of my time has been devoted to problems in mathematical physics. In this field as in chemistry I have always been interested not merely in the detailed advances of science but also in the general trend, or, as we might call it, the philosophy of science, and this habit has led me to devote a great deal of thought not merely to the inanimate sciences but also to the larger and even more perplexing problems of biology...

Perhaps he appraised his own work best in a letter he wrote in 1928 to Professor J. R. Partington of London, who had proposed nominating him for the Nobel Prize and had asked for some particulars regarding his work. Lewis answered:[126]

It is very kind indeed of you to wish to submit my name for the Nobel Prize, and of course I am delighted to have you do so, even though the effort seem [sic] a little visionary.

While I have flirted with many problems, I was for many years pretty loyal to the main task which I had set for myself, namely, to weave together the abstract equations of thermodynamics and the concrete data of chemistry into a single science. This is the part of my work in which I feel the greatest pride, partly because of its utility, and partly because it required a considerable degree of experimental skill. It is one thing to learn an experimental method and apply it with great exactness to all the problems which come to hand; it is another thing to have a definite problem which requires the use and often the invention of many different methods. That part of my work therefore which has given me the greatest amount of personal satisfaction was the study of the free energy of formation of the most important compounds, and in particular the electrode potentials of the elements. I began my work in this field soon after the appearance of Wilsmore's summary of previous work on electrode potentials. In spite of the care which he himself displayed it was impossible to conceal the slovenliness of experimental method and of theoretical treatment which was then current. In order to provide the adequate theoretical treatment I invented the somewhat trivial but very useful 'activity' and set about determining activity coefficients. On the experimental side it was necessary to consider all the factors which determine the constancy and reproducibility of electrodes, and to eliminate uncertainties in the liquid potentials.

For eight years I carried on experiments with the sodium electrode until finally Kraus and I obtained a cell with a sodium electrode which for months was as constant as the standard cell with which it was compared. Each new problem presented its own difficulties and required new technique. The results obtained are those which are tabulated on page 433 of Lewis and Randall. All my papers dealing with potential measurements and the calculation of free energy from equilibrium measurements are included in the fifty papers which are listed on pages 617 and following of our book on Thermodynamics. If I have any claim to recognition I think it would be based chiefly on these papers. . .

Notice that Lewis made no mention of his theory of valence - a wise decision for two reasons. First, the valence theory at that time, particularly in Europe, was too closely associated with Langmuir's name and, in the minds of many people, there would be a question as to whom to give major credit. Second, Nobel Prizes are generally awarded for work which is largely experimental and free from questionable theory. This latter fact probably accounts for Lewis's emphasis in the letter on the experimental problems associated with his thermodynamic work.

A number of other people were also nominating Lewis for the Nobel Prize. F. G. Donnan of London wrote the following in a letter of 1929:[43]

I send you my best congratulations on the award to you of the Davy Medal by the Royal Society. This is a timely, though belated, recognition of your great work in physico-chemical science. Some of us in England have been nominating you for a Nobel Prize in recent years, and are very disappointed you haven't got one yet. The ways of the Swedish Academy are rather mysterious, and certainly difficult to understand. Certain recent recipients of the Prize, though no doubt very worthy and excellent persons, do not strike one as particularly brilliant solutions of the yearly puzzle set by Nobel. . . .

The people who nominated Lewis for the Nobel Prize from 1922 through 1935 are listed in the accompanying table.[148] The most persistent and persuasive of these was W. W. Campbell, the famous astronomer who served as president of the University from 1923 to 1930. Here is one of his shorter nominating letters, dated December, 1930:[26]

The Nobel Committee for Chemistry
Stockholm 50
Sweden
Gentlemen:
    In response to your courteous invitation dated September, 1930, I herewith very respectfully nominate Gilbert Newton Lewis, Professor of Chemistry and Dean of the College of Chemistry in the University of California, for the Nobel Prize in Chemistry, 1931, *for his achievements in the fields of thermodynamics and the theory of valence.*
    In *thermodynamics*, his advances in theoretical, mathematical and experimental methods and his systematic determination and tabulation of free energies, have already revolutionised the application of this science to chemistry. To be noted also are his experimental and theoretical researches on the activities of solutions which led to his discovery of the principle of the ionic strength, and served

Nominators of G. N. Lewis for the Nobel Prize, Through 1935*

Prize Year	Name
1922	F. G. Donnan, London
1924	J. B. Clark, New York
	T. W. Richards, Cambridge, Mass.
	C. D. Walcott, Washington
1925	E. V. McCollum, Baltimore
	V. Lenher, Madison
1926	W. W. Campbell, Berkeley
	J. Walker, Edinburgh
1929	A. J. Allmand, London
	W. W. Campbell, Berkeley
	J. B. Clark, New York
	W. D. Harkins, Chicago
	J. R. Partington, London
	H. I. Schlesinger, Chicago
	S. Smiles, London
	J. Stieglitz, Chicago
1930	W. W. Campbell, Berkeley
1931	W. W. Campbell, Mt. Hamilton, Calif.
1932	W. W. Campbell, Cedar Rapids, Iowa
	W. Foster, Princeton
	K. Landsteiner, New York
	A. W. C. Menzies, Princeton
	W. Palmaer, Stockholm
1933	I. Langmuir, St. Moritz
	C. A. Mann, Minneapolis
	W. Palmaer, Stockholm
	M. C. Sneed, Minneapolis
	O. Stern, Hamburg
1934	W. W. Campbell, Washington
	F. Haber, Cambridge
	W. Palmaer, Stockholm
1935	E. Abel, Vienna
	D. A. Deissman, Berlin
	M. Planck, Berlin

* Nobel archival material is available for historical research only if more than fifty years old.[148]

as the foundation for testing the theory of Debye. Viewed as a whole his work constitutes a unified and vigorous system, most productive of results.

Of his numerous achievements in *valence theory* and related fields, perhaps the most significant is his logical deduction, from the facts of chemistry alone, of the shared electron pair as the chemical bond. This concept, at the time of its publication some fifteen years ago, and for long afterwards, was viewed with disfavour or ignored by most other contributions [sic] to the subject. It has, however, been completely substantiated by recent developments in quantum mechanics. The confirmation thus afforded of this important result, achieved long before the means for its theoretical elucidation had been conceived, focusses attention at the present time upon the striking character of the original deduction. The keen insight and scientific acumen with which he built on this discovery his theory of chemical valence are now receiving the recognition which they deserve. His theory has reconciled the discordant views of the organic and inorganic chemist and given an interpretation of the generalizations of Werner concerning valence and coordination number. . .

Respectfully submitted:
W. W. Campbell

Why didn't Lewis ever get the Nobel Prize? Here are some thoughts on the matter.

First, he might well have been given the Nobel Prize for his work in thermodynamics. That work, carried out over a period of twenty-five years, was summarized in the text by Lewis and Randall. In it, Lewis made thermodynamics a science easily used by the ordinary chemist. He showed, among other things, that even a relatively short table of free energies enables the calculation of equilibrium data for thousands of reactions. However, in order for Lewis to get the Nobel Prize for his work in thermodynamics, a nomination from Nernst was probably a necessity, and, according to Joel Hildebrand, Nernst did not feel that Lewis deserved the prize. After all, van't Hoff had received the prize in 1901 for his discovery of the law of osmotic pressure in solutions, Ostwald had received it in 1909 for studies of the principles governing chemical equilibria, and Nernst himself had received it in 1921 for his work on thermochemistry. Why should an upstart American who had merely acquired some good data and organized it well be specially honored?

Second, Lewis might well have been given the prize for his

work on chemical bonding. But, as we have already pointed out in Chapter 11, Langmuir stole the show in this field with his many lectures and articles based on Lewis's ideas.

Third, Lewis might have been given the prize for his work on deuterium. In 1934, the Nobel Prize was awarded to Lewis's former student, Harold C. Urey, for his discovery of deuterium. It would not have been unreasonable for that prize to have been split between Urey and Lewis - half to Urey for the discovery, and half to Lewis for the isolation and chemical characterization. It is undoubtedly significant that, although Lewis had a grand total of twenty-five papers on deuterium published in 1934 (the year Urey received his Prize), *he abruptly stopped his work on deuterium that year and never published a single paper on that topic thereafter.*

Fourth, and finally, he might have been given the prize for his concept that we now refer to as the Lewis Acid-Base Theory. Although Lewis succinctly described this concept in 1923, he wrote nothing more about it until the late 1930s, when he began to collect some supporting experimental data.[133] In the meantime, Sidgwick introduced his "coordinate bonds," formed by the interaction of donor and acceptor molecules, and Ingold introduced the name electrophile for oxidizing agents or electron acceptors and the term nucleophile for reducing agents or electron donors.[90] However, after Lewis's belated elaboration of his acid-base concept, the chemical community began to use the concept and to give him credit for it. In 1946, Luder and Zuffanti wrote a book entitled *The Electronic Theory of Acids and Bases* which brought the idea of Lewis acids and bases to the attention of many chemists.[140] Perhaps if Lewis had lived a few more years he would have been suitably honored for this important contribution to chemistry.

Lewis's Last Years

When World War II came, Lewis was approaching the traditional retirement age. Perhaps for this reason, and because he had dissociated himself from the National Academy of Sciences, he was never offered any administrative position having to do with wartime research that he felt worthy of consideration. He certainly didn't want a war job that mainly involved carrying papers around; he once remarked, "I refuse to accompany a flying briefcase."[138]

Around 1942 David Lipkin (Lewis's research assistant) and Sam Weissman (an NRC Fellow at Berkeley) told Lewis that they were thinking of going to work at Los Alamos. This irritated Lewis. He said, "Why do you want to do that? You should think about it more carefully." Later he went to them and said, "Are you really committed to going to Los Alamos? I have spoken to Birge about you, and he says that he probably would be able to offer you both instructorships in the Physics Department if you stayed here." Nevertheless, they both went to Los Alamos.[138]

Around 1941 Lewis did a little fiddling around with gas masks and some thinking about high nitrogen-content explosives, no doubt at somebody's bidding, but he had little enthusiasm for these projects, and no progress was made.

When the war was over, all the rest of the chemistry staff were covered with glory for their war-related work, but he had little to celebrate. The colleagues he had brought with him from MIT in 1912 either had left the department or had died. (Tolman and Randall left in 1916 and 1944 respectively; Bray died in February 1946.)

Perhaps he felt that the Nobel Prize was beyond hope. After all, Lewis and Randall had been published more than twenty years earlier. And his contributions to the electron-pair bond idea (diluted, unfortunately, by Langmuir's contributions) were being rapidly overshadowed by modern quantum chemistry. Urey had been awarded the Nobel Prize for the discovery of deuterium, so it was unlikely he would receive the Prize for his isolation of deuterium. The only other contribution for which he was well known, the Lewis acid-base concept, had not yet achieved its ultimate popularity and widespread application.

It is possible that the melancholy associated with the end of the war, disappointment about the Nobel Prize, and a deterioration in health may have led Lewis to despair in his last year. One of Lewis's bridge-playing cronies, Gerald Marsh, said that on the afternoon of March 23, 1946, Lewis appeared to be morose while playing cards at the Faculty Club. He then went to his laboratory in Gilman Hall, where he was later found dead near a broken ampule of hydrogen cyanide. Now, the fact that Lewis had an ampule of the deadly poison, hydrogen cyanide, in his laboratory is not as sinister as it might first appear. He had been studying the variation of the absorption spectra of dyes with solvent dielectric constant, and hydrogen cyanide, which has an extremely high dielectric constant, was one of the solvents he was using. In a retrospective symposium honoring G. N. Lewis, Michael Kasha attempted to quash the suggestion that Lewis committed suicide, but his arguments were not compelling.[96] Hildebrand believed he took his own life. Pitzer has pointed out that somebody as smart as Lewis might well commit suicide in such a way as to make it appear accidental.

CHAPTER
17

Wheeler

There is no question that the rapid rise of the College of Chemistry to a position of prominence among the universities of the world can be credited mainly to G. N. Lewis. However, it is equally certain that Lewis's coming to Berkeley, and the ease with which he was able to carry out his program for building up the department, were due largely to the efforts and support of the "benevolent despot," President Benjamin Ide Wheeler.

Wheeler was born in Randolph, Massachusetts in 1854. He graduated from Brown University in 1875 and taught classical languages at Providence High School and Brown until 1881. He then spent four years studying at various German universities and received the Ph.D. degree at Heidelberg in 1885. During his stay in Germany he acquired a lasting love for German culture. On his return to America, he taught German at Harvard for a year and then was appointed professor of comparative philology and Greek at Cornell.[143, 207]

When offered the presidency of the University of California in 1899, Wheeler made four demands:[237a] "(1) That the President should be in fact, as in theory, the sole organ of communication between the Faculty and Regents, (2) that the President should have sole initiative in appointments and removals of professors and other teachers and in matters affecting salary, (3) that the Board, however divided in opinion during discussion, should in all things the President is called upon to do regarding the Faculty, support him as a unit, (4) that the President should be charged with the direction, subject to the Board, of all officers and employees of the University." The Regents accepted these conditions, and Wheeler accepted the presidency, with a salary of $10,000 per year.

Perhaps, when Lewis made his rather strong demands upon being invited to join the faculty in 1911, Wheeler was reminded of the demands that he himself had made twelve years earlier.

Wheeler was a man of great vigor, well suited for the booming years of the University. He rode about the campus on a horse. He dressed elegantly every day as well as on special occasions. He had a rich voice and was in demand as a speaker throughout the nation. His speech was perfect - completely acceptable to the intellectual and yet easily understood by the ordinary citizen. At Cornell he had been a friend of Theodore Roosevelt even before Roosevelt was governor of New York, and the Regents and faculty were much impressed when Roosevelt accepted Wheeler's invitation to speak at the 1903 commencement exercises.

A master stroke of Wheeler's was his appointment of Armin Leuschner, the distinguished astronomer, as dean of the graduate school. Leuschner educated not only Wheeler, but also a series of presidents after him, on the importance of research in graduate study.[40, 80]

Naturally, Wheeler's autocratic ways were not popular with everyone. Evidence of criticism is found in a 1903 letter that O'Neill wrote while he was touring the world, visiting various oil fields and chemical manufacturies. He wrote to Wheeler from Japan as follows:[158]

> At Yokohama I received a number of newspapers containing articles attacking you and your administration. I feel that they do not carry much weight and that they do not reflect the opinions of any considerable body. But the fact that any such articles are published arouses my anger. When I think of how you work for us all the time, Sundays, vacations, and all this time how you never spare yourself, pushing on incessantly trying to carry us with you, all for the enhancement and honor of the University, and of how well you have succeeded, and then find that there are some people who are trying to misinterpret all your motives, searching out little things, and grossly exaggerating them, giving false impressions whenever they can, and by innuendo and unkind suggestions, try to make out that you and your administration are a failure, I get mad all over. I want to assure you that there are many of us who appreciate what you have done for the University and feel an intense indignation at these unwarranted attacks. I wish I was back now to help, in what little way I can, to convince the community of the true condition of things. I am sure you must at times feel discouraged. I want to assure you that you have many loyal friends and that one of them is
>
> Yours most sincerely
> Edmond O'Neill

Wheeler had one serious crisis during his twenty-year administration. He had been a visiting professor at Berlin in 1909-10, and during his stay he became acquainted with Kaiser Wilhelm. In 1913 he visited Germany again and had long talks with the Kaiser.[143, 204] In 1916 he was a patron of a "German Relief Bazaar" held in San Francisco, and wrote an essay on "America's Debt to German Education" for its brochure.[238] In the midst of the anti-German sentiment of 1918, Wheeler became the object of attack from the Regents and others in the Bay Area. Soon after the United States' entry into World War I, a step which Wheeler deplored, the Regents circumscribed his authority by appointing an Advisory Committee of three deans to provide a channel of communication between the Regents and faculty. At the same time, an Emergency Council was established to facilitate war work within the University.[55]

Although Wheeler's pro-German sympathies were largely forgotten when the war ended in November 1918, these actions by the Regents and faculty are sometimes said to be the cause of Wheeler's resignation the next year. However, for several years he had been showing definite signs of senility, and he would probably have resigned soon in any event.[40, 150] He died in Vienna in 1927 while visiting his son, who was studying there.

William C. Bray

Bray was born in 1879 at Wingham, Ontario, Canada. When he was three years old, his father died, and, when he was twelve, his mother died. He then went to London, Ontario, to live with a great-uncle and aunt. In 1898 he entered Toronto University, where he soon came under the influence of the famous chemist, W. Lash Miller. His first publication, in 1903, "The Rate of Reaction in Solutions Containing Potassium Iodide, Potassium Chlorate and Hydrochloric Acid," was based on work he performed as an undergraduate and set the course he followed for the rest of his life: the study of the kinetics and mechanisms of inorganic reactions in aqueous solutions.[84]

He graduated with honors and was awarded a travelling fellowship which he used to go to the school of chemistry in Leipzig, headed by Ostwald. There he worked with R. Luther and was awarded the Ph.D. in 1905. In Leipzig he joined the "American Colony Club," where he made contacts that led to his being invited to join the group of physical chemists gathered by A. A. Noyes at MIT.

During his seven years at MIT, Bray produced eleven papers, including four long, classic papers with Noyes and Spear on "A System of Qualitative Analysis for the Common Elements." This work changed qualitative analysis from an empirical set of procedures to a systematic scheme based on the Law of Mass Action and the Ionic Theory.

In 1912 he accompanied Lewis to Berkeley. There he was put in charge of the laboratory work in freshman chemistry. He believed that the freshman course should be built around laboratory work and that the students should work, under supervision, in small groups. With this in mind he designed the freshman chemistry building with many rooms, each providing space for twenty-five students. The laboratory work was a carefully planned sequence of assignments designed to give an understanding of chemical equilibrium and the principles of qualitative analysis. Bray also devised an upper-division laboratory course on equilibria and kinetics in inorganic chemistry, known as Chem 120 (later changed to Chem 107). The simple yet revolutionary teaching methods used in these Bray-devised courses have directly or indirectly benefited thousands of American chemists.

Bray also carried out pioneering research in inorganic reaction kinetics - research that helped to establish what became known as the Berkeley school of inorganic chemistry. Because Bray's teaching was essentially an extension of his research (and vice versa), a discussion of either of these activities is almost as revealing as a discussion of both. Henry Taube, now at Stanford University, carried out his Ph.D. research with Bray during the period 1937-40. In his Priestley Medal address of 1985, Taube described Bray's teaching methods so well that I have, in the following paragraphs, simply excerpted directly from that address. In Taube's words,[212]

"Chemistry 120 was a very important part of the training of both undergraduate and graduate students. Though the course was not a formal requirement for the latter, the recommendation to those of us assisting in the instruction in general chemistry, that we audit Chem 120, was so strongly made as to be tantamount to a requirement. Moreover, mastery of the principles introduced in Chem 120 - principles many of us embraced rather reluctantly - proved to be a requirement for effective instruction in general chemistry, the laboratory work in that course involving as it did a great deal of reaction chemistry of the kind that is the basis for qualitative analysis. . .

"In Chem 120 we learned to think about reactions in an orderly way, and for most of the graduate students auditing the course, this was a new experience. Undergraduates on the whole performed better than graduate students. Many had taken general chemistry in the same department, and since this course also reflected Bray's approach in teaching chemistry, they were well prepared for the advanced course. But a more important reason for inferior performance on the part of many of the graduate students was this: Because of sloppy habits of thought already ingrained, they came to the course not just unprepared, but in fact disprepared. . .

"To compound our difficulties, the principles which underlay the course seemed at first hearing to be so obvious and lacking in depth that we did not take them seriously until the first examination, when many of us learned that we did not at all understand the implications or applications of the seemingly simple principles. . .

"For me, and I dare say for many of my peers, the reaction to the subject matter of the course began with a feeling of superiority to such simple issues, and of irritation at being expected to deal with them. To this there was soon added a feeling of frustration when we discovered how difficult it was for us, with all our sophistication, to get things right. Eventually the feeling of superiority was replaced by enough humility to make learning possible. And finally a sense of appreciation developed as we began to experience the power of looking at equilibrium and rate phenomena in the way that Bray advocated. This appreciation eventually extended to the teacher, but in some cases this phase did not set in until several years after the course was completed.

"With the limited time that we devoted to the course, coverage of many of the aspects of the dynamics of chemical systems could not be and was not extensive. Those of us who were Bray's students had the opportunity to learn from this extended contact, and whether or not we were students, we had before us his publications as models of how to deal with the dynamics of reactions in solution, and, I must add, of how to present findings and conclusions clearly, concisely, with precise choice of words. The important point about the course was not its coverage but the preparation it provided in applying the principles to new problems.

"Bray had an important role as a teacher also outside the contacts provided by work in the courses, and in retrospect it is clear that he kept our education in mind in all the functions of the department. During the discussions that took place in the teaching assistant-faculty gatherings that preceded the periods of laboratory instruction, we were given many opportunities to observe how the members of the faculty dealt with the unexpected and puzzling observations frequently encountered in the laboratory work of the students. Bray was clear-minded in his approach and candid in admitting the limits of his knowledge and understanding when these did not carry him to a complete resolution of the matter at issue.

"One of the most important instruments of instruction in the department was the weekly seminar, and here Bray played a quite special role: that of asking the simple question which was needed to emphasize or to clarify an important point made by the speaker. Each of us eventually learned that this was done only for our edification. . .

"Bray was not a particularly good lecturer, and I don't think he was very popular. He was rather reserved, and did little to reveal his underlying warmth and generosity. He was as well very sensitive and thus understood how students tended to react to him. In the course of a serious discussion of teacher-student relations, he once remarked to me: 'I irritate them into learning,' a remark which, in view of my own early reactions to him, I could not disagree with. Despite these superficial, apparent failings, he was a superb teacher, a point that was not appreciated by many until some time after they had left the university."

Only a limited number of graduate students were smart enough to take advantage of the opportunity to work with such a masterful chemist. One such student, aside from Taube, was Robert E. Connick, who stayed on to become a permanent Berkeley faculty member.

I have appended to this history a list of Berkeley faculty members, including a selection of four significant publications for each faculty member. In the case of Bray, I had extreme difficulty choosing publications because so many of them are landmarks in chemistry and worthy of mention. Finally I decided to make an exception for Bray and listed seven publications! Perhaps I was compensating for the fact that Bray's accomplishments have usually been greatly underrated.

I have already mentioned his early work on qualitative analysis. The titles of six other classic publications are:

"A General Relation between the Concentration and the Conductance of Ionized Substances in Various Solvents," with C. A. Kraus;

"Valence and Tautomerism," with G. E. K. Branch;

"A Periodic Reaction in Homogeneous Solution and Its Singular Relations to Catalysis;"

"The Catalytic Decomposition of Hydrogen Peroxide in a Bromine-Bromide Solution, and a Study of the Steady State," with R. S. Livingston;

A Course in General Chemistry, with W. M. Latimer; and

"Kinetic and Equilibrium Measurements of the Reaction $2Fe^{+++} + 2I^- = 2Fe^{++} + I_2$," with A. V. Hershey.

Bray became a U.S. citizen in 1913. During World War I he and several associates worked on the problem of devising a gas mask to absorb carbon monoxide, which, as a product of incomplete combustion in gun emplacements, was killing seamen and soldiers. This work, sponsored by the Defense Research Section of the Chemical Warfare Service, led to the preparation of "hopcalite" (Hopkins-California), a catalyst for the low-temperature oxidation of carbon monoxide. He directed research at the Experimental Station, American University, Washington, D.C., and in 1919 he served as Associate Director of the Fixed Nitrogen Research Laboratory. For two years during World War II he served as chairman of the Chemistry Department and acted as a consultant for defense projects. However, in 1945 he suffered a heart attack from which he never completely recovered, and he died in February, 1946.

Taube referred to Bray as "Teacher and Herald of Inorganic Reaction Kinetics." Yost and Russell,[245] in the dedication of their book *Systematic Inorganic Chemistry*, referred to him as "Able Scientist, Inspiring Teacher." At an ACS meeting, Latimer once stated that it was largely Bray's philosophy that guided the development of inorganic chemistry at Berkeley and that "when it came to working out the chemistry of plutonium in a short time, I think that the performance of the boys with our Berkeley thermodynamic reaction-kinetic training was a real tribute to the philosophy of William C. Bray."[113]

Richard C. Tolman

Tolman was born in 1881 in West Newton, Massachusetts. After receiving a B.S. in chemical engineering at MIT in 1903, he spent a year engaged in academic and industrial research in Germany. Then he returned to MIT, where he became a friend of A. A. Noyes and G. N. Lewis and, in 1910, obtained a Ph.D. in physical chemistry. After spending a year at the University of Michigan and a year at the University of Cincinnati, he went to Berkeley as an assistant professor of physical chemistry in 1912, and thus, with Bray, was one of the first two faculty members appointed during Lewis's reign at Berkeley.[99]

Tolman was a brilliant chemical physicist. He wrote articles and books on relativity theory and, with one of his first graduate students, T. Dale Stewart, studied the inertia of electrons in metals. Unfortunately, in 1916 he was attracted away from Berkeley by a professorship in physical chemistry at the University of Illinois with an annual salary of $3000.[121]

Tolman was ambitious, and he may have moved to Illinois partly to be free of Lewis's control.[150] However, he did not stay at Urbana long either. Upton Sinclair tells a story which makes the University of Illinois administration of those days sound like Joe McCarthy's Committee on Unamerican Activities.[204] A rumor that certain faculty members had expressed disloyalty to their country came to the attention of the board of trustees. Apparently somebody had heard something he didn't like at the country club, where some faculty members were drinking at a supper party. A "Committee to Investigate Rumors of Disloyalty" was appointed, met in November of 1917, and examined five professors in a formal trial which included the call of witnesses. Tolman, who was known to have socialist leanings in those days, was one of the five under investigation. Mrs. Mary E. Busey, one of the trustees, exclaimed, "To think that members of my faculty should behave in this way!" Tolman asked, "My faculty? Do you mean to say we are your hired servants?" "Well," replied Mrs. Busey, "you are in my employ!" The upshot of the matter was that the committee members found no evidence of disloyalty in the faculty ranks. However they did announce that America's participation in the war did not permit full freedom of speech and that "not even neutrality should be tolerated."[67]

This witchhunt may have been the cause of Tolman's resignation of his faculty position at the end of the academic year, when he accepted the rank of major in the army to serve as chief of the newly established Dispersoid Section of the Chemical Warfare Service. This group studied the production of toxic and nontoxic smoke screens and candles and tested airplane ammunition using a "hang-fire measurer," developed by Tolman.

At the end of the war, he was recruited by his friend Noyes, who, as chairman of the Committee on Nitrate Supply, was urging the government to continue the program during peacetime. Thus in 1919 Tolman joined The Fixed Nitrogen Research Laboratory of the Department of Agriculture. He served first as associate director and then as director. The laboratory became a Mecca for top-notch young physical chemists who studied a wide range of pure and applied scientific problems. Tolman even found time, with coworkers, to extend and to refine his study of the inertia of electrons in metals, which had been started in Berkeley. In the acknowledgments section of the paper reporting this work, the authors stated their desire "to express to the Government their appreciation of the policy of encouraging the staff of a government laboratory to devote a portion of their time and facilities to the investigation of fundamental scientific questions which have no immediate bearing on the main problem of the laboratory. It is believed that such a liberal policy is of great importance in maintaining a proper scientific attitude on the part of the staff of a research laboratory."[219]

In 1922 Tolman was appointed Professor of Physical Chemistry and Mathematical Physics at Cal Tech, again through the efforts of Noyes, who in the meantime had moved from MIT to Cal Tech. Tolman's career at Cal Tech was long and productive; he served as Dean of the Graduate School for twenty-four years. He was a meticulous teacher who covered the blackboard with equations and notes even before the start of a class. Because of his dry wit and sense of humor, Tolman became Cal Tech's unofficial toastmaster, a job he enjoyed as much as his teaching and administration.[66]

His tenure at Cal Tech was interrupted by World War II, during which he served on the National Defense Research Committee and as scientific advisor to General Groves during the development of the atomic bomb. After the war, he returned to Pasadena where, in 1948, he died.

George Ernest Gibson

Gibson was born in Edinburgh, Scotland, in 1884. His ancestors had alternating names of John and George. His great grandfather, John Gibson, was Sir Walter Scott's lawyer; his financially independent grandfather, George Gibson, experimented with kites and hot air balloons, and his father, John Gibson, was Professor of Chemistry at the University of Edinburgh.[59]

George Ernest Gibson received a B.Sc. degree at the University of Edinburgh in 1906, remained for two years of graduate work, and then went to Breslau, where he worked with Professor Otto Lummer and obtained a Ph.D. in 1911. After two years of teaching and research at Breslau and Edinburgh, he was appointed instructor of chemistry at Berkeley the year after G. N. Lewis's arrival.

Lewis put Gibson in charge of two new honors courses, Thermodynamics and Advanced Physical Chemistry. Gibson's translation of Sackur's *Textbook of Thermochemistry and Thermodynamics* served as the thermodynamics textbook until Lewis and Randall's text appeared in 1923. Gibson's research at Berkeley was in the areas of spectroscopy and low temperature calorimetry. The research of three of his early graduate students, Latimer, George S. Parks, and Giauque, was designed to test the validity of the low temperature calorimetric method for evaluating absolute entropies of elements and compounds. These three students later served as nuclei (Parks at Stanford, and Latimer and Giauque at Berkeley) for the spread of low temperature thermodynamic studies in the United States through their own students.

I remember listening to a seminar given by Gibson in 1952. Although the ideas were brilliant, I got the impression that he had made no preparation for the seminar and that he was figuring out what to say as he went along. Several times he got into blind alleys that took several minutes to get out of, and throughout the seminar his thought processes were embarrassingly apparent to his listeners. This behavior was not a consequence of old age. Albert Loomis remembered that it was much the same in 1916:[16] "I learned all my thermo from Gibson. Now Gibson was a good teacher, but he tended to make mistakes at the board. He'd be writing along, and we'd know he was getting into trouble because his ears would start to turn red. When he'd reach the point where he knew something was wrong, he'd turn to us and say, 'All right, you fellas help me out here. You can see this better than I can.' I'd take notes during class and then I'd go home every night and write them up in a better notebook. But I'd find mistakes, so the next day at the beginning of class I'd raise my hand and say, 'Professor Gibson, there's something I don't understand about what you were saying yesterday.' Then we'd go over the mistakes in class. Finally it got so that I didn't even have to raise my hand anymore. Gibson'd just say right off, 'All right Mr. Loomis, what have you got for us today?'"

Despite Gibson's absentmindedness, which sometimes made his graduate students feel as if they were working all alone, he was keenly alert to current developments in research and always had interesting problems to suggest. He was selected as Ph.D. research director not only by Latimer, Parks, and Giauque, but also by such men as Phipps, Eyring, Rice, and Seaborg. He was proud of the fact that two of his students became Nobel laureates.

When Glenn Seaborg arrived in Berkeley in 1934 to do graduate work, he had no idea with whom he would work. He chose to work with Gibson for two reasons.[151] One was that Gibson was working in nuclear chemistry. The other was that he had a reputation for not paying much attention to his graduate students. And that's what Seaborg wanted. He asked around, and people warned him away from Gibson, saying that some of his students took a long time to finish. Seaborg just thanked them and then signed up with Gibson anyway. Seaborg essentially carried out his own Ph.D. research. After a year or so, Gibson didn't follow the work very closely, and occasionally Seaborg would go to him to explain what he was doing. When the time came, Gibson merely signed the thesis.

Gibson carried a tremendous number of physical constants in his head and would make mental calculations (usually with mistakes) at the drop of a hat. He enjoyed music and for a while played violin in the University Symphony Orchestra. In his later years he became interested in Oriental philosophy and became proficient in the translation of Sanskrit. He died in 1959.

CHAPTER
21

Joel H. Hildebrand

Joel Hildebrand was like a juke box. Whenever you pushed one of the buttons - that is, whenever you mentioned something related to one of the many memories in his vast cranial storehouse - the appropriate record dropped onto the turntable, the tone arm moved into position, and you were told a fascinating anecdote. The mechanism always worked perfectly, and the record always sounded exactly the same as it did the last time it was played. One particular anecdote, The Story of the Impertinent but Pertinent Student (which can be found in Chapter 13), was like an old Caruso recording: we heard it played over and over again. The faculty became so familiar with that story that we used to smile or wink at one another during, or in anticipation of, its recitation.

Joel was born on November 16, 1881, in Camden, New Jersey, and died on April 30, 1983, in Berkeley. He explained his longevity by saying, "I selected my ancestors carefully."[81] There is very little about his life that Joel himself has not already related. So most of this biographical sketch is taken from his own writings.

"Gilbert N. Lewis wrote in a preface, 'Science has its cathedrals, built by a few architects and many workmen.' Most of these cathedrals of science have been built largely during the span of my life; to have been one of the workmen has filled my years with excitement and satisfaction, and I am happy to tell about some of the things I have seen under construction. I have lived during all but five years of the life of the American Chemical Society, and half of the life of the United States of America.

"I was introduced to science by an occasional lecturer in an elementary school. He made hydrogen, blew bubbles that rose to the ceiling, and burned it to water. He electrified a rod that first attracted and then repelled pith balls coated with tin foil and exhibited many other wonders. I was fascinated and repeated at home everything I could.

"I remember high school in a suburb of Philadelphia with pleasure and gratitude. . . The principal of the school had studied chemistry one year at Harvard and offered a course in it. When he found that I knew more chemistry than he did he gave me a key to the laboratory and his Harvard text, *Chemical Philosophy* by Prof. Josiah Cooke of Harvard. . . Cooke classified the elements into 'artiads' and 'perrisads,' with even- and odd-numbered valences, respectively. Since the valence of oxygen is 2, the valences of nitrogen in N_2O, N_2O_3 and N_2O_5 are odd, 1, 3, and 5. There is another oxide, called nitric oxide, that we now write as NO, but Cooke wrote as N_2O_2 in order to have a third valence bond uniting two nitrogen atoms. Other writers wrote it NO. Not being a natural philosopher, I performed an experiment to select the right formula by applying Gay-Lussac's law of simple multiple volumes of reacting gases. I made nitric oxide and oxygen and collected each over water in graduated cylinders, and noted their volumes. I then poured a measured volume of the oxide upside down into the oxygen, where it formed brown fumes which dissolved into the water. The volume of the nitric oxide was twice the volume of the oxygen that reacted, therefore the equation is $2NO + O_2 = N_2O_4$. Experiment refuted 'chemical philosophy.'

"I graduated from the University of Pennsylvania in 1903 from the College of Arts and Science with a double major in chemistry and physics instead of from the professional curriculum in chemistry, where I would have been trained as an assayer or commercial analyst. I became a graduate student, aiming at an academic career. I spent the first two years on inorganic and organic preparations for which I have been grateful. There was no physical chemistry. The head of the department had a low opinion of this new-fangled subject. He said, 'The real question is, can you analyze sulfuric acid? I don't care whether you do it by ionic theory or by mass action, but can you analyze it?' But since other institutions were beginning to include physical chemistry, he decided that his department must yield to the trend. He did not want to call some outsider, thinking it safer to groom me for the job; being home-trained, I would be more conservative - and cheaper.

"So, in the summer of 1906, I went to Berlin to study with Prof. J. H. van't Hoff and Geheimrat professor Walther Nernst, the most prestigious physical chemists of the time. . . I returned from Europe in the summer of 1907 to become the first teacher of physical chemistry at the University of Pennsylvania. My salary was $1000. I was provided with the facilities supposed to suffice for a chemist in those days: beakers, flasks, burets, pipets, and a balance. I did my own glassblowing. There was no shop; I could borrow a needed screwdriver from the janitor. I begged and got a Wolf potentiometer. There was no galvanometer, so I made a Lippmann electrometer. . . I had an 18-hour teaching load.

I carried on my research in the student laboratory while students worked at their assignments. Before our first child was born, my young wife would bring supper to the laboratory so that I could make a series of measurements."[82]

"On [a] Saturday morning early in 1913, I was working on a paper describing following the course of chemical reactions with a hydrogen electrode, when a visitor entered. We had never before met, but I discovered that he was the rather well-known Dr. Frederick Cottrell of the Bureau of Mines. He stayed for some time, with no pauses in our conversation. When I returned home, I told my young wife about the visit, saying that he seemed to be looking me over with some object in view. I added that I could not have made a very good impression, because I was coming down with a cold.

"Some time later, I received an invitation from Gilbert Lewis to deliver three lectures at the University of California, Berkeley, where he had gone in 1912 with a group of young men to bring to life a moribund College of Chemistry. I accepted, although I had little expectation of leaving the center of civilization in the East to go to a rather unknown institution in the Far West. I could at least stop off to see the Grand Canyon.

"I made the trip in March, delivered my lectures and met a group of young iconoclasts for whom chemistry was an alluring field to investigate - not just a lot of information to try to memorize. There were Gilbert Lewis, Richard Tolman, and William Bray, who had heard me present some results of my research at a meeting of the American Chemical Society in Washington. Fred Cottrell attended one of my lectures. In the evening, he came to the Faculty Club where I was staying and talked at length about the University of California and its Department of Chemistry, of which he had recently been a member."[150]

"[I received] two flattering offers. . . one from the U.S. Bureau of Standards in Washington offering a salary of $3500. . . and the other from the University of California, Berkeley. Lewis offered me an assistant professorship at $2000 and I accepted, rejecting the offer from the Bureau of Standards because I wanted to teach and because I preferred to investigate questions I invented myself instead of those handed to me by a director of research. I sensed an eager curiosity at Berkeley about natural phenomena that was quite absent from the department in Philadelphia, where a research conference was conducted by a professor who did no research. Arriving in Berkeley, I felt that I had escaped from a dungeon into sunshine.

"At Penn, all Ph.D. theses had to be worked under the 'head.' He explained that this practice saved his underlings from envying one another. Lewis, on the other hand, sent new graduate students to consult various members of the staff about research projects. The chief at Penn had earned his Ph.D. in Germany, where there was only one full professor in an institute, who ruled like a feudal lord."[82]

"Our curriculum became a departmental enterprise. In order to have good graduate students we began with freshman. I lectured, Bray wrote the laboratory manual, and nearly all of us handled laboratory and quiz sections. This made for continuity between earlier and later courses and a sense of unity among the staff. . .

"At the time I began to teach freshmen, all the texts on the market were almost entirely descriptive. They dealt with 'occurence, preparation, properties, and uses,' to be memorized and recited. There was little to challenge thought. . . I became convinced that a new kind of text was called for, and wrote *Principles of Chemistry*, first edition 1918, second in 1926."[81]

The chapter on chemical equilibrium in that text contained a discussion of the important fact that, in order to get the desired amount of product from a chemical reaction, it may be necessary to use an excess of one or more of the reacting substances. Joel wrote:[77] "This excess is in no way indicated by the equation, nor does the presence of this excess change the proportions in which the substances react. We may illustrate this important point by imagining a Western celebration in which a large number of cowboys are to ride wild horses. Now in order to have fifty mounted cowboys it would be necessary to have more than fifty cowboys and fifty horses present, for we will assume that cowboys are constantly being unhorsed. It might be necessary to have, say, seventy cowboys in order to have all the horses mounted most of the time. This does not affect the fundamental reversible reaction, which is

Man + Horse = Mounted horseman

If the men are in excess of the horses we will not have two men trying to ride one horse, nor, if the horses are in excess, will one man try to ride two horses. After equilibrium has been reached, in which there are, on the average, a certain number of each of the three varieties represented by the equation, if more men arrive, the reaction corresponding to the equation as read from left to right will take place in a few more cases, shifting the equilibrium so as to use up riderless horses, while if some of the unmounted men leave for the nearest saloon, the net result will be that the reaction as read from right to left will take place until a new condition of equilibrium is reached. Again, starting with sixty horses, in order to get fifty horsemen it might be necessary to have several hundred men, if bank-clerks were substituted for cowboys." But back to Joel's main narrative.

"Soon after the outbreak of World War I, the introduction of poisonous gases, liquids, and vapors by the Germans presented to the U.S. forces then in France a lot of problems in chemistry that West Point-trained officers were not prepared to solve. When the first small contingent of the Chemical Service Section of the National Army, which included Gilbert Lewis as a major and me as a captain detailed from the Ordnance Reserve Corps, arrived in France early in January 1918, we learned that the U.S. Army then in France had suffered more casualties from enemy gas, especially 'mustard gas,' than from all other weapons combined. Our job was clear.

"Our chief, eventually a major general, Amos A. Fries, was an army engineer who had built San Pedro Harbor. He was open minded and imaginative, and Lewis and I had every opportunity for doing our best; Lewis became finally lieutenant colonel and chief of the Defense Division of the Chemical Corps of the AEF. I became commandant of Hanlon Field, near Chaumont, which included the Experimental Field and the Officers Gas School. In 1922 we each received a Distinguished Service Medal at a ceremony at the San Francisco Presidio.

"In World War II I was, first, a consultant on the design of the 'weasel,' a kind of snowmobile that was to be used in driving the Germans from Norway. I was sent on a top-secret mission to Chile to report on the feasibility of trying it out in powder snow in August. In May of 1943 I joined the American Embassy in London as a scientific liaison officer for the Office of Scientific Research and Development. My purview included war gases, incendiaries, obscuring smoke, and fog clearance from airfields.[81] I believe my own most useful service was the sponsoring of a series of conferences on smoke during the weeks preceding D-Day. Officers of our Strategic and Tactical Air Forces, our ground forces, and our Navy, who were responsible for smoke during the impending operations, felt the need of coordinating their efforts during the invasion. . . . After spending months sending communications to Washington with little evidence that they had any effect, it was gratifying to feel that here was an effort that would get into the war rather than into a filing cabinet.[78] . . . After the war I was awarded the 'King's Medal for Service in the Cause of Freedom.'[81]

"In 1916 I published a paper on 'Solubility' in which I interpreted deviations from Raoult's law in terms of internal pressures. This laid the basis for the gradual construction of the theory of regular solutions.

"An early deduction was that helium would be found to be less soluble in any liquid than any other gas. On Jan. 29, 1924, I wrote to Dr. Samuel C. Lind, then director of the division of chemistry of the Bureau of Mines, which controlled stocks of helium, proposing that the bureau study the applicability of helium-oxygen mixtures to deep diving. The project was investigated first in the bureau, then in the experimental diving unit of the Navy, directed by its able medical officer, Albert R. Behnke. . . The use of helium for deep diving is now standard practice. And it all began with simple curiosity about the solubility of gases in liquids. Knowledge of nature's ways is a prolific source of beneficent results."[82]

"I recently read a dictum that little creative work can be expected from a man after the age of thirty-five. That is unquestionably true, because few persons do anything very creative even before thirty-five. But there is no arbitrary age deadline after which a person can no longer enjoy the pleasures of the mind. There are notable instances of extraordinary creativity continuing to twice thirty-five and beyond. . . These years of pseudoretirement have been among the happiest of my life. I am busy at what I like best to do. I devise questions that I and my young coworkers hope will evoke answers from nature, who is far more pleasant to deal with than are most people. We have been getting some beautiful answers. Plato said that the heavenly bodies must move in circles because a circle is the most perfect geometric figure. He was wrong; the most perfect geometrical construction is a straight line connecting experimental results on one axis with the parameters of your theory on the other. We have obtained a number of such lines."[81]

Joel was an active member of the Sierra Club for more than thirty years. He joined the club in the early 1930s and resigned as honorary vice-president in 1965, after an effort to curtail the activities of the club's executive director. He was president of the club from 1937 to 1940, during the campaign for establishing Kings Canyon National Park. He helped draft the bill creating the park on behalf of the club and thus ensured that the park remain a wilderness area.

In 1938 Joel initiated the club's burro trips, which serve as the model for most club outings even today. He was a leader in ski mountaineering who advanced the sport in California by improving ski techniques, devising ski tests, and stimulating competition. He managed the U.S. Olympic Ski Team in 1936.[102]

In the first chapter of *Going Light with Backpack or Burro*, Joel wrote a valuable creed for all of us:[75] "If you want good fishing, you may have to go where there are mosquitoes as well as fish. If you want to camp amid the inspiring scenery of timberline, your nights will be cold. This is a fine lesson to learn and willingly accept, for these are only the just prices that have to be paid for the good things of life - prices that have not been inflated by greed."

November 16, 1981, was Joel's hundredth birthday. On that day the University held a day-long celebration in his honor, complete with speeches, testimonials, songs, and an elaborate luncheon. The Chevron Research Company announced the establishment of the Hildebrand Chair in Chemistry, to provide research funds for a junior faculty member in the College of Chemistry. The Shell Development Company announced the establishment of a new ACS award, the Hildebrand Award in the Theoretical and Experimental Chemistry of Liquids, with Joel as the first recipient. A year and a half later, at age 101, he died peacefully in his sleep.

Gerald E. K. Branch

Branch was born in 1886 in the British West Indies. In 1904 he entered the University of Edinburgh to study medicine, but he gave up medicine and studied chemistry under the famous F. G. Donnan at Liverpool University, where he graduated with honors in 1911. He obtained a master's degree, working with Titherly, in 1912.[63] At the suggestion of Donnan (a friend of G. N. Lewis), he went to Berkeley for his Ph.D. There he worked with Lewis on "The Free Energy of Formation of Formic Acid." Immediately upon obtaining his Ph.D., he was made an instructor in the Chemistry Department.

When I started graduate work at Berkeley, all beginning graduate students in chemistry were required to take Chem 103, an upper-division course in physical organic chemistry, taught by Branch. At that time Branch was sixty-three years old - well past his prime - and he had acquired quite a reputation for his idiosyncrasies. In his lectures, he adhered very closely to the textbook (Branch and Calvin, the writing of which we shall describe in the chapter on Calvin), so that there really was not much need to attend the lectures. Branch spoke so very softly that he could hardly be heard beyond the third row of seats in the lecture hall. Once a student in the middle of the lecture hall suddenly died of a heart attack, and the word went around that Branch had finally bored someone to death in his class. His exams (or "exes," as he called them) were almost identical from year to year, so any student with access to copies of previous exams had a tremendous advantage. For example, it became well known that his final exam invariably had a question on the rather obscure Hixon-Johns method (a method of plotting the logarithms of equilibrium constants, etc. which showed the similarities of the effects of groups on various reactions).

I remember going to chat with Branch about some topic related to my Ph.D. prelim exam. (We were free to consult anybody we wanted to in order to prepare for these exams.) I was overwhelmed by his office. He had papers piled everywhere, so that he had to do his writing on a book on his lap. But he very graciously helped me as much as he could with my problem, and I felt compassion for him. I learned later that, after he died, an amazing collection of items - including old journals in their original wrappers and uneaten lunches - was removed from his office.

Despite idiosyncratic behavior in his later years, he made significant contributions to chemistry and the University, as summarized in the biographical sketch on Branch in the UC serial publication *In Memoriam.* This sketch is much more interesting than most from this series - probably because Ernest Gibson had a hand in writing it - and I reproduce here excerpts from that publication.[63]

"Branch may be considered as having established, at the University of California, the first modern school of theoretical organic chemistry. His extensive study of the relationship of the structure of organic acids with acid strength gave rise to many of the basic notions of induction and mesomerism (resonance) stemming from Gilbert N. Lewis's theory of chemical bonds. Branch's views contributed much to the development of this theory. . .

"Many of Professor Branch's students extoll the inspiration of his teaching. Dr. Bert Tolbert's remarks are typical. '. . . in his office conferences, Professor Branch would cover great realms of theory and inductive reasoning, many times leaving me far behind, but he would patiently and simply repeat and explain until everything was completely clear. Another item that stands out was his method of helping in the laboratory work. I learned that the primary requirement was a tremendous quantity of test tubes and an array of all the common solvents and reagents. With this very limited set of tools, Professor Branch would cover a fantastic multitude of exploratory experiments and derive thereby the optimum pathway for our research. He instituted a series of weekly meetings at his home in the evening to write up a series of papers for publication and to review the material for my thesis. The opportunity to become thoroughly acquainted with my professor and his wife was probably one of the most memorable parts of this instruction period.'

"Like his friend Gilbert Lewis, Professor Branch in his leisure hours was a delightful and inspiring companion. His keen analytical mind made him pre-eminent in chess and games of cards. At the Faculty Club, his only rival at chess was the late Arthur Ryder, Professor of Sanskrit. Mr. Fred N. Christensen remarks: 'As a student, I remember that nearly every semester he would give a simultaneous exhibition for us in Stephens Union, taking on all comers.' Mr. W. P. Barlow tells that Branch's performance at a simultaneous exhibition, while on sabbatical leave in England, was praised in the *Chess Magazine.* He also tells that Branch and he once played a simultaneous exhibition with twenty-five children at the Blind School of California in Berkeley.

"As in science, so in chess he was untiringly kind and considerate with beginners.

"On the morning of the day of his death, April 14, 1954, during a lecture he felt an oncoming [heart] attack. He took a dose of nitroglycerine and finished the lecture.

"That afternoon he returned to his office and there his wife found him when she came to fetch him home, at rest forever from his labors."

Merle Randall

In 1909 Randall started his graduate work in chemistry at MIT, where he began a long association with G. N. Lewis. He received his Ph.D. in 1912 and, in the same year, accompanied Lewis to Berkeley, as Lewis's research assistant. In 1917 he was promoted to assistant professor, but he was still essentially an assistant to Lewis. From the first year that Lewis and Randall came to Berkeley until 1923 they collaborated on the writing of the book entitled *Thermodynamics and the Free Energy of Chemical Substances*. Actually, it was a rather unbalanced collaboration. Randall was essentially Lewis's amanuensis. Lewis would dictate, and Randall wrote it down. Albert G. Loomis, a graduate student in the years 1916-19, occupied the laboratory next to the room where Lewis and Randall were writing their book. Loomis had taken a course in thermodynamics from Gibson and was known for the fact that his notebook was very thoroughly and carefully written. Loomis recalled, "I could hear Lewis pacing up and down, talking. That was the way they worked, Lewis talking and smoking his cigar, and Randall taking it down. Well, every once in a while, Lewis would send Randall into my office to borrow my notebook - not to see if he were right, you understand, just to make sure that he had covered all the material."[16]

From the very beginning, Randall was in charge of the so-called technical chemistry courses, but he also taught physical chemistry and quantitative analysis. His major research field was thermodynamics; he was particularly interested in the determination of the free energies of various compounds and in the activity coefficients of various electrolytes. Probably Randall's most notable research student was Frederick D. Rossini, who went on to an illustrious career in thermodynamics at the Bureau of Standards, Carnegie Tech, Notre Dame, and Rice University.

Randall also became interested in the separation of the isotopes of oxygen and hydrogen by distillation processes. He and his students constructed an enormous still in Gilman Hall for the fractional distillation of water. It had a reflux column, filled with metal shoe-eyes, that reached from the sub-basement to the third floor. He and his student, James Hyde, used this column to prepare some water enriched in oxygen-18. That water sample was used in collaborative research with Sam Ruben and Martin

Kamen to show that the oxygen from water, not the oxygen from carbon dioxide, is the origin of photosynthetic oxygen.[95, 189]

However, during his last years in the department, Randall was a source of irritation to the rest of the faculty. He had students engaged in activities related to his consulting - activities of questionable merit and propriety. The limit was reached when he required his students in quantitative analysis to buy a privately printed textbook on physical chemistry that he and Leona E. Young had written.[178] He and Young had never been able to find a publisher for this book (a fact that the faculty took as evidence that the book was of low quality), and the book had very little relevance to quantitative analysis.[170] Hildebrand, who was department chairman in 1941-43, had the uncomfortable job of convincing Randall to take an early retirement. Indeed, Randall retired from the University in 1944 and spent his remaining years in consulting work. He became consultant and director of research for the Stuart Oxygen Company of Berkeley and consultant and vice president of a small Oakland company called Pioneers, Inc.[187]

Randall and the president of Pioneers, Jess M. Ritchie, concocted a substance which they marketed as a battery additive under the trademark Battery AD-X2. They claimed that this material, when added to lead storage batteries, would reduce sulfation and would bring "dead" batteries back to life.[185] The material was simply a powdered mixture of anhydrous sodium sulfate and nearly anhydrous magnesium sulfate. The fact that Randall was working with magnesium sulfate-containing battery additives was well known in those days. At a Christmas party of the local American Chemical Society Section, Randall was presented with a bag of Epsom Salts (magnesium sulfate) by Santa Claus.[170]

However, soon after Randall's death in 1950, AD-X2 was not a source of humor to chemists in the National Bureau of Standards. The product caused a scandal in the U.S. Department of Commerce and led to an unwarranted tarnishing of the public image of the Bureau of Standards. Indeed, some people believe that the Bureau of Standards has never fully recovered from the AD-X2 affair.

The affair started in the years 1949-51, when the NBS issued several circulars and reports implying that no material such as AD-X2, when added to the electrolyte of a lead acid storage battery, could improve the battery's performance or materially reduce the rate of pernicious sulfation.[147] Of course, Ritchie objected to these reports, and in 1952 the Senate Small Business Committee arranged for independent tests of AD-X2 to be conducted at MIT. The report issued by MIT stated that their tests "demonstrate beyond a reasonable doubt that this material is in fact valuable, and give complete support to the claims of the manufacturer." The NBS countered with still additional tests in 1953 that confirmed its previous findings. The Post Office then issued a fraud order against Pioneers, but this was almost immediately withdrawn, pending further investigation, at the request of Secretary of Commerce Sinclair Weeks. Weeks also requested the resignation of the Director of the NBS, Allen V. Astin. This latter action caused a public uproar. President Eisenhower then put pressure on Weeks so that he requested the the National Academy of Sciences to appoint a committee to study and report on the work of the NBS on AD-X2. This committee found fault with the conclusions drawn by the MIT group and concluded, without reservation, that the quality of work of the NBS in the field of lead acid storage batteries was excellent. They also stated: "We find no data obtained from any well-designed scientific experiment which is inconsistent with the hypothesis that AD-X2 behaves like a corresponding mixture of sodium and magnesium sulfates, and is substantially neutral in its effect upon a lead acid storage battery. . . ."

Another committee, headed by Mervin J. Kelly, President of Bell Labs, and containing members selected from several scientific and engineering societies, was appointed to study the functions of the NBS in relation to national needs. Kenneth Pitzer represented the American Chemical Society on this committee and was probably the most knowledgeable and influential member of the committee. The committee report included a number of valuable recommendations, such as the transfer of "weaponry" projects to the Department of Defense. Weeks accepted these recommendations and even used them to his advantage so that his capitulation was not so obvious when he finally reinstated Astin as director of the Bureau in August, 1953.[45, 53, 221, 222]

Alpha Chi Sigma

In the spring of 1902, several chemistry students at the University of Wisconsin got together to form an organization for promoting good fellowship and scholarship. After several preliminary meetings, the Alpha Chi Sigma fraternity was formally launched on December 11, 1902. In 1904 the group was incorporated as a national chemical fraternity, and the officers were given the titles Master Alchemist (president), Vice Master Alchemist (vice-president), Reporter, Recorder, Treasurer, and Master of Ceremonies. It was not long before groups at other universities petitioned to start their own Alpha Chi Sigma chapters, and by the end of 1911 a total of seventeen chapters had been chartered, each identified by one of the first seventeen letters of the Greek alphabet.[2,3]

However, at that time there was no chapter west of the Rocky Mountains. At the University of California, a chemistry honorary society called the Mim Kaph Mim (which later became the local chapter of the national chemistry honorary society, Phi Lambda Upsilon)[36] had been organized in 1901. However, some of the upper-classmen of the College of Chemistry felt that another society, having both a social and a professional nature, would benefit the College. Therefore, in August 1912, they formed the California Chemical Association and called a meeting for September 19, 1912, that was attended by twelve men. H. E. Wales was elected president, H. W. Noble, secretary, and L. L. Lieb, treasurer, and seven additional men were admitted to membership. It was soon recognized that the aim of this association (to bring students closer together and to help them aid one another in their work) could be furthered if the association became part of a national organization, and it was decided to apply to the Supreme Council of Alpha Chi Sigma for a charter. In the meantime, meetings with technical talks were held on alternate Tuesdays.[5]

Late in November the group learned that their petition had been granted. They immediately made plans for an installation ceremony to be held on January 16, 1913, at the Hof Brau Cafe in San Francisco. Harry A. Curtis, professor at the University of Colorado and Vice Grand Master Alchemist of the fraternity, came to officiate at the installation. The banquet menu was as follows:

Oysters on Half Shell
Celery, Olives, Crab Salad
Consomme Royal
Filet of Bass, Vin Blanc
Spring Chicken, Maryland
Ice Cream, Assorted Cakes
Roquefort Cheese
Cafe Noir
Punch, Cigars, Cigarettes

The charter members of the Sigma chapter were:

Ewald Anderson
Frank Mead Bacon
Jesse Wright Barnes
George Henry Bell
Herbert Spencer Blakemore
Chester A. Cromwell
William Newton Davis
Laurance Winant Dickey
DeRalph Frizell
Lloyd Linwood Lieb
Roscoe C. Lyans
Herbert Nelson Massey
Haymond Walter Noble
Willard Holmes Nutting
Joseph Pavliger
Charles C. Scalione
Thomas Dale Stewart
Ernest Fredrick Thoenges
Harold Edward Wales

Paul S. Burgess, Paul V. Faragher, and Merle Randall (Alpha Chi Sigma members from other chapters) also joined the Sigma chapter at that time. It should be noted that two of these early fraternity members - Stewart and Randall - eventually became professors in the College of Chemistry. For many years, Stewart served as the Faculty Advisor for the chapter.[5, 6]

The first formal meeting of the Sigma chapter was held on January 21, 1913, when the California Chemical Association was dissolved and T. Dale Stewart was elected Master Alchemist. During the first few months of its existence, the chapter was very active. The members held weekly meetings in Room 10 of University Hall at Telegraph and Bancroft, initiated new members in the Old Chemistry Building, held a dance in University Hall, and took several trips to industrial plants in the Bay Area.

In the fall of 1913, the chapter moved into a house at 2600 Bancroft Way. At a social event at that house, Alpha Chi Sigma and Phi Lambda Upsilon members held a joint "jolly-up" in which students burlesqued the various faculty members of the College of Chemistry.[37] The chapter history book[5] indicates that "Prof. Tolman was much pleased with the humor of the situation in which he saw one of his own pupils, brother Stewart, carrying out an imitation of one of his own recitation sections. . . . The spirit of the evening was quite evident in the spirit which would cause our dignified 'Eddie' O'Neill and 'Pa' Booth to rag furiously for a minute." A 1915 entry in the history book stated: "The chapter house was opened as a general boarding house during the summer session. Owing to the great demand for accommodations on the part of visitors to the [Panama-Pacific] Exposition, all available space (even including the club room) was rented out. We made a substantial profit."

The chapter soon moved to a house at 2435 Haste Street and then, in 1922, it purchased and moved into a house at 2610 Durant Avenue that had previously been owned by the Sigma Nu fraternity. This purchase was made possible by a loan from the father of one of the members, William Hampton.[202] Around 1928 that house and the adjacent property was bought, for a goodly sum, by investors who then built the Durant Hotel. The chapter stayed in a house on College Avenue until about 1931, when it finally acquired the large Spanish mission-style house it now occupies, at 2627 Virginia Street. This location, on the north side of campus, is far from "Fraternity Row" (Piedmont Avenue, on the south side of campus), and, indeed, the AXΣ members hold themselves aloof from most of the activities of the Interfraternity Council. In the days when the Dean of Students sent out an annual list of the fraternities in order of grade-point averages, the AXΣ house was always at the top of the list, a fact that undoubtedly did not endear it to the other "Greeks" on campus. It should be pointed out that only twelve out of the approximately 78 Alpha Chi Sigma chapters operate houses.[4, 15, 202]

Although a women's chemistry organization called Alchemia (or Al Chemie) existed when Alpha Chi Sigma was chartered at Berkeley, this organization does not appear to have lasted long.[5, 6] Thus Berkeley women had no organization comparable to Alpha Chi Sigma until 1971, when, in a revolutionary step, women were first admitted to the fraternity.[3]

As of 1986, the national fraternity had elected eleven of its members to a "Hall of Fame." The Sigma chapter has the distinction of having three of its members, Frederick Cottrell, Joel Hildebrand, and Gilbert Lewis, in this prestigious group.[3]

Wendell M. Latimer

Wendell Latimer was descended from a long line of Latimers going back to 1660 in New London, Connecticut. He was proud to be a member of the Society of Mayflower Descendants from the Reverend Brewster, whose granddaughter married a Latimer. His father, originally from Illinois, moved to Garnett, Kansas, in 1886, where he took over the management of a bank. There he met and married a native Kansan woman who soon became the mother of Wendell Latimer. When Wendell was eight, his father died, and he and his mother moved to his grandfather's farm, where he lived the life of a typical farm boy. In 1911 he entered the University of Kansas as a pre-legal student and became active in the debating clubs. However, he became disgusted with the methods which he had to use to win debates; it appeared that logic counted less than the technique of "building straw men and tearing them down with irony and sarcasm." So he changed his curriculum and, during his last two years, completed majors in both mathematics and chemistry.[83, 110]

After receiving the A.B. degree in 1915, he stayed on at the University of Kansas for two years as an assistant instructor in chemistry. During this time he earned a Master's degree, carrying out research with Professor Hamilton P. Cady in which he measured the dielectric constant of liquid ammonia from -40° to 110°. Cady was an extremely modest, even self-effacing, scientist who was responsible for the surge of interest in liquid ammonia as a solvent in the first part of the century.[20] Latimer referred to him as an inspiring teacher with a truly great mind. Undoubtedly Cady played an important role in shaping Latimer's scientific character. I am particularly proud of the fact that, about thirty-six years later, Latimer and I coauthored a paper on absolute entropies in liquid ammonia.[114] This paper was the only one Latimer ever published having to do with liquid ammonia. Undoubtedly our collaboration was a consequence of Latimer's early work with Cady and my previous work with Audrieth, who was a great proponent of "the nitrogen system of compounds" and of the use of liquid ammonia as a solvent.

Cady sent not only Latimer, but also his own son, George, to be a graduate student at Berkeley. George worked with Joel Hildebrand on fluorine chemistry and then joined the staff at the

University of Washington, where he had a full, productive career in inorganic fluorine chemistry. George's son, Howard, later got his Ph.D. at Berkeley working with Robert E. Connick.

During the summer of 1916, Latimer attended the University of Chicago, where he took two courses given by William D. Harkins. He was much impressed by Harkins' ideas on the nucleus.

When Latimer arrived in Berkeley in 1917, he signed up to work with Gibson on low temperature calorimetry. In 1918, when most of the staff were in France, he was chosen to give the freshman lectures, an honor that he credited to his early debating experience. He was awarded the Ph.D. in 1919 and was retained as an instructor.

Latimer's first published paper, perhaps his most important, was coauthored in 1920 with Worth Huff Rodebush.[111] The title, "Polarity and Ionization from the Standpoint of the Lewis Theory of Valence," gives little hint of the most important topic discussed in this publication, namely, hydrogen bonding. The authors felt obliged to get permission from Gilbert N. Lewis to publish the paper because they used his new theory of valence. It is interesting that only after considerable argument was Latimer allowed to keep the discussion of hydrogen bonding in the paper. This paper is a classic because for the first time it described the bonding of protons between highly electronegative atoms as a phenomenon characteristic of associated liquids. However, it may be an exaggeration to say, as Joel Hildebrand once did, that Latimer and Rodebush "discovered" the hydrogen bond.[76] The principles of hydrogen bonding as applied to aqueous solutions of amines and tetraalkylammonium hydroxides had been roughly outlined in 1912 by Moore and Winmill.[146] And in his book on valence, Lewis pointed out that the idea of hydrogen bonding had been first suggested by Maurice L. Huggins, an undergraduate at Berkeley.

Incidentally, Rodebush was a professor of chemistry at Illinois who gave the elementary physical chemistry course when I was a student there in the forties. He was a handsome man, but a poor lecturer. He required his students to use the text by Rodebush and Rodebush (written with his wife, Esther Kittredge Rodebush).[186] This was surely the worst textbook that I have ever been required to read, and it probably was very effective in deterring students from careers in physical chemistry.

Esther Rodebush's sister was Mabel Kittredge, the long-time secretary and virtual manager of the College of Chemistry. Most graduate students referred to her and greeted her as "Miss Kittredge." It was only after I had been at Berkeley for a year or two that I learned that she was married and that her last name was really Wilson. Apparently she joined the chemistry department when she was unmarried, and most people never accommodated to the name change when she married. Some students were scared to death of Miss K. She wielded all the authority of the Dean and was not about to be intimidated by upstart graduate students. Others, who (like myself) were somewhat meek and subservient on first encountering her, got along famously and enjoyed her favor. But I digress.

In 1921 Latimer installed a hydrogen liquefaction apparatus in the basement of Gilman Hall.[177] He was the first in the United States to liquefy hydrogen and to make thermodynamic measurements in that temperature region. He used low-temperature heat capacity data in conjunction with the third law of thermodynamics to calculate the entropies of aqueous ions. Latimer was probably the first to grasp the importance of such entropy data. The entropy values allowed him to use thermal data to calculate free energies, and thus the driving forces, of inorganic reactions. When he began this work, not a single ionic entropy was known. Over a period of thirty years, he determined values for practically all the known stable inorganic aqueous ions. Aside from the value of the derived thermodynamic data, these entropy data have also increased our understanding of the general theory of strong electrolytes.

The many data on aqueous ions which Latimer obtained allowed him to prepare extensive tables of oxidation-reduction potentials, relating the various oxidation states of practically every element. These potentials, which he summarized in his classic book, *Oxidation Potentials*, have been invaluable in the systematization of inorganic chemistry.[109]

Latimer's Fun and Games

Latimer suffered a number of personal tragedies which might have embittered a weaker, less resilient, man. His father died when he was a child, his first wife died after a few years of marriage, and his first son died at age nineteen, apparently by suicide.[38] Nevertheless, throughout his life, Latimer was fun to be with. He had a sharp wit and a playful spirit combined with a gregarious nature.

Joel Hildebrand told the story of Latimer as a graduate student, presenting something or other in the research conference.[83] Gilbert Lewis constantly interrupted him, finally saying, "The trouble with you is that you don't take your audience into consideration." Wendell replied: "The trouble with me is that I can't keep my audience quiet long enough to say what I have to say." Lewis left him alone after that.

As a professor, Latimer entered the lecture hall of his undergraduate course in inorganic chemistry one November morning and found that somebody had attached to the blackboard a piece of paper with the words "Go Stanford" written in red. Without hesitation, he whipped out his Zippo lighter and, to the great delight of the class, ignited the paper and laughed as it was converted to ashes.

In the old days, most of the teaching staff were involved with the teaching of the freshman chemistry laboratory. Each laboratory room held about two dozen students, and a professor and a teaching assistant were assigned to each laboratory room. At the beginning of each semester, Latimer would enter his assigned room and, to the amazement of the students, begin to call upon the students by name. He knew the name of each student in the room! Of course, there was a trick. The students had previously been assigned to particular lockers in the room, and they were already seated at their respective lockers when Latimer entered. He had merely memorized the seating chart for the room. But the students never forgot that trick.

Latimer usually had no trouble holding the attention of his classes during lectures. He often had a firecracker ready to light in case some student dozed off.[58] Firecrackers also played an important part in his celebrations. About a month or so after I arrived at Berkeley, when I was working in my lab on the main floor of Gilman Hall, I suddenly heard a tremendous volley of firecrackers out in the hall. Everybody in the building rushed to find out what was happening. This was Latimer's way of announcing that William Francis Giauque had just won the Nobel Prize in Chemistry.

In the spring of 1963, eight years after Latimer's death, the dedication ceremonies for Latimer Hall were held in the plaza just outside the main entrance of the building. Probably a lot of people wondered what the devil George Pimentel and I were up to when, completely unannounced, we set off a bunch of firecrackers during the middle of this formal affair.

The Christmas season encouraged Latimer's playfulness. In the days when the fall semester ended right before Christmas, Latimer was known to send passing grades to barely deserving students over the signature Santa Claus. And he usually started each Faculty Club Christmas party by inserting a cigarette between the lips of the stuffed moose head that looked over the chemists' table.

During the Depression, Little Willie rhymes were popular. Latimer contributed the following.

LITTLE WILLIE RIMES FOR CHEMISTS
Synthesized by Wendell M. Latimer

Little Willie, good as pie,
Fed the cat on alkali.
Now the process, with yields first-rate,
Produces potassium pussiate.

Little Willie, hard as rocks,
Put fulminate in Daddy's socks.
Now Daddy really wants to know
How long it takes to grow a toe.

Little Willie, tried and true,
Fed his sis on methylene blue.
Now Sister has a perplexed look
Whene'er she sees a babbling brook.

Little Willie, happy and free,
Took a breath of H_3P.
Now Willie belches rings of smoke,
And thinks it's quite a parlor joke.

Little Willie, calm and placid,
Boiled his ma in nitric acid.
Now Mother dear is just a plastic,
Transparent, clear; but non-elastic.

Little Willie, full of glee,
Put radium in Grandma's tea.
Now Grandpa thinks it a lark
To see her glowing in the dark.

Little Willie, mean as hell,
Fed the goat some cal-o-mel.
Now just look at poor old Nannie,
Sitting there upon her fannie.

Little Willie, I hate to tell,
Soaked his dad in HCl.
Now the chemist at his sink
Wonders what made all the stink.

Little Willie, the so and so,
Put H_2S in our H_2O.
Now this was not so bad at all,
For we drink nought but alcohol.

The following facts may help the non-chemist to understand some of the above rhymes. (1) Fulminates are explosive. (2) The ingestion of methylene blue causes the urine to be colored blue. (An old fraternity trick was to put methylene blue into blueberry pie, where it wouldn't be noticed.) (3) When PH_3 is prepared by the hydrolysis of calcium phosphide, it is usually contaminated with P_2H_4, which is spontaneously inflammable. So when the generated gas is bubbled up through water, each bubble produces a poof and a smoke ring. A well-known lecture demonstration of the good old days. I don't understand why Latimer wrote H_3P instead of the usual PH_3. It's as unusual as writing OH_2 instead of H_2O. The scanning and rhyming would be unchanged. (4) Calomel, Hg_2Cl_2, has been used as a cathartic.

There are very few people who met Latimer who didn't like him. One reason for this is the fact that he was adept at defusing those who were temporarily angry at him. Once G. Frederick (Fat) Smith of the University of Illinois wrote an angry letter to Latimer, upbraiding him for allegedly telling a reporter that perchloric acid is a very hazardous material and that even a matchstick dropped into perchloric acid would cause a violent explosion. Smith concluded his long letter thus:[205]

"I suppose it will be natural for you to make no reply to these comments. If not, I will threaten to corner you at the next national meeting and get your comments by word of mouth. Maybe we can perform the cellulose experiment to convince you at that time."

Latimer replied:[106]

Dear Professor Smith:
   I am indeed surprised that I have been quoted so widely on the subject of perchloric acid. I held a two minute telephone conversation one evening with a reporter on a Hearst paper and what he may have done with that conversation is unknown to me as I did not even see or hear my name mentioned. He wanted to know if perchloric acid was explosive. I recall that I said it could be handled safely but mixtures with organic materials were highly explosive. I had in mind a mean explosion one of our men had a few years ago with barium acetate in perchloric acid.
   You should know that university men are more or less helpless against the type of reporter who wishes to use their name to give authority to his story. I hope I am doing a good job teaching my students both the virtues and the dangers of perchloric acid. I believe that you will find me not uninformed on both aspects of the case. I know absolutely nothing of the Los Angeles explosion and have not expressed myself as to a probable cause.
   I resent the implication that I don't answer my friends' letters if they are written in a heated tone. The next time I see you I want you to buy me a drink to make amends for such an insinuation.
                    Sincerely,
                    Wendell M. Latimer

   Latimer suffered fools without insult or belittlement. Once a man from the editorial department of a prominent San Francisco newspaper went to see Latimer to describe "The Seed Pod Theory of the Atom" and to present him with a manuscript on this topic. Later Latimer sent him this letter:[107]

Dear Mr. ----:
   I have studied your Seed Pod Theory of the Atom and think I can understand how one could get this point of view from a study of 17th or 18th century writers. My difficulty in accepting the theory stems from my knowledge of modern spectroscopy. The most accurate measurements in science are the frequency of spectral vibrations, and the quantum mechanic modification of the Bohr atomic picture is so successful in the interpretation of the spectra in terms of electronic levels that I have great confidence in the accuracy of the picture.
   I suggest that you spend some time reading a modern text on spectroscopy and see the complex problems which are

solved by our modern atomic picture.
It was a pleasure to meet you and see your manuscript.
                                        Sincerely,
                                        W. M. Latimer

When I was doing my graduate work under Latimer, I noticed that he was practically never in his office between noon and 1:30 or 2:00 in the afternoon. I learned that he spent most of this time at the Faculty Club playing hearts. This hearts game is a tradition at the Faculty Club that started in the 1930s. In those days it was sometimes played in the private room that Lewis rented. (For much of the year, Lewis's family lived in Inverness, about 70 miles away on the coast of Marin county, to which he commuted on weekends.) In the heyday of the hearts game, there would be as many as three tables, with four players each, going after lunch, with many kibitzers. During the thirties and early forties, the regular players were Gerald E. K. Branch, G. Ernest Gibson, Latimer, Arthur Hutson (from the English Department), Lewis, and Gerald Marsh (from the Speech Department). Around 1948, Charles Tobias (a recent immigrant from Hungary in the Department of Chemical Engineering) also joined the group. Even today the game is played almost every weekday, but Tobias is the only remaining "oldtimer." Hearts players have their idiosyncracies; in fact, to this day there are "plays" named after the individuals who frequently perpetrated them. For example, there are the "Full Gibson," the "Latimer Pass," the "Tobias Hold-up," and the "Hutson Memorial Discard." More recent developments have been the "Markowitz Gofer" and the "Diliberto."

You may wonder how it is that a game generally thought to be a simple children's game could engage the attention of intelligent men for so many years. I believe the reason is that the rules of the Faculty Club game are superior to those of the game as it is usually played. In all hearts games, each heart in a trick counts one point against the person winning the trick, and the queen of spades counts thirteen points against the person winning it. However, whoever wins all the hearts and the queen of spades has "goferred" and acquires twenty-six points in his favor. The Faculty Club version differs from most versions in three important respects. First, winning the jack of diamonds counts ten points in one's favor. Second, the number of players in a given game is restricted to four, and only four. Third, the amount by which one wins or loses is calculated by summing the differences between one's score and the scores of the other three players. The next time you play hearts, try these rules. You'll find that this version of the game is much more interesting and challenging than the usual versions.

Latimer, Nuclear Chemistry, and War Projects

"To you, Wendell, we bring today the remembrance of the things you did for us when we were beginning, when we hardly knew which way was forward to what the true values in science were. We came to you in the great days with Gilbert, Ernest, Gerry, Bill, Ermon, Rolly, and all the rest. I think there has never been a greater group than you were - never in the history of all of science. I used to think so when I was a young graduate student, but now thirty years later, in what is supposed to be the full wisdom and maturity of my years, I still believe as I did then. You were the best; you made science in the University of California, and in physical chemistry and nuclear physics throughout the country. You strong men welcomed Ernest Lawrence and kept and supported him in his bold attack on the atomic innards which armed this country with the personnel and know-how required by the Manhattan District Engineers and for the whole development of the atom in peacetime. You knew what was important and went for it boldly and imaginatively, and so attracted to you the means and men needed."

So spoke Willard F. Libby on the occasion of the dedication of Latimer Hall on May 3, 1963.[137]

In the fall of 1930, Libby worked as a Chem 180 senior research student under Latimer. He was assigned to build a fabulous new instrument which had been described in *Naturwissenschaften* just two years earlier by H. Geiger and W. Mueller.[57] This project was Berkeley's entry to the field of nuclear chemistry and resulted in the first Geiger counter built in the United States. Libby stayed on to do graduate work under Latimer, working on problems of soft beta-emitters. He developed many of the techniques which later were important in his carbon-14 dating work. After Libby received his Ph.D., he and Latimer started a seminar on nuclear problems which ran for many years. They attracted such men as Kennedy, Ruben, Seaborg, and Wahl and helped lay the foundation for the discovery of plutonium.[110] The separation of plutonium from uranium involved the application of oxidation-reduction chemistry, and Latimer, with his encyclopedic knowledge of oxidation potentials and inorganic chemistry, was just the man to help develop the separation processes.[74] Oddly enough, Latimer's heavy smoking indirectly helped the radiochemical work. He smoked Regent king-size cigarettes, which came in neat flat boxes that were ideal for holding the little metal plates on which radioactive samples were deposited for counting. Hundreds of these boxes accumulated in Gilman Hall during the war.

However, it was not just the atomic bomb that occupied Latimer's attention during the war. He supervised studies of the effect of weather conditions on the behavior of poison gases and the turbulence and diffusion associated with bomb bursting. This work was carried out in conjuction with William D. Gwinn, Thomas H. Norris, Kenneth S. Pitzer, and Samuel Ruben.[69] One of the gases studied was the very deadly S_2F_{10}. Testing was done near Davis in Yolo County, on the slope of Mount Shasta, in Florida, Canada, and on an island off the coast of Panama. The work took Latimer to England in 1943 and to Panama, Australia, and New Guinea in 1944. A publication on the "Pancake Effect" in gas clouds resulted from this work.

After the war, Latimer's services were so frequently called upon that he had to refuse some interesting and prestigious appointments. For example, in 1946 the president of the National Academy of Sciences invited Latimer to spend six or eight months as scientific advisor to General MacArthur and the Japanese.[92] This job would have been similar to one that Roger Adams (of the University of Illinois) had in Germany. Latimer's devotion to the University is shown in his reply:[105]

Dear Dr. Jewett:

The proposal to visit Japan as the representative of the National Academy of Sciences is certainly very attractive. Shortly after I received your letter, Dr. Harry C. Kelly stopped at Berkeley, on his way back to Japan, to visit Dr. Ernest Lawrence, and I had the opportunity of discussing with him the problem of the orientation of science in Japan. The situation certainly deserves the attention of the Academy and Dr. Kelly should be given all possible assistance.

However, I am convinced that it would be unwise for me to leave the University of California for six months at this time. Our department has suffered serious loss in the deaths of Professors G. N. Lewis and W. C. Bray, and we are in the process of rebuilding. We have hopes of molding a group of brilliant young men into an outstanding organization and I feel that I have very definite obligations to our department in this program. Moreover, I am directing the chemistry research in our Manhattan Engineering District Contract and

I hesitate to break my contracts with this research for a period as long as six months. Also, I am not at all certain that the Security Office would give approval for me to leave the country.

The decision has been a difficult one to make and I know I would have enjoyed the opportunity of participating in a program of such unusual international importance.

Very sincerely yours,
Wendell M. Latimer
Dean of the College of
Chemistry

In 1946, Latimer sent President Sproul a report in which he listed the contributions of the chemistry department to various war projects as follows:[115]

1. The discovery and isolation of the element plutonium, and the establishment of the essential features of its chemistry. This work provided the foundation for the successful production of the element at the DuPont Richland Plant and was a major factor in the atomic energy program.

2. Continued investigation of the properties of plutonium and other transuranic elements. The next 20 years will see the development of a great atomic power industry which will have profound influence upon industrial expansion in the state by providing the equivalent of cheap coal. Many of the basic patents upon which this new industry operates will rest upon the fundamental discoveries made in this laboratory.

3. Oxygen was a most essential war item and this department made two significant contributions to this program. (a) The development of mobile truck units for the production of liquid oxygen. (b) The development of the cobalt-amine regenerative cycle for the extraction of pure oxygen from the atmosphere. Oxygen is a $100,000,000 a year industry in this country and the new principles and applications arising from this research may have a large money value.

4. Research in Chemical Warfare. Chemical warfare was not employed in World War II due very largely to the fact that the enemy was aware of the high state of efficiency attained by this branch of the American Army. This department held large contracts for research in this field, and among the contributions were the discovery of a new method of impregnation which greatly enhanced the efficiency of charcoal (many million gas masks were filled

with this charcoal), studies on new gases, new recording instruments for gas detection, field experiments on the efficiency of large bombs, and studies on the effect of meteorological conditions on the travel of gas clouds.

5. The principal product of a university is, naturally, trained personnel, and students from the department of chemistry held positions of prominence in many war research programs throughout the country. As an example, in the field of atomic energy, in addition to the work on this campus, the following men with the Ph.D. from this department may be cited: Dr. Harold Urey, director of the Columbia University project for the separation of U^{235} by diffusion; Dr. Willard F. Libby, associate director of the same project; Dr. F. H. Spedding, director of the Ames Iowa project for the production of metallic uranium; Dr. Monte Evans, superintendent of design and construction of the DuPont Richland plant; Dr. John Chipman, director of the refractory laboratory at the Massachusetts Institute of Technology; Dr. J. W. Kennedy, director of chemical research at Los Alamos; and Dr. T. R. Hogness, associate director of the Chicago University Metallurgical Laboratory. In addition to these names, there were at least a hundred younger men working in the various laboratories of the project.

6. Department Personnel on War Research.

Dr. W. C. Bray, consultant for division 10 NDRC.

Dr. W. F. Giauque, director of NDRC contract on mobile liquid oxygen truck.

Dr. G. E. Gibson carried out investigations on the theory of the effect of oil on waves - Woods Hole Navy project.

Dr. Joel H. Hildebrand, liaison officer NDRC London office, in charge of work on Chemical Warfare incendiaries and explosives.

Dr. W. M. Latimer, director Manhattan Engineering district contract; official investigator NDRC Chemical Warfare and regnerative oxygen contracts; War Department mission to England and to South West Pacific.

Dr. Axel R. Olson, official investigator NDRC contract on Chemical Warfare munitions.

Dr. K. S. Pitzer, Technical Director NDRC Special Munitions Laboratory; also participated in Chemical Warfare research, University of California.

Dr. G. K. Rollefson, participated in work on the Manhattan Engineering District plutonium contract.

Dr. G. T. Seaborg, on leave to Chicago, directed work on the chemistry of plutonium.

Dr. T. D. Stewart, in charge of department program for ESMWT training.

Dr. Melvin Calvin, official investigator regeneration oxygen project; research associate plutonium contract.

Dr. R. E. Connick, on leave as research chemist on the plutonium contract.

Dr. W. D. Gwinn, Field director Chemical Warfare project, Florida and Panama; research chemist plutonium contract.

Dr. W. K. Wilmarth, research associate plutonium contract.

Dr. T. H. Norris, research associate Chemical Warfare contract.

Although the fundamental research program of the department was greatly restricted, a number of important contributions were made. Professor Lewis continued his research on the nature of phosphorescence and succeeded in elucidating this complex phenomenon. Professor Pitzer, in cooperation with the U.S. Bureau of Standards and the American Petroleum Institute carried forward the Thermodynamics of the Hydrocarbons, a research which has been of great value to the petroleum industry. Professor Branch published a number of papers on the Absorption Spectra and Constitution of Dyes. Professor Olson continued his research on the Mechanism of Hydrolytic Reactions. Professor Frank published a remarkable series of papers on Free Volume and Entropy in Condensed Systems. While this work has little popular appeal, it does constitute a notable advance in the theory of solutions.

CHAPTER 28

The Oppenheimer Hearings

After the war, atomic scientists were divided into two camps with respect to the hydrogen bomb, or "super" bomb, as it was referred to by Teller. There were those who felt that it should be developed as soon as possible to maintain an edge on the Soviet Union. And there were those who opposed such development either because they felt they had committed a sin by helping to develop the atom bomb or because they felt the hydrogen bomb was technically infeasible. Latimer and most of the Berkeley atomic scientists were in the first camp. In October 1949, Lawrence, Alvarez and Latimer went to Washington and brought the issue to a head by talking to members of the Joint Congressional Committee on Atomic Energy and to Admiral Strauss.

I have already mentioned Latimer's part in helping to organize the Livermore Radiation Laboratory for the development of hydrogen bombs. A much clearer picture of his activities in this area as well as insight to his personality can be gotten from his testimony before the personnel security board in the matter of J. Robert Oppenheimer, held in 1954.[220] The following quotations are verbatim except for minor editing to eliminate repetitions and to make for easier reading.

Q. Doctor, did there come a time when you began thinking about a weapon which is called the H-bomb?

A. Yes. I suspect I started worrying about the H-bomb before most people. Just as soon as it became evident to me that the Russians were not going to be cooperative and were distinctly unfriendly. I felt that it was only a question of time that the Russians got the A-bomb. I haven't much confidence in secrecy keeping these things under control very long. It seemed to me obvious that they would get the A-bomb. It also seemed to me obvious that the logical thing for them to do was to shoot immediately for the super weapon, that they knew they were behind us in the production of a bomb. So I suspect it was around 1947 that I started worrying about the fact that we seemed to be twiddling our thumbs and doing nothing.

As time passed, I got more and more anxious over this situation that we were not prepared to meet, it seemed to me, a crash program of the Russians. I talked to a good many people about it, members of the General Advisory Committee.

Q. Do you recall who you talked to about it?

A. I talked to Glenn Seaborg for one. I didn't get much satisfaction out of the answers. They seemed to me most of them on the phony side.

Q. Doctor, may I interpose right here before we go on to ask you a couple of questions, first, why did it seem obvious to you that the Russians would proceed from the A-bomb to the H-bomb?

A. They knew they were behind us on the A-bomb, and if they could cut across and beat us to the H-bomb or the super weapons, they must do it. I could not escape from the conclusion that they must take that course of action. It was the course of action that we certainly would have taken if we were behind.

Q. The second question is, you said that we seemed to be twiddling our thumbs in the matter. What was the basis for that feeling on your part?

A. In the period between 1945 and 1949 we didn't get anywhere in our atomic energy program in any direction. We didn't expand our production of uranium much. We didn't really get going on any reactor program. We didn't expand to an appreciable extent our production of fissionable material. We just seemed to be sitting by and doing nothing.

Q. Reverting again to your narrative, you said you talked to Dr. Seaborg and others about going ahead with the H-bomb, and their answers, you said, seemed to be phony. What did you mean by that?

A. I can't recall all the details during that period. When the Russians exploded their first A-bomb, then I really got concerned.

Q. What did you do?

A. In the first place, I got hold of Ernest Lawrence and I said, "Listen, we have to do something about it." I think it was after I saw Ernest Lawrence in the Faculty Club on the campus, the same afternoon he went up on the Hill and Dr. Alvarez got hold of him and told him the same thing. I guess the two of us working on him at once with different impulses got him excited, and the three of us went to Washington that weekend to attend another meeting, and we started talking the best we could, trying to present our point of view to various men in Washington.

On that first visit the reception was, I would say, on the whole favorable. Most people agreed with us, it seemed to us, that it should be done.

Q. Do you recall whom you saw on that occasion?

A. Around the Commission I think Dean was the only Commissioner there. I talked largely to the chemistry group there, to Dr. Pitzer and Dr. Lauritsen, and Dr. Lawrence and Dr. Alvarez talked to a good many other men. They talked to, as I recall, members of the joint congressional committee, and to various men in the Air Force and Army.

Q. Do you recall whether you talked to any other scientists who were not with the Commission?

A. Yes. I talked to Dr. Libby and Dr. Urey in Chicago. I talked to everybody I could, but I don't remember now. I definitely tried to build up pressure for it.

Q. What was the reception of your suggestions received at that period of time? I am speaking of the time 2 or 3 weeks after the Russian explosion.

A. It was favorable, I would say. We met practically no opposition as I recall.

Q. Will you tell us whether or not that situation changed?

A. It definitely changed within a few weeks. There had been a lot of back pressure built up, I think primarily from the Advisory Committee.

Q. Would you explain that to us a bit?

A. I don't remember now all the sources of information I had on it, but we very quickly were aware of the fact that the General Advisory Committee was opposed.

Q. What was the effect of that opposition by the committee upon fellow scientists, if you know?

A. There were not many scientists who knew the story. I frankly was very mystified at the opposition.

Q. Why?

A. Granted at that time the odds of making a super weapon were not known, they talked about 50-50, 10 to 1, 100 to 1, but when the very existence of the nation was involved, I didn't care what the odds were. One hundred to one was too big an odd for this country to take, it seemed to me, even if it was unfavorable. The answers that we kept getting were that we should not do it on moral grounds. If we did it, the world would hate us. If we didn't do it, the Russians wouldn't do it. It was too expensive. We didn't have the manpower. These were the types of argument that we got and they disturbed me.

Q. Did you ascertain the source of any of this opposition?

A. I judge the source of it was Dr. Oppenheimer.

Q. Why?

A. You know, he is one of the most amazing men that the country has ever produced in his ability to influence people. It is just astounding the influence that he has upon a group. It is an amazing thing. His domination of the General Advisory Committee was so complete that he always carried the majority with him, and I don't think any views came out of that Committee that weren't essentially his views.

As far as the security board was concerned, probably the most important part of Latimer's testimony was the following.

Q. Would you care to give the board, sir, any comments you have upon the basis of your knowledge of Dr. Oppenheimer as to his character, his loyalty and his associations in that context?

A. That is a rather large order.

Q. I know it is, Doctor.

A. His associations at Berkeley were well known. The fact that he did have Communist friends. I never questioned his loyalty. There were elements of the mystic in his apparent philosophy of life that were very difficult to understand. He is a man of tremendous sincerity and his ability to convince people depends so much upon this sincerity. But what was back of his philosophy I found very difficult to understand.

A whole series of events involved the things that started happening immediately after he left Los Alamos. Many of our boys came back from it pacifists. I judged that was due very largely to his influence, this tremendous influence he had over those young men. Various other things started coming into the picture.

For example, his opposition to the security clause in the atomic energy contracts, opposition on the floor of the National Academy which was very intense and showed great feeling here. These various arguments which were used for not working on the H-bomb, the fact that he wanted to disband Los Alamos. The fact of the things that weren't done the four years that we twiddled our thumbs. All these things seemed to fit together to give a certain pattern to his philosophy. A man's motives are just something that you can't discuss, but all his reactions were such as to give me considerable worry about his judgment as a security risk.

Q. I will put it in very simple terms, Doctor. Having in mind all that you have said, and you know, would you trust him?

A. You mean in matters of security?

Q. Yes, sir.

A. I would find - trust, you know, involves a reasonable doubt, I would say.

Q. That is right.

A. On that basis I would find it difficult to do so.

Much later, the testimony went as follows.

Q. Wasn't it true that many scientists after the explosion at Hiroshima and perhaps even before that, were terribly troubled by this weapon?

A. Oh, yes.

Q. Weren't you, sir?

A. I was more troubled by what the Russians might do along the same line.

Q. I would like to ask you whether you were troubled by this weapon.

A. No.

Q. Were you troubled by the fact that 70,000 people were killed at Hiroshima?

A. I felt that you might even have saved lives. I had been in the Pacific and I had seen something of the difficulty of getting the Japanese out of caves. I went over there on a special mission that involved that problem. I felt that if we had to land our boys on the coast of Japan, and knowing what I know about the difficulty of getting Japanese out of underground positions, that the loss of life might be very much greater.

Q. I think we all understand that consideration, Dr. Latimer, and I think we all share it. What I would like to know is whether you were troubled by the fact that 70,000 people were killed at Hiroshima.

A. I suppose I was troubled to the same extent that I was troubled by the great loss of life which occurred in our fire bombs over Tokyo. The two things were comparable in my mind. I am troubled by war in general.

CHAPTER
29

Humanum Est Errare

Even the most brilliant people make mistakes. In fact, if one habitually does novel, exciting things in science, the odds are fairly high that some of them are "crazy" or at least wrong. Around 1927, Fred Allison of the Alabama Polytechnic Institute started research on the so-called magneto-optic method.[1] The experiments involved passing the light from a spark through a Nicol prism and an aqueous solution in a magnetic field. Electrical adjustments were then made until the intensity of the very dim flash of light was minimized. Allison obtained separate minima for each salt in the solution. Any concentration greater than about 10^{-8} molar caused a minimum, but the effect disappeared sharply at lower concentrations. Even isotopes of elements gave separate minima. For example, in the case of lead salts, Allison found sixteen different minima which he interpreted as evidence for sixteen different isotopes. This method became a means of detecting previously undiscovered elements. Thus, alabamine (now astatine) and virginium (now francium) were "discovered."

Well, around 1932, Latimer became interested in this method. Let me quote Irving Langmuir as he told the story in a retrospective talk in 1953:[104]

"Latimer said, 'There's something funny about this Allison effect, how they can detect isotopes.' He had known somebody who had been down with Allison and who had been very much impressed by the effect, and he said to Lewis, 'I think I'll go down and see Allison, to Alabama, and see what there is in it. I'd like to use some of these methods.'

"Now people had begun to talk about spectroscopic evidence that there might be traces of hydrogen of atomic weight three. It wasn't spoken of as tritium at that time, but hydrogen of atomic weight three that might exist in small amounts. There was a little spectroscopic evidence for it, and Latimer said, 'Well, this might be a way of finding it. I'd like to be able to find it.' So he went and spent three weeks at Alabama with Allison, and before he went he talked it over with G. N. Lewis about what he thought the prospects were, and Lewis said, 'I'll bet you ten dollars you'll find there's nothing in it.' And so they had this bet on. He went down there and he came back. He set up the apparatus and made it work so well that G. N. Lewis paid him the ten dollars. He then discovered tritium and he published an article in the *Physical Review*. Just a little short note saying that, using Allison's method, he had detected the isotope of hydrogen of atomic weight three. And he made some sort of estimate as to its concentration.

"Well, nothing more was heard about it. I saw him then, seven or eight years after that. I had written these things up before, about this Allison effect, and I told him about this point of view and how the Allison effect fits all these characteristics. Latimer said, 'You know, I don't know what was wrong with me at that time. After I published that paper I never could repeat the experiments again. I haven't the least idea why. But those results were wonderful; I showed them to G. N. Lewis and we both agreed that it was all right. They were clean-cut. I don't know what else I could have done, but later on I just couldn't ever do it again.'"

During the discussion after Langmuir's talk, the following exchange took place between Herman A. Liebhafsky and Langmuir:

Liebhafsky: I just wanted to point out that perhaps the neatest comment [on this topic] was made at the University of California when this business was discussed at the Research Conference there in about 1930 or '32. Professor Birge said that this effect was just Allison wonderland.
Langmuir: Did you ever hear Latimer talk about it?
Liebhafsky: Well, Latimer was pushing it, and you've got to allow for Latimer's persuasiveness. There were people on the faculty that I'm sure never believed it.
Langmuir: But it was funny that G. N. Lewis would believe it.
Liebhafsky: Well, you know that there is a very close personal relationship between Latimer and Lewis.
Langmuir: I understand that Lewis got back his ten dollars.

Actually, six years after the tritium paper, Latimer and his coworker in the tritium discovery work published a retraction:[112]

"We were led to conclude from visual observations that the minima reported by Allison in his magneto-optic method were reproducible. Our conclusions are certainly wrong as we have not been able by any purely objective method to check these results. In order to clear up the record we wish to make this retraction.

"There have been so many cases of erroneous deduction resulting from visual observations at very low light intensities that the problem is worthy of serious consideration. In addition to the magneto-optic effect, we may list the numerous N-ray experiments, the Davis and Barnes experiments on the capture of electrons by α-particles, and the Pokrovskii experiments on the emission of α-particles from lead by x-ray excitation.

"In all of these cases the experimenters have been convinced that their observations are real and that their eyes cannot deceive them. This effect might be explained as arising from slight movement of the eye so that the light falls upon a less sensitive region of the retina. To the observer this would appear to be a change of intensity. There may also be some question as to the nerve centers which respond to low order stimuli and the possibility that such centers may be lacking in the usual power of discrimination. However, an element of suggestibility or hypnotism must also be present."

Even Lewis, the most revered of all Berkeley chemists, was not immune to self-deception. In 1914, he published an article on his theory of ultimate rational units in which he made some nonsensical calculations.[134] Lewis believed that it should be possible to find relations between all the measuring units of physics and chemistry that would give a set of dimensionless universal constants. These he called the ultimate rational units. Following this rationale, he came up with an expression equating the Stefan's law constant to a function of fundamental constants. Plugging in the known values for the constants, he calculated a Stefan's law constant that was very close to the experimentally measured value. Similarly, he calculated a value for Planck's constant that was quite close to the experimental value. However, it turns out that the agreements between theory and experiment were completely accidental - sort of like coming up with your phone number after taking the square root of the logarithm of your street address.

There is no evidence that Lewis ever discarded this idea.[135] In fact, nine years later, he derived a formula for the entropy of a monatomic gas which, although incorrect, gave values that agreed well enough with experiment that he believed the equation to be correct. This equation can be found in chapter 32 of the classic book on thermodynamics that he wrote with Merle Randall.[129] Lewis predicted that "new experimental determinations will bring the entropies constantly nearer to those calculated from the equation." This equation for the entropy of a monatomic gas is as follows:

$$S = R\ln(T^{3/2}M^{3/2}V) + C.$$

If we equate the constant C given by Lewis to the generally accepted constant C of the Sackur-Tetrode equation, we obtain the relation

$$h = [2.301(2^{9/2}\pi^{5/2})e^2]/c,$$

where h is Planck's constant, e is the electronic charge, and c is the velocity of light. This result is wrong and is not even dimensionally correct.

Lewis went astray again in 1925, when he considered the logical consequences of his belief in the "symmetry of time."[211] After discussing "the law of entire equilibrium" (which others referred to as the principle of microscopic reversibility), he wrote:[131]

"The law of entire equilibrium might have been called the law of reversibility to the last detail. If we should consider any one of the elementary processes which are occurring in a system at equilibrium, and could let us say, obtain a moving-picture film for such a process, then this film reeled backward would present an equally accurate picture of a reverse process which is also occurring in the system and with equal frequency. Therefore in any system at equilibrium, time must lose the unidirectional character which plays so important a part in the development of the time concept. In a state of equilibrium there is no essential difference between backward and forward direction in time, or, in other words, there is complete symmetry with respect to past and future. I believe that some of the ideas contained in this paper have been suggested by the work of Einstein, but he has not proposed this law of equilibrium. Indeed one of the first applications which I shall make, in a subsequent paper, will be to the interaction between matter and light, where I shall attempt to demonstrate the invalidity of Einstein's derivation of Planck's radiation formula."

Indeed, Lewis soon thereafter wrote a paper, "The Nature of Light," in which he stated[132] that "an atom never emits light except to another atom, and that it is as absurd to think of light emitted by one atom regardless of the existence of a receiving atom as it would be to think of an atom absorbing light without the existence of light to be absorbed. I propose to eliminate the idea of mere emission of light and substitute the idea of transmission, or a process of exchange of energy between two definite atoms or molecules. Now, if the process be regarded as a mere exchange, the law of entire equilibrium . . . requires us to consider the process as a perfectly symmetrical one, so that we can no longer regard one atom as an active agent and the other as an accidental and passive recipient, but both atoms must play coordinate and symmetrical parts in the process of exchange."

This paper was received with considerable skepticism by the eminent physicists of the day. Finally, Lewis wrote to Einstein,[118] "The paper on The Nature of Light I should like very much to get your views upon. Although I state that it is an extension of your principle of relativity, it may be a step that you would be quite unwilling to take." Einstein soon responded,[46] "The ideas you suggest . . . are the same as I have agonizingly turned over in my own mind without coming to a conclusion. . . . I am completely convinced of the validity of your 'law of entire equilibrium.' But I can not agree with your opinion that this law proves the incorrectness of my derivation of Planck's law." He then explained why.

Einstein's remarks were devastating. Lewis was forced to reevaluate his ideas on radiative processes, but for several years he continued to publish papers in this field. In "The Conservation of Photons" he wrote,[132a] "It would seem inappropriate to speak of one of these hypothetical entities as a particle of light, a corpuscle of light, a light quantum, or a light quant, if we are to assume that it spends only a minute fraction of its existence as a carrier of radiant energy, while the rest of the time it remains as an important structural element within the atom. . . . I therefore take the liberty of proposing for this hypothetical new atom, which is not light but plays an essential part in every process of radiation, the name photon." Lewis's "photon" was not exactly our familiar light quantum. However, in the 1927 Solvay conference, Arthur H. Compton adopted the word with its modern meaning:[31] "In referring to this unit of radiation I shall use the name 'photon,' suggested recently by G. N. Lewis. This word avoids any implication regarding the nature of the unit, as contained for example in the name 'needle ray.'"

The word "photon" was immediately accepted by the scientific community, but Lewis's principle of the symmetry of time was ignored. No one seems to have developed his concept. Other scientists who later wrote about time reversal in quantum mechanics apparently were not aware of Lewis's work.

I don't mention these aberrations of the two chemists most responsible for the fame of the Berkeley College of Chemistry in order to demean them. Rather, my intent is to suggest that the rest of us should not be afraid to occasionally do or say unconventional things. Conversely, let us not be too harsh with others when they make incredible proposals, whether or not they are later shown to be correct. It is well to remember that, when Roentgen's discovery of x-rays was announced in the latter part of 1895, Lord Kelvin was completely skeptical and regarded the announcement as a hoax.[215]

CHAPTER
30

William F. Giauque

I took a full year of Advanced Chemical Thermodynamics from Professor F. T. Wall at Illinois, but it was not until the fall of 1949, when I started taking Chem 114 (Advanced Thermodynamics) at Berkeley, that I really began to understand the importance of thermodynamics in chemistry. I was fortunate to have Giauque as my instructor in both Chem 114 and the follow-up course in statistical mechanics, Chem 216. Giauque taught a no-nonsense course in which he emphasized practical applications and problem sets. He taught straight out of Lewis and Randall.

The day after the announcement of his Nobel Prize, we were scheduled to have a quiz in Chem 114. When he walked in the classroom door, we all clapped. He then said, on one of the rare occasions when he smiled for us, "All right, but we're still going to have the quiz today."

Giauque was born in 1895 in Niagara Falls, Ontario. His father was an American citizen, and therefore he was able to adopt U.S. citizenship even though he was born in Canada. His father died when Giauque was thirteen, and thereafter all members of the family had to engage in part-time jobs. His mother did seamstress work for the family of John W. Beckman of the American Cyanamid Company. After graduation from high school, Giauque worked for two years for Hooker Electrochemical Company and became fascinated with chemistry. When the Beckmans moved to Berkeley, California, Mrs. Beckman wrote to the Giauques of her husband's high regard of G. N. Lewis and the Berkeley chemistry department. Therefore Giauque went to Berkeley for both his undergraduate and graduate work in chemistry.[169]

Some remarks of Giauque regarding Latimer are of interest.[58] "My earliest personal recollection of Latimer is 1919. I was an undergraduate. He was seated before a potentiometer determining low temperature heat capacities, and as I watched he explained the measurements. Suddenly he announced that he had a dinner engagement and asked if I could complete a series of measurements he had started. I was anxious to try. However the potentiometer had an unusual feature in that a foot pedal switch was included in the galvanometer circuit. I filled his data book with the largest array of open circuit galvanometer readings on record. He never asked me to collaborate again but he did let me watch him and I learned much about high vacuum technique and how to silver dewar vessels, etc., when such things were not so common. Later I learned most of the fundamentals of gas liquefaction by watching him build and operate the first successful hydrogen liquefier in the United States. These things obviously had an influence on my later work."

After completing his Ph.D. work with Gibson in 1922, Giauque accepted a faculty position in the Berkeley chemistry department in spite of a strong interest in chemical engineering.

In his studies of entropy, Giauque realized that the entropy of a molecule can be calculated either from spectral data or from low-temperature calorimetric data. It was while studying the spectra of molecular oxygen that Giauque discovered the oxygen isotopes. There were some faint lines in the oxygen spectra that remained unexplained, and this was an intolerable situation to Giauque. After consideration of various possibilities, he realized that these anomalous lines could be explained by the isotopic molecules $O^{16}O^{17}$ and $O^{16}O^{18}$. But his calculations predicted some further lines that had not been reported. He wrote to Babcock, whose spectra he was using, asking about these missing lines. Indeed they were there, but Babcock had not reported them because he had thought that they were not part of the oxygen spectrum. Giauque was then able to announce the discovery of oxygen-17 and oxygen-18.

Most people would have ignored these minor deviations from the expected. They might have ascribed the faint lines to an impurity or to unknown higher energy levels. But Giauque was like a bulldog; he wouldn't let go until he could explain the discrepancy.

Such attention to detail characterized all of Giauque's research. His meticulous measurements of the entropies of carefully selected molecules enabled him to establish the validity of the third law of thermodynamics. Apparent exceptions to this law were always found to be explicable in terms of structural anomalies. He was awarded the Nobel Prize for his "achievements in the field of chemical thermodynamics and especially his work on the behavior of matter at very low temperatures and his closely allied studies of entropy."

When he was in Stockholm to receive the Prize, he sat next to one of the royal princesses, an intelligent woman who, said Giauque, spoke better English than he did. She asked him, "Professor, just what is the importance of reaching these extremely low temperatures?" Giauque claimed that he struggled for half an hour and was unable to explain its significance to her.[101]

Although Giauque was known for his rather gruff and forbidding demeanor, he was certainly not humorless, as I have already indicated. Once he even introduced humor into a serious scientific article, a feat that very few have accomplished. This occurred in a 1939 paper[61] in which he pointed out the folly of using a temperature scale based on two fixed points, such as the ice point (0° C) and boiling point (100° C) or the ammonium chloride-ice eutectic (about 0° F) and the human body temperature (about 100° F). He proposed a redefinition of the temperature scale in which one fixed point, the ice point, is arbitrarily defined. To help make his point, he added "A Parable of Measures to Improve Weights," which follows, in highly abbreviated form.

"An early scientist, who deserves much credit, desired a standard of weight. He selected two convenient stones. The lighter stone was very smooth, hard and dense, and gave every indication of durability; the heavier stone was definitely of lower quality.

"Now the accumulation of information available to this scientist being much less than that of the present, he failed to see the matter with as much clarity as might reasonably be expected of his current successors. His solution of the problem was to state that the heavier stone weighed 100 convenient units more than the lighter standard, which was taken as the zero of weight.

"This system served very well for a time, but presently weights below zero were found to be necessary and the tradesmen scarcely knew whether they were buying or selling when the customers asked for 50 units of bread and minus 10 units of cheese.

"A temporary respite from this difficulty was obtained in the following manner. A practical scientist decided to search for the lightest stone to be had. The search took him far and wide and, having failed to see nothing, he returned with a somewhat lighter standard for the new zero of weight. As a heavier standard he decided to use the weight of man, and the difference between the two standards was again defined as a certain number of units. . . . This scheme was of some temporary help to the tradesmen; but it was not long before someone found weights below zero again and the whole . . . system became unpopular among scientists although it is still used by a few practical groups.

"Eventually it became apparent that weight had an absolute value and the standards were themselves determined in terms of convenient units. The lighter stone was found to weigh about 273 convenient units, but as always, there were experimental errors,

and various contemporaries used values ranging from 270 to 276.
. . . In order to preserve the units in general use it was decided
to adopt only the unexcelled lighter stone as a standard of 273
convenient units and soon everyone wondered why they had done
otherwise."

David Lyon recalled his first year as a graduate student with
Giauque:[141] "When I came here in 1942, I brought some of my
midwestern heritage - including the belief that April Fool's Day
and Halloween had to be recognized with certain events. For
April Fool's, I corrupted a fellow student to help me with my
pranks. We figured out how to adjust the clocks in the lab so
they would run backwards. We came in late the evening before
and set all four clocks so that they would run backwards but
show the right time when people came to work the next morning.

"When the technician got to work at the liquid air plant, the
clocks said 7:45, but soon he noticed they said 7:30 and then 7:15.
He told Professor Giauque something was wrong. When Giauque
figured it out, he bellowed, 'This is a scientific laboratory! This
is no place for nonsense.' But later I saw him take one of the
clocks to his desk and take it apart to see how we had done it.
His curiosity and sense of humor just got the best of him."

Giauque's research productivity did not lessen during the
latter part of his career. In fact, he published more papers
during the last thirty years of his sixty-year stay in Berkeley
than during the first thirty years.

It is remarkable that, although Giauque was an adept experimentalist, he never owned an automobile until he succumbed to
family pressure after receiving the Nobel Prize. Even then he
refused to drive and was chauffeured by his wife almost until
her death in 1981. He died the following year.

CHAPTER
31

Willard F. Libby

Libby was born in 1908 in Grand Valley, Colorado, but he grew up on a ranch in Sebastopol, California. Sebastopol is located northwest of Berkeley, about forty miles north of the Golden Gate, in rich Gravenstein apple country. After graduating from high school, Libby wanted to be a businessman and a farmer, but his father recognized his genius and told him to go to college. Stanford was well known to the family but too expensive. So he went to Berkeley and moved into a boarding-house on Bancroft Way which, it happens, was run by Miss Kittredge's mother. He signed up in petroleum engineering but was influenced by the other students in the boardinghouse, most of whom were chemists, and after two years he transferred into chemistry. The only C grade Libby ever received was in Bray's tough course in inorganic chemistry, Chem 120. He was unable to do any better in the course and consequently regarded Bray with fear and respect ever after.[12]

In Chapter 27 we saw that Libby did undergraduate and graduate research with Latimer in nuclear chemistry. He completed his Ph.D. work on the natural radioactivity of samarium and neodymium in 1933, when jobs were very scarce. He lost out on a Harvard instructorship to Duncan MacDougall, a cryogenist from Giauque's laboratory. However, this blow was a blessing in disguise: the atomic world was just opening up, and Berkeley was the best place for someone familiar with the Geiger Mueller counter and chemical purification techniques. He was given a half-instructorship at Berkeley (at $1000 per year) and so was able, in a state of near poverty, to continue his research in nuclear chemistry. Libby never forgot the time when Carlos, the janitor who pushed his broom in the old Rat House, took pity on him and asked, "Would you like to borrow some money?"

At the time of Pearl Harbor, Libby was on sabbatical leave at Princeton with a Guggenheim Fellowship. Let's let Libby himself continue the story, as he told it to Mary Terrall in an interview in 1978:[214]

"I went to Dr. Urey, who was at that time the most prominent scientist at Columbia, even eclipsing Enrico Fermi, who was still there, and simply volunteered. This was the day after Pearl Harbor. I had written a paper at Berkeley a couple of years before on a new idea I had for separating isotopes. I thought maybe he might be interested in that, and he was. In fact, I was impressed that he had already read it and knew about it. And then he told me that he wanted me to join him and do the chemistry for the diffusion plant.

"[The diffusion process] is an old idea. I think the English were the first ones to say that you could do it, and the people in the physics department at Columbia. John Dunning, who was dean, and several others had said they could envisage how if you made a porous solid, like a brick, and then passed a gas through it, it would separate. My job was to make the brick such that it wouldn't react with uranium hexafluoride. Uranium hexafluoride is probably the most reactive gas known, so I had quite a job. I'm very proud of it. I think it's better than my carbon-14 dating, frankly. Never been published; it's still classified. But I'm very proud of it. We worked on that for four years. . . .

"The process wasn't invented until you could make a material which could stand the UF_6. What the physicists and the engineers would say: 'If you have such a material, then that's fine.' But I found the material and proved that it would work, and that's the contribution. . . . I've never seen a piece of research move so perfectly. We knew we had to find a material whose growth rate was controlled by electron tunneling. That I knew. That's the way I guided the whole thing. So we tested three or four likely candidates and the fourth fit. And that's the material." The patent applications for the barrier material, in the names of Libby and Anthony Turkevich, are still classified some forty years later and have never been issued by the U.S. Patent Office.

While working on the Columbia project, Libby had to contend with General Groves, who was in charge of the entire Manhattan Project. "Well, let me tell you how we'd treat the general. There was only one boss and that was General Groves. And every time he'd come around, we'd burn him up a slab of Transite. Do you know what Transite is? Well, I can take you out there; I have one out there on my barbecue. It's solid concrete. So we'd take a slab of Transite, and we'd light it up and burn it with fluorine. And the old general would just laugh like hell; he just loved that. Here we were burning concrete; he thought we were the greatest chemists in the world."

After the war, Libby joined a great exodus from Columbia to the University of Chicago, where he began his studies of radiocarbon dating. At the top of the earth's atmosphere, cosmic rays produce neutrons which combine with nitrogen to form carbon-14. This radiocarbon, along with ordinary carbon, spreads throughout the atmosphere and is assimilated by plants and animals. If the specific radioactivity of ancient living matter was the same as that of living matter today, then the level of radioactivity in any organic matter should be a measure of the time of the organism's death. This assumption is the basis of the method that has allowed the determination of the ages of materials such as wood, charcoal, shells, and skeletal remains.

"At Chicago, the first thing we had to do was measure the half-life, because the Martin Kamen-Sam Ruben work was brute force; they estimated the half-life to be 25,000 years. Well, when you have one estimate of three months and another one of 25,000 years, the first job is to measure it. So that was the first thing. Fermi used to ask me, 'Why are you spending your time measuring the half-life of carbon-14?' I said, 'Well, it needs to be done.' He said, 'But you could work on these others.' I said, 'Yes, I know.' He didn't know what I was after, and I didn't tell him. I didn't tell Urey either. And the reason I didn't was that I've learned one thing: if you have a really original idea, they won't support it. It has to be mediocre in order to get support, and I've had a hell of a lot to support. But if it's really original - like, suppose I have an idea to cure cancer - you couldn't possibly get support for it. There would be fifty-nine reviews against it. The peer-review system is built to kill new science. And it's killing this country. . . . We fill the library with pretty mediocre stuff."

Radiocarbon dating continually expands into new areas. It is being used to determine the age of soils and ocean-bottom water, the rates of exchange of atmosphere between the stratosphere and troposphere and between the hemispheres, and the rate of absorption of atmospheric carbon dioxide by the oceans. In a study closely related to radiocarbon dating, Libby used tritium to determine the recent history of water samples. First he determined the concentration of tritium produced by cosmic rays and then determined the concentration in various water samples to trace the source and circulation of water. The method has been a valuable analytical tool in studying the circulation of water in the atmosphere and in the oceans.

While working on these dating problems, Libby was engaged in a side project in biology. Here is the story as told to Mary Terrall:[214]

Libby: The main thing we did was called a horse farm where we built a large greenhouse and we grew plants with radiocarbon. That is, we had an enclosed space about the size of this living room, and we put radioactive CO_2, intensely radioactive, and put a whole bunch of different vegetables to see which ones could take the beating and which ones couldn't. And as a result, we got a whole barnload of radioactive harvest. And it was just at the point when I was going to put animals in there that President Eisenhower appointed me to the AEC, and that stopped that.

Terrall: What were you planning to do with that?

Libby: Make a radioactive horse.

Terrall: Why?

Libby: Horse serum, biochemicals - for research purposes.

Terrall: Were the radioactive plants used for anything then?

Libby: Yes, some of them were used, but not as much as they should have been. A very interesting thing happened. The little chemical companies were synthesizing carbon-14 compounds and they didn't like competition. The AEC had the policy of not competing with industry. And then I became AEC commissioner, so I had to enforce that policy. So we kind of closed down the horse farm, but other things were happening then.

In 1954, Libby accepted a five-year appointment as the scientific Commissioner of the AEC. In that position he encouraged the development of nuclear power reactors, launched a program for studying the worldwide movement of fallout in the atmosphere and stratosphere, and helped organize the International Atomic Energy Agency and the first Atoms for Peace Conference.

At the conclusion of his AEC term, Libby went to UCLA to continue his academic life. The chemistry department there was not strong, and Libby helped to raise the department to its present eminence. He was the prime mover for the establishment of a UCLA space research program, and he instituted a graduate curriculum devoted to training the "environmental doctor." He regularly taught the freshman honors course. In 1960 he was awarded the Nobel Prize for his carbon-14 dating research - work which had been accomplished mainly at Chicago.

Libby always went after the big and important problems. He was always trying to make a big leap forward in knowledge. He had many dazzling ideas, and enough correct ones to put him among the few top-notch scientists of the century. He was tough with his students, each of whom he treated in a special way in order to get the best response. Sometimes his method was to provoke anger, sometimes to embarrass by criticism, and sometimes to simply dare by making an extreme statement. But most of his students felt privileged to work with him and profited greatly from their association with him.

Ever since his days in Sebastopol, where his father instilled conservative beliefs in him, Libby was a political conservative. He was incensed by Linus Pauling and Bertrand Russell, who led the movement to ban atmospheric testing. He claimed that these scientists were speaking out of their fields and were taking advantage of their positions for political purposes. He liked to point out that public health records showed no correlation with the fact that Denver has three times the cosmic ray dose rate of Los Angeles. He was also a strong supporter of home fallout shelters, and became known for the fact that he had one of his "Poor Man's Fallout Shelters," supported with railroad ties, in his back yard. Unfortunately, the great Bel Air brush fire of 1963 destroyed Libby's fallout shelter, along with his home, and thus provided some support for those who felt that simple home fallout shelters were a waste of time.

During the 1970s, Libby was one of the 141 members of the Board of Directors of the Committee on the Present Danger, an organization concerned about the perceived state of the country's defenses and the consequences thereof.[191] During the 1950s this organization had relatively liberal members. However, when it was reorganized in the 1960s, the membership became distinctly more conservative and included people such as Eugene V. Rostow, Robert S. Mulliken, and Edward Teller. But despite the potentially influential positions that Libby held, he did not grandstand. He exerted his influence by the quiet lobbying of influential people outside of government.

Libby died on September 8, 1980. His UC biographers paid tribute to him by declaring:[11] "In the breadth, profundity and diversity of his many contributions, Professor Willard F. Libby must rank among the foremost scientists whose lives and spirits have graced this planet." The citizens of Sebastopol in Sonoma County are now frequently reminded that Libby was a local boy who made good. A portion of State Highway 116 between Sebastopol and Forestville has been named the Willard Libby Highway.[191a]

CHAPTER
32

Melvin Calvin

Picture two small boys playing with grasshoppers on a hot summer day in a back yard in Detroit, Michigan, around 1920. The boys found that if the grasshoppers were held under water, they would eventually stop kicking. But when the apparently drowned grasshoppers were then put in the sun to dry out, they eventually recovered and hopped away. The boys even tried to determine if there was a correlation between the time for which they were held under water and the time required for them to recover. One of the boys was Melvin Calvin, and, with his friend, he was carrying out his first experiment (a biological one, at that). About sixty years later, Calvin theorized that when they held a grasshopper under water, the breathing system (a series of pores in the grasshopper's abdomen) was blocked, and that when the pores dried out, the breathing system was opened up again.[152]

Calvin was born in 1911 in St. Paul, Minnesota. His family moved to Detroit, and he received his undergraduate training at the Michigan College of Mining and Technology. Then his family moved back to St. Paul, where he carried out his graduate work at the University of Minnesota. In 1935, after completing his Ph.D. work with Glockler on the electron affinities of iodine and bromine, he went to Manchester, England, to work for a couple of years with Michael Polanyi on porphyrin chemistry. While Calvin was in Manchester, Joel Hildebrand happened to visit the laboratory, was impressed by Calvin, and discussed with him the possibility of his joining the staff at Berkeley. When Joel returned to Berkeley, he convinced Lewis to offer Calvin an instructorship, which was accepted. Thus in 1937 Calvin became the first non-Berkeley-trained faculty appointee in 24 years, that is, since the appointments of Hildebrand and Gibson in 1913.

Soon after Calvin arrived in Berkeley, Lewis found a common interest that he used to determine whether Calvin would stay at Berkeley or not. He said, "Let's write a paper on the color of organic substances."[23] They laid out in the seminar room in Gilman Hall all the references to the color of organic substances which were available. They then searched out, read, and discussed the references for several months. After Lewis had absorbed and digested the material, he felt it was time to write. The process was similar to that used for the writing of Lewis and

Randall. Lewis walked around the table in the seminar room and dictated, and Calvin wrote. It went very smoothly, and little revision was necessary. The final paper, "The Color of Organic Substances," was published in *Chemical Reviews* in 1939 and is generally regarded as a landmark publication in physical organic chemistry. Lewis decided that Calvin could stay at Berkeley.

Soon thereafter, Lewis encouraged Calvin to start a similar writing project with Gerald Branch, the writing of *The Theory of Organic Chemistry*. Lewis said that Branch had it all in his head, but he couldn't seem to get it written down. An arrangement was worked out in which Calvin went to Branch's house for dinner once or twice a week. Esther Branch cooked dinner, and then Branch and Calvin went to work. Calvin added to material that Branch had written earlier in the week. Then they would rewrite the material and plan next week's task. After about fifty dinners at the Branches' house, the book was finished and eventually published in 1941. Another classic publication.

Calvin carried out research in collaboration with Lewis from 1937 to about 1944. During that time they studied, among other things, the paramagnetism of the phosphorescent state. Lewis surmised that this state was long-lived because it was a triplet state, and hence should be paramagnetic. They set out to prove it by measuring the deflection of an illuminated phosphorescent sample in a magnetic field. The experiment was best described by Calvin in a 1976 talk on G. N. Lewis.[22]

"For the balance, we needed two quartz fibers, about 2 meters long from which to suspend the sample. . . . Lewis got the glassblowing torch at one end of the 50-yard long hall on the top floor of Gilman Hall. He took the quartz rod about 4 mm in diameter, and stood over the torch, turning the rod. When the rod was just the proper temperature, he handed me one end of the fiber, and I had to run down the hall with it, while he held the other end. We kept repeating this performance until we got a couple of good fibers, which were then hung up inside glass tubes about 1 inch in diameter, with ground joints at either end. The sample was suspended from these fibers and the tip of the sample carrying rod was watched through a microscope.

"The next step in the experiment was to turn on the magnetic field and then turn on the light. My job was to tell him which way and how much the sample moved. I said that it 'jerked' the right way, but it came to rest going the wrong way. This went on for several days. We were illuminating the sample at one end of the magnetic field, and the illuminated part of the sample should have come into the field, but instead it jerked and then went back the other way. Lewis didn't believe these observations. He then let me turn on the light and watched himself; the results were the same - it went the wrong way.

"As you can imagine, this was a rather nervous time for me, as the results were going the wrong way, and Lewis knew that they shouldn't behave in that fashion. He could not understand the results. Late one afternoon we were down on the lower floor of Gilman Hall in the magnet room and the door was open. . . . Giauque came by and asked what the matter was (he could feel the tension), and Lewis explained what was happening. Giauque asked what gas we had in the glass tubes, and Lewis replied that there was air in the tubes. Giauque said that you shouldn't have air in the tubes as oxygen is paramagnetic. When we changed the air in the tubes to nitrogen, all the experimental results were proper, and as expected. The sample became heated by the light, which warmed the oxygen, and the volume magnetic susceptibility becomes less, so that the oxygen moves out of the field."

During the war, Calvin must have been one busy fellow. He not only helped Lewis with his work, but he also taught classes and directed a research project for the preparation of compounds which would reversibly absorb oxygen gas. These compounds were needed for providing oxygen to breathe in submarines and for use in welding on naval tender ships.

During the early war years, Calvin, Seaborg, and Kennedy lived in the Faculty Club. At that time, one couldn't have liquor in the Club except privately. So the chemists who lived in the Club would gather in one of their rooms before dinner and have cocktails. Calvin remembered an important conversation among the nuclear chemists that took place during one of these cocktail hours. The gist of the conversation was as follows. The separation of uranium-235 was anticipated to be a very difficult job. It was known that plutonium-239 was fissionable, and that the isolation of plutonium could be done chemically rather than by an isotope separation process. Thus the notion of going the plutonium route in the construction of an atom bomb was discussed, if not born, over cocktails. The idea was entirely new to Calvin, and he believed that it was new to the others as well.[152]

The first synthesis of carbon-14 was carried out by Sam Ruben and Martin Kamen in 1940 in one of Ernest Lawrence's cyclotrons. They immediately began research on the photosynthetic process using carbon-14 as a tracer, but this work was interrupted when the war started and essentially stopped when Ruben died in 1943 and when Kamen was banished from the Radiation Laboratory by a misguided federal security program.[95] After World War II enough of this isotope was becoming available to make possible its extensive use as a tracer in the study of biological processes and chemical reactions. Latimer and Lawrence decided that such work should be continued and that Calvin was the man to carry on the work. In 1945, Lawrence invited Calvin to form a group of chemists to exploit this newly available isotope of carbon. He offered, as a laboratory, the space that was left in the old radiation laboratory after removal of the 37-inch cyclotron. In order for carbon-14 to be used as a tracer it had to be incorporated into a variety of key compounds. Calvin organized a small team of talented chemists who made the key compounds and used them to deduce the mechanisms of important biological processes.

Very soon Calvin's small group became the world's source of carbon-14-labeled organic compounds. Because of the tiny amounts of carbon-14 available, the group had to learn to handle efficiently extremely small amounts of organic compounds. They began their studies of photosynthesis in the late 1940s. Calvin fully realized the importance of this project, and it is not much exaggeration to say, as did one of my colleagues, that Calvin attacked the project like Eisenhower planning the D-day invasion.

They fed the carbon-14-labeled CO_2 to growing plants and then isolated and identified dozens of labeled intermediate compounds. The main analytical technique which they used for the separation and identification of the intermediates was two-dimensional paper chromatography. Calvin had a hard time convincing his critics that this technique was reliable for the identification of compounds. However, in spite of a heart attack in 1949, he did. Eventually all the major aspects of the photo-synthetic process were unravelled during the 1950s, and in 1961 Calvin was awarded the Nobel Prize for that work.

In 1963 Calvin and his coworkers (including Professors Rapoport and Sauer) moved into a brand-new, specially designed building, to be the official home of the Laboratory of Chemical Biodynamics and part of the Lawrence Radiation Laboratory. This building, designed largely by Calvin, is a three-story cylinder, often referred to as "The Round House." The round design is reminiscent of his old laboratory, which had originally housed a cyclotron. This design was intentional; it forces the workers, whether they be chemists, physicists, or biologists, to work elbow to elbow. Thus scientists from different disciplines are brought together to share their ideas and approaches.

Although Calvin retired from the directorship of the Biody-namics Laboratory in 1981, when he became seventy years old, he continues an active research program, directed from his quarters in Latimer Hall. Current research projects include the study of "petroleum plantations" (that is, the "milking" of gasoline-like fuel from plants such as Hevea) and the development of artificial photosynthetic systems to convert either water into hydrogen, or carbon dioxide into a useful reduced compound.

I have always found it a pleasure to chat with Melvin Calvin. He doesn't put on airs or try to conceal his ignorance about a topic. In fact, his curiosity is insatiable, and he is almost always asking questions. Generally I find myself a little embarrassed when talking with Melvin because I am unable to provide answers to the questions he poses - questions whose answers I probably should know. But of course, the ability to ask good questions is a necessary qualification of a top-notch scientist. Melvin has the other qualification as well: the ability to find answers to the questions.

It is an interesting fact that metal chelate compounds have played an important part in almost all of Calvin's research. During his post-doctoral research with Polanyi, he worked with phthalocyanine complexes:

Polanyi recognized the similarity of this structure to those of the biologically important porphyrins, which are derived from the structure:

Calvin's second involvement with chelate molecules was during his search for an efficient oxygen carrying compound. At first, it was suspected that heme (the iron-porphyrin complex that forms the heart of hemoglobin) would be an important reference molecule in that search. However, it turned out that cobalt chelate complexes derived from an aldehyde or ketone and an amine were the best synthetic oxygen carriers. The basic structure of most of the useful compounds was as follows:[24]

The third time that metal chelates became relevant was during the photosynthesis work. The key molecule involved in the reduction of carbon dioxide in the photosynthetic cycle is chlorophyll, a magnesium-porphyrin complex.

The fourth study of metal chelate compounds was in Calvin's recent work aimed at producing an artificial photosynthesis assembly capable of converting solar energy into storable high energy compounds. In this connection, manganese porphyrin compounds have been studied as potential redox catalysts.[206]

It is clear that the early work with Polanyi strongly influenced the course of Calvin's subsequent research. In spite of this common thread in his work, it is nevertheless clear that his research is multidisciplinary. Calvin received his education in physical chemistry; he has carried out enough work on the chemistry of metal chelates to make him famous as an inorganic chemist, and yet he is best known for his work in bio-organic and biophysical chemistry and has even ventured into botanical studies. He is our best evidence of the virtue of eliminating formal disciplinary boundaries in a department of chemistry.

When Calvin was asked about his scientific style, he said,[152] "When I was making the choice of chemistry . . . it was chosen not because it was of service to man as such, that is, the practical aspect; it was chosen because it seemed to me a necessity to society, and therefore would assure me of being necessary to society and thus earning a living. It wasn't a choice because of service. It wasn't an altruistic choice; it was a very selfish kind of choice, a choice which was motivated, not by wishing to serve humanity, but by wishing to be of service, therefore be necessary, and therefore be assured of a livelihood.

"In recent years in common with most scientific people as they get older, most of them will begin to think more in terms of the social value of what they do. ... As you age, you think more about what the social meaning of what you're doing is, and this doesn't stem from the motivations that you hear in the public domain today - the social responsibility of scientists and all that. It doesn't come from that origin at all; it comes simply from aging and experience. There's a gradual diminution of creative capability with age - it sort of falls off a little bit - and so you compensate for it by picking things and thinking about things that are of service to your fellow man. And there it becomes a true altruism, but it's a true altruism, I think, which is dependent upon a security which comes only with age, you see. In other words, I can do it now with some confidence and security, which I couldn't have done 40 years ago, and so the motivations were different then than they are now."

CHAPTER 33

Kenneth S. Pitzer

Pitzer's paternal grandfather was a very successful farmer in western Iowa.[170] However, because most of his family suffered from hay fever and asthma, he moved, while still deriving income from the Iowa farm, to Boulder, Colorado, and then to Pomona, California. In California he bought an orange grove and a walnut orchard. In fact, the whole family went into the citrus business. The youngest son, Russell, who was Kenneth's father, did the best financially. Whenever he had the money to spare and there was an orchard for sale, he bought it. Although there were heavy losses due to a bad freeze in 1913, the citrus business was very prosperous during the 'teens and '20s. Kenneth's father then sold the orchards and put the money into Los Angeles apartment buildings. About that time, he was persuaded by academics from the nearby Claremont Colleges that there was a need for a college for women emphasizing social sciences rather than the fine arts, as was Scripps College.

Federal loan money was available for the building of schools, and Kenneth's father gave several million dollars as an endowment for Pitzer College. The money was largely used to cover the interest payments on the loan. With the aid of other endowments, Pitzer College has developed over the years into a very highly regarded college, now coeducational.

Kenneth Pitzer was born in Pomona in 1914. There was never any doubt that he would eventually pursue a scientific or other intellectual profession. His mother had been a mathematics teacher and, although his father was not particularly interested in science, he had a keen intellect and respected professional people of all kinds. Two uncles were very interested in mechanical and scientific things, and their encouragement focussed young Kenneth's interest in the direction of science or engineering. Pomona was only twenty-five miles away from Cal Tech, so, after graduating from high school in 1931, it was quite natural for him to go to Cal Tech for his undergraduate work. There he decided to be a chemist because of the influence of A. A. Noyes. This was the same Noyes who had organized the famous group of physical chemists, including G. N. Lewis, at MIT during the first decade of the century. At Cal Tech, Noyes took a great interest in freshmen. He encouraged the Institute to buy a building down in the spectacular Newport/Balboa Beach area, right next to his own house. He converted a room in the Institute building to a chemical laboratory and each summer invited a few students for research activity and found them some small financial support. Pitzer was invited there the summer after his freshman year and was very excited by the experience. The work that summer, plus a little work at the end of the freshman year and during the sophomore year, led to two important papers on the higher oxidation states of silver.[183]

Pitzer remembers some research he carried out with Pauling during his senior year:[198] "I was attending some of Pauling's graduate lectures, and along the way it was proposed that I do a fairly simple crystal structure problem. Rhenium hadn't been discovered long before and became available in a significant quantity only at that time, essentially. I think it was Yost actually who got a few grams of rhenium. Pauling, I judge, noticed in the literature that this tetraamminocadmium rhenate had cubic symmetry. Now cubic crystals are relatively simple to solve. So, it went through his head, I'm sure, 'I'd like to give Pitzer some simple problem that he can work out in a month or two, and Yost has just got some rhenium, and here's a cubic crystal.' So, he proposed that with some guidance from Yost I prepare the crystal and then do the x-ray diffraction on it. . . . It was rather a nice little structure, and it was an experience very valuable to me ever since. Having done that much serious work on crystals, I'm now even to this day quite at home with the languages of crystal symmetries and all that infrastructure of theory which most chemists don't have and which puts them off. I've said many times that this whole modern era of solid-state physics could well have been essentially done by chemists as a part of chemistry, except most chemists were put off by the basic infrastructure theory of crystals and didn't want to get into it. Therefore the physicists who felt more at home with that much additional mathematical theory took the whole thing up."

When the time came to choose a graduate school, Pitzer investigated Harvard, Princeton, and Berkeley. Harvard didn't seem to be very cordial. He was soon to be married, and Princeton was highly prejudiced against married graduate students - undoubtedly because of the influence of Hugh Taylor, the department head. Everybody at Cal Tech was enthusiastic about Berkeley, so he chose Berkeley without much further thought.

Pitzer described his choice of research director thus: "Now Latimer had quite an active program at the time I came: heat capacity measurements in relation to the Third Law of

Thermodynamics and in terms of chemical thermodynamics of various inorganic species (ions, solids, or the like) with an underlying quantum-statistical mechanical guiding theory. . . . This seemed interesting to me, so I chose to do that. Latimer was very much inclined to give his students general guidance and support but a minimum of supervision. That was fine with me. I was perfectly willing to make my own decisions. I was physically located right next to Giauque's laboratory, and Giauque's office was right in the lab, essentially. So in many respects I got as much advice from Giauque as I did from Latimer by just knowing that he had the answer and he was right there. And I was brash enough to go in."

At the time Pitzer entered graduate school, the problem of internal rotation about the single bond in ethane was one of the great puzzles of physical chemistry. In Pitzer's words, "There was a controversy in the literature. . . . Chemists through the years had said there was free rotation about single bonds without knowing just how free 'free' needed to be. There were a few papers calculating thermodynamic properties for hydrocarbons on the assumption of completely free rotation that led to disagreements with entropies measured by low-temperature heat capacities and the Third Law.

"A man by the name of Ralph Witt had come very early in the thirties . . . as a National Research Council Fellow . . . to work with Giauque. Giauque never did understand why he insisted on measuring ethane. But he did. . . . Giauque assigned a new graduate student by the name of J. D. Kemp, who just needed to learn the ins and outs of the lab, and they measured the low-temperature heat capacity of ethane. Then Witt left and Kemp did something else for his thesis - it was nitrogen oxides as I recall.

"But he had this investment in these measurements on ethane which Witt [didn't] seem to show much interest in. Then I arrived on the scene claiming to know something about quantum mechanics! So Kemp interested me in the problem . . . I said, 'I don't see anything too difficult about this problem. Why don't we go ahead and solve the statistical mechanics for the restricted rotor?' . . . And so we went ahead and did it. I did most of the statistical mechanics, but Kemp knew what was going on. We wrote a letter on the result, but then there were two full papers: one was a Witt-Kemp paper on the experimental Third-Law measurements, and then Kemp and I wrote a paper on fitting the data with a potential barrier of around three kilocalories."

When Pitzer completed his Ph.D. work in 1937, he was appointed to the staff of the Chemistry Department. He soon had a disagreement with G. N. Lewis. "One of my arguments with him was that we ought to have a quantum mechanics course in chemistry (which after two or three years we finally got). . . . He wanted to keep it as an undergraduate course. He believed almost as a religion that there ought not be any formal classroom courses labeled graduate courses. I think he was just trying to keep the amount of time that graduate students spent in formal instruction to a minimum. And if they had to take courses that were labeled undergraduate honors courses, then there wouldn't be many of them that they hadn't already taken. They would free themselves from the guidance of a formal course and start really working as independent scientists sooner. It was a good basic philosophy. If it had been carried to the extreme, it would have been overdone. But these pseudo-graduate courses existed, including the one in quantum mechanics that Bill Libby and I started the first year, and then I taught for several years thereafter. Many, many years thereafter. It was molecular quantum mechanics, if you wish, in chemistry."

With graduate student William Gwinn (soon to become an instructor in the Chemistry Department), Pitzer extended the theory for internal rotation to molecules with unsymmetrical groups and prepared convenient tables for the contribution of internal rotation to various thermodynamic properties. In a landmark paper in *Science* in 1945, Pitzer showed that internal rotation potentials contributed to the strain energies of ring molecules. Later, he made more detailed calculations of the structures of cyclopentane and cyclohexane and their derivatives, showing that the chair form of cyclohexane was more stable than the boat form and that the properties of substituents in cyclohexane are determined by their location as "equatorial" or "axial" according to the geometry of the chair form. The concept of pseudorotation in cyclopentane was introduced with Kilpatrick. These researches provided the basis for the entire field of conformational analysis that now plays a major role in structural organic chemistry.

During World War II, Pitzer was first involved with the micrometeorology of gas clouds under Latimer, as discussed in Chapter 27. However, much of his time was spent on a project near Washington, D.C., to help the Office of Strategic Services, a predecessor of the CIA. This project involved the study of devices for guerrilla warfare and intelligence. He worked on time-delay devices of the type that one could put in the oil spouts of trucks to prevent the trucks from operating or of the type that would wreck trains. Regarding this work, Pitzer said, "By far the biggest thing of military significance, of course, was that the entire railway system of France was tied up after D-Day. The Germans, insofar as they could resupply their retreating forces, had to do so by highway transport. There are some interesting - now open, published books - accounts of how those railways were tied up. I don't say that this wouldn't have happened to a considerable degree without our work, but our time-delay devices and our various types of railroad intercepting devices were all used by British agents."[198]

Although none of Pitzer's war-time work involved the atom bomb, his administrative ability and scientific expertise became so well known that, in 1949, he was appointed Director of Research of the Atomic Energy Commission. Now, the AEC was a fairly new institution at that time. During the war it had been possible to get top-notch scientists to stop what they were doing and to do things that were very important to the war effort. But in peacetime there was not that level of drawing power for recruitment, even in the relatively exciting new technological area of atomic energy. This recruitment problem was one that Pitzer and the various AEC laboratory directors faced in 1949. The question of competition between National Laboratories and universities also arose. Pitzer believed in and pursued the policy that the AEC should have a substantial number of small research projects in universities, generally on subjects that had reasonable relevance to AEC objectives, but independent of the major laboratories.

He returned to Berkeley in 1951 as dean of the College of Chemistry and continued Latimer's post-war rebuilding of the College. After Latimer's death in 1955, Pitzer also inherited control of the Radiation Laboratory chemistry group that had originally been Latimer's Manhattan Project group. This group was eventually expanded in scope to include members of other University departments such as Metallurgy and Ceramic Engineering, and became known as the Inorganic Materials Research Division. The administrative tasks associated with these jobs plus his own research work would have been enough to keep two ordinary men fully occupied. But he also had to attend to a multitude of incidental problems that are typical of the continual harassment of a dean. I remember two scandalous incidents. One involved the College glassblowers, who were moonlighting in their own private glassblowing shop in Berkeley. Pitzer summarily dismissed them from their College positions when it was discovered that they were using University-purchased glassware in their private venture. Another incident involved smoothing over the ruffles associated with a love affair between one of the married instructors and the wife of one of the graduate students.

The story goes that the instructor used to post one of his graduate students as a guard outside of his trysting room.

In 1961, Pitzer left Berkeley to become president of Rice University, in Houston, Texas. There he led the fight to admit black students. Ken recalls, "The trouble for all practical purposes wasn't on the campus - the campus was ready for it. The problem was in getting the alumni and the community to come around. A small portion of the alumni were the most difficult; they were the ones who actively opposed it."[42]

From 1968 to 1971, Pitzer served as president of Stanford University. However, this was during the height of the student uprisings, when all kinds of disruptive activities occurred, including an occasion when somebody threw a pail of paint on Pitzer as he was attending a banquet on the Stanford campus. Pitzer was unable to effectively pursue his main interest, i.e., the administration of research on the campus, and he resigned under some pressure from the alumni.

He was welcomed back as a professor of chemistry to the Berkeley College of Chemistry, where his research of the past fifteen years has been so dazzling that, for that work alone, he would now be world-famous.

One area of research has involved the thermodynamics of concentrated solutions of electrolytes and, more generally, ionic fluids. Pitzer found that a blend of theory for the coulombic effects with a few empirical parameters for short-range forces fits the data remarkably well. Others have applied his methods to deduce the phase relationships between various minerals and sea-water brines.

Another area of research involves relativistic effects on chemical properties. The work started out as simple scientific curiosity: can one explain chemistry with nonrelativistic quantum mechanics, or does one have to use relativistic equations? Pitzer found that when you apply relativistic equations to the heavier elements, they appear to have dramatically different properties than when you use nonrelativistic equations. Thus he has been able to explain a number of phenomena that have baffled inorganic chemists for many decades. For example, it appears that the so-called "inert pair" effect (as evidenced by the extraordinary stability of the lower oxidation states of the heavier elements of the families of elements following the transition elements) is a consequence of relativity. Similarly, the fact that the mercurous ion is dimerized as Hg_2^{2+} can be explained. Even the lanthanide contraction (which makes the elements following the lanthanide series smaller than expected from periodic table trends) can be shown to be partly due to relativistic effects.[42]

Pitzer is convinced that if one is going to be fully effective in chemistry, one must carry a certain amount of factual knowledge in one's mind. He feels that the teaching of chemistry in terms of systemization with theories has been somewhat overdone because much is known experimentally that has not been reduced to any sort of quantitative theory. He says,[198]

"There are people here in this department who very openly have no pretenses of doing any experiments. I think I contributed some to their success in guiding them as young people, not to do experiments, but to maintain contact with experiments, so that you're doing theory on something that is really of interest to the main body of chemistry, which is experimental.

"A man like Fritz Schaefer, for example, on the faculty here. When I came back first to the department in '71, I urged him very strongly, 'Now, you're doing beautiful quantum-mechanical calculations, but be sure you do a reasonable number of them on molecules where somebody is interested in the answer besides a few spectroscopists or other theorists. I think the breadth of his reputation in chemistry as a whole depends greatly on that.'"

Ken's favorite activity when he's not working is sailing. He designs and builds with his own hands the boats that he sails. His sixteen-foot sailboat, named "The Susan" after his engineer granddaughter, "was designed to sail very nicely without being an extreme hot rod." The boat is kept at Clear Lake in northern California wine country, where he also has a small fruit orchard with apricots, peaches, plums, and grapefruit. He tends the orchard himself. "I need the exercise," he says. "I do this instead of playing golf."[42]

Samuel Ruben

Ruben was born in San Francisco in 1913; he obtained the B.S. degree at Berkeley in 1935 and stayed on to do graduate work with Latimer on the production and identification of artificial radioisotopes.[108] During part of his graduate work, he collaborated with Martin D. Kamen (a recent chemistry Ph.D. from Chicago, working for the Radiation Laboratory) and James Cork (a visiting physics professor from Michigan) on a study of the so-called "resonance transmutation" of platinum by deuterons. This work showed that the bombardment of platinum by deuterons produced a large number of nuclear isomers. This discovery was quite surprising and helped to establish nuclear isomerism as a phenomenon of widespread occurrence. The experience led to a friendly partnership between Ruben and Kamen in which they, with their chemical expertise, exploited the combined facilities of the Radiation Laboratory and the Chemistry Department. Ruben initiated a study, with Kamen and Zev Hassid, of the metabolism of glucose, using carbon-11, an isotope with a 21-minute half-life. The procedure involved feeding plants $^{11}CO_2$, waiting for a predetermined period (a few minutes to an hour), adding a carrier compound, followed by extraction and isolation of the carrier and determination of radioactivity, if any, in the carrier. The carbon-11 was produced on the cyclotron by bombardment of boron with deuterons. In his memoirs, Kamen describes the work:[95]

"At the Rat House, Sam and Zev [W. Z. Hassid] would be waiting for me like sprinters at the starting gate. Beakers would be filled with boiling water or other solvents and pipettes ready to suck up measured volumes of radioactive solutions onto absorbent blotters, which would be held by tongs over hot plates and dried. All the necessary reagents and apparatus would be in place. The counter would be ticking away establishing the background activity. Each experiment had to be planned ahead in every detail so that no time was lost in confusion or delay in deciding what procedure to follow. Anyone looking in on the Rat House when an experiment was in progress would have had the impression of three madmen hopping about in an insane asylum. . ."

Although they did not identify the CO_2 fixation product, they did contribute to the understanding of the photosynthetic process. Their experiments showed the existence of two systems: a complex set of dark reactions for CO_2 uptake, and a light-dependent process for the simultaneous evolution of molecular oxygen.

However, it was clear that the half-life of carbon-11 was too short for these studies. They very much needed carbon-14, which was expected to have a half-life considerably longer than that of carbon-11. Late in 1939, Ernest O. Lawrence was anxious to show that cyclotron-produced isotopes were useful as tracers, so he authorized Kamen to make long-term bombardments using the cyclotron, with the aim of making carbon-14. In February 1940, Kamen completed a month-long bombardment of carbon with deuterons, hoping for the reaction $^{13}C + d \longrightarrow {}^{14}C + p$. Ruben converted the carbon to CO_2 and found that the sample had about 800 counts per minute, significantly greater than the background of a few hundred counts per minute. This was adequate evidence to claim the formation of a long-lived radioactive carbon, presumably carbon-14.

It happened that, the very next day, the Swedish Consul presented the Nobel Prize to Ernest O. Lawrence in Wheeler Hall auditorium. After giving the presentation address, R. T. Birge mentioned the recent discovery of astatine by Corson, Segre, Hamilton, and McKenzie. He then announced,[14] "I now, for the second time this evening, have the privilege of making a first announcement of very great importance. This news is less than twenty-four hours old and hence is real news . . . Now, Dr. S. Ruben, instructor in chemistry, and Dr. M. D. Kamen, research associate in the Radiation Laboratory, have found by means of the cyclotron, a new radioactive form of carbon, probably of mass fourteen and average life of the order of magnitude of several years. On the basis of its potential usefulness, this is certainly much the most important radioactive substance that has yet been created."

Ruben did not have the courage to be present, and Kamen had a sinking feeling that the whole report might be wrong. However, further work verified their discovery.[95] Even better, it was found that neutron irradiation of nitrogen (as ammonium nitrate) gives much better yields of carbon-14. Indeed, this latter process is still used for the commercial production of carbon-14, except that the high neutron fluxes are obtained from atomic piles rather than from cyclotrons.

Because Ruben had been made an instructor in 1939, he was able to continue his study of photosynthesis using carbon-14 with the aid of graduate students. But after the war started, Latimer asked him to work on a project of the Office of Scientific Research and Development. This was a study of the dissipation of phosgene on the beaches of Marin county, with the aim of learning how to immobilize beach defenses in a possible invasion of Europe. On September 27, 1943, he was in the open courtyard of the Old Chemistry Building, preparing to transfer some phosgene to a vacuum line. First he had to cool a glass vial containing the phosgene in liquid nitrogen so as to freeze out the gas. Unfortunately, the glass cracked when it was plunged into the liquid nitrogen, and the liquid phosgene was sprayed into the air by the violently boiling nitrogen. Ruben received a lethal dose and was dead the next day. He had no insurance, and his wife Helena then had to earn money as well as to raise their three young children. For many years, she worked for the Radiation Laboratory as an x-ray diffraction technician in the group under the direction of David Templeton.

It has often been claimed that, if Sam Ruben had lived, he and Kamen would have been contenders for the Nobel Prize for their discovery of carbon-14. As it was, Kamen was not awarded the Nobel prize probably because of the death of his coworker. In his memoirs, Kamen spends considerable time bemoaning the injustice of the fact that most of the papers he wrote with Ruben had Ruben's name first and that thereby he lost recognition.[95] Kamen felt that he was the main contributor in the discovery of carbon-14. He claimed that Mrs. (sic) Kittredge, the departmental secretary, was responsible for the order of names. Allegedly she gave Ruben the impression that if his name was not first, Latimer might not be inclined to promote him. And Ruben was as ambitious as any of his colleagues in his striving for tenure.

Glenn T. Seaborg

Glenn Seaborg started keeping a diary a few months before his fifteenth birthday. He had the section covering the period August 1934 to April 1942 typed up and published, and kindly provided me with a copy.[197] I have made considerable use of it in writing the first part of this chapter.

In 1934 Seaborg completed his undergraduate work at UCLA. In August of that year he moved to Berkeley to start graduate work in chemistry. During his first two weeks there, he talked about possible research projects with Rollefson, Olson, Gibson and G. C. Nutting (an instructor). He also attended his first classes, taught his Chemistry 1A laboratory section with Giauque, and attended the nuclear science seminar conducted by Libby. He decided to do his research with Gibson on nuclear chemistry, which meant that he would work in room 118 of the old Radiation Laboratory, where he would be closely associated with Dr. Robert D. Fowler. Indeed, because of Gibson's lackadaisical method of research direction, Fowler was his de facto research director during the first year. Seaborg spent a lot of time preparing instrumentation. He made an ionization chamber and linear amplifier for use in the measurement of alpha particles, a cathode ray oscillograph, and a Geiger counter.

Seaborg also caught a lot of colds, which he blamed on Berkeley's weather - damp and cold compared to Los Angeles's. To improve his health, he spent the summer of 1935 working for his board and room at a ranch in Pahrump, Nevada (near Death Valley).

In the fall of 1935, a new graduate student, David C. Grahame, joined the group and, for the next couple of years, worked fairly closely with Seaborg. As a graduate student, Seaborg lived in a boarding house most of the time. However, one year he lived in a rooming house and ate his meals in restaurants. He mentioned that occasionally he had dinner at the Hotel Whitecotton on Shattuck Avenue, where a multi-course dinner was served for 45 cents - a price he couldn't afford very often. Usually he ate at the more reasonably priced True Blue Cafeteria on Center Street. For relaxation, he went to the movies about twice a week. He also took a class in Elementary Tap Dancing in the Men's Gym, and, near the end of the semester, took part in a tap dancing exhibition at a fraternity house. That would have been something to see!

Of course every graduate student had to present a research conference on some article from the literature, and Seaborg chose to discuss the now-famous paper by Hahn, Meitner, and Strassmann in which they reported evidence for the elements of isotopes with atomic numbers of 93, 94, 95, and 96, obtained by the neutron bombardment of uranium.[70] Clearly a harbinger of future work to be done by Seaborg.

Seaborg got involved in a lot of different projects. For example, on April 3, 1936: "I ran into Jack Livingood, a staff physicist who works in the Radiation Laboratory. He mentioned that he was having a tin target bombarded with 3.5 microamperes of 5.2 Mev deuterons in the 27-inch cyclotron and asked if I would be willing to perform the chemical separations on the target necessary in order for him to identify the transmutation products." Seaborg agreed, and two months later Livingood and Seaborg completed and mailed to *Physical Review* an article, "Deuteron-Induced Radioactivity in Tin," Seaborg's first published scientific paper.

Soon thereafter, Livingood and Seaborg discovered several radioisotopes of iodine. Seaborg had the satisfaction, some twenty-five years later, of knowing that his mother's life was prolonged by almost ten years because of treatment with one of these isotopes, iodine-131. In fact, he now classifies his part in the discovery of these and other radioisotopes that are commonly used in medical diagnosis and therapy second in importance only to his discovery of transuranium elements.

When Seaborg completed his Ph.D. work in 1937, Lewis asked him if he would like to be his research assistant (a position analogous to the modern "post-doc"), at a salary of $1800 per year. Seaborg had been fervently hoping to stay on at Berkeley in some capacity and enthusiastically accepted Lewis's offer. During his two-year tenure in this job, he was able to continue a rather substantial effort in nuclear chemistry, with Lewis's blessing. However, considerable time was spent helping Lewis carry out experimental studies of "generalized acids and bases" (now called Lewis acids and bases) and other research.[194] The daily schedule during those years is described in Seaborg's diary:[197]

"Lewis arrives each day between 10 and 11 a.m. in his green Dodge car which he parks on South Drive between the chemistry buildings and the Men's Faculty Club. We then usually work together in Room 119 until about noon or 1 p.m., when he goes to the Faculty Club to play cards with his friends (he doesn't eat any lunch) while I go to lunch. Lewis usually returns to the laboratory at about 2 p.m., and we work together until late afternoon (4:30 p.m. to 6 p.m.). This gives me time to work on my other research projects before he arrives, during the noon break, and after he leaves in the afternoon."

The experimental work of Lewis and Seaborg on acid-base reactions served as the basis for a lecture which Lewis was to give at the Franklin Institute in Philadelphia in May 1938. Seaborg was responsible for preparing the equipment required for demonstrations that Lewis wanted to give. This led to an amusing incident in the laboratory.

"Today I helped Professor Lewis pack his suitcase for his demonstration lecture at the Franklin Institute next Friday morning. He is travelling to Philadelphia by train. I was pleased to see him bring into our laboratory and place on the bench two suitcases because I felt this would give me ample room to pack the material for his demonstration experiments. However, he told me that he would need much of this space for his cigar boxes. (He smokes 'Alhambra Casino' cigars incessantly and will need a good supply to keep him going during his visit to Philadelphia.) He filled one entire suitcase and part of the other with cigar boxes which meant that I had to exercise some ingenuity in order to get the equipment, chemicals, etc. into the remaining space."

A collaborative research with Emilio Segrè was one of several nuclear projects that Seaborg was involved with during the time that he was helping Lewis. On September 14, 1938, he and Segrè mailed to *Physical Review* a paper entitled "Nuclear Isomerism in Element 43." In it they reported that a new isotope of element 43 decays with a half-life of six hours by the emission of a line spectrum of electrons. They explained this as due to an excited state reverting to the ground state by the emission of conversion electrons and gamma rays. A week later, Lawrence told Segrè that he believed, after reading the paper and conferring with Oppenheimer, that they should withdraw the paper from publication. Oppenheimer felt it highly unlikely that such a high degree of internal conversion of a gamma ray could be correct. Segre and Seaborg were confident of their interpretation. However, after discussing the matter, they reluctantly sent a telegram to the journal withdrawing the paper. The October 1 issue of *Physical Review* had a letter by Pontecorvo entitled "Nuclear Isomerism and Internal Conversion," in which he reported, for rhodium, a transition similar to the one that Segrè and Seaborg observed for element 43. When they showed this letter to Lawrence, he conceded that they should resubmit their paper. Unfortunately they were scooped; the same issue had a paper by Kalbfell entitled "Internal Conversion of gamma-ray in the 6-hour Element 43," based on work with an element 43 sample that Segrè and Seaborg had given him. In June of 1939, Lewis said that he had been taking up too much of Seaborg's time and that he was putting him on the staff of the College of Chemistry as an Instructor. That appointment marked the beginning of the most productive two decades in Seaborg's research career, during which he and his coworkers prepared, identified, and chemically characterized ten new elements and significantly changed the form of the periodic table of elements.

But it wasn't all work and no play. For example, on the evening of May 11, 1940, Seaborg, Kennedy, Ruben, and Libby went out with Henry Taube to celebrate his new Ph.D. Seaborg wrote, "After a visit to Trader Vics on San Pablo Avenue, where we drank 'Zombies,' we then went to the Club Shanghai, a Chinese night club on 10th St. in Oakland, owned by Dr. Fong Wan, a well-known herbist. The floor show (TAI and MAI SING, a popular dance team ala Fred Astaire) was in progress when we entered, and Henry made quite an entrance as he pitched headlong onto the floor, the result of too many 'Zombies.' Needless to say, we had some difficulty taking Henry home." Years later, Glenn said, "I wonder if any of the people in that night club who witnessed our arrival would have believed that three of us [Libby, Seaborg and Taube] were to win Nobel prizes."

Incidentally, Henry Taube was made an instructor in 1940, but he served as such only one academic year. The next year he moved to Cornell, later to Chicago, and finally to Stanford, where he is today.

In July of 1940, William G. Young, chairman of the UCLA Chemistry Department, offered Seaborg an assistant professorship. Seaborg said that he would take the offer seriously and would let him know his decision. A couple of weeks later, Seaborg made this entry in his diary:

"I met with Professor Lewis in his office this morning to tell him about my offer of an assistant professorship from Chairman William Young of UCLA. Although I didn't say it, my inference was that I would be happy to consider an equivalent offer from him. Admittedly, I was concerned that he would suggest that I accept the offer and would wish me luck. To my delight he made no such suggestion but exhibited a degree of indecisiveness. He asked when I intended to give Professor Young my answer, and I said (realizing that I should give Professor Lewis time to consider the matter) that I would phone him tonight from the Faculty Club after 7 p.m. when the rates are cheaper. Lewis then thanked me, and the conversation was ended.

"Shortly after 7 p.m. I headed for the phone booth in the Faculty Club; this in full view of the occupants of the main lounge. As I hoped, Professor Lewis was there, much later than his usual departure time. He motioned for me to come over and asked whether I had called Chairman Young yet. I replied that I was about to do so; he then said, with a smile, that he had decided to recommend me for an appointment as an assistant professor at Berkeley for the next academic year, i.e., 1941-42, although he cannot guarantee that President Sproul will accept the recommendation. . . . Lewis then asked if I still intend to phone Chairman Young. I replied, 'Yes, but now I shall do it in order to tell him that I have decided to accept your offer.' I immediately phoned Bill Young to tell him of the Lewis offer and my decision. His response was that he was disappointed but that he understood my decision."

In 1985, Seaborg stated,[167] "My colleagues and I synthesized, identified and determined the key nuclear properties of plutonium in late 1940 and early 1941 in Berkeley using the cyclotron of . . . Lawrence. My coworkers were Joe Kennedy and Ed McMillan, junior faculty members, Emilio Segrè, a research associate, and Art Wahl, a graduate student.

"The experiments, performed at our initiative before the United States entered World War II, were part of our regular academic research program, and the results were voluntarily withheld from publication and kept secret when their importance became apparent to us.

"On the stormy night of Feb. 23, 1941, Art Wahl performed the oxidation that gave us proof that what we had made was chemically different from all other known elements. It was the first realization of the alchemist's dream of large-scale transmutation, the first synthetic element seen by man.

"That experiment, and the first identification of the element with the atomic number 94, took place in room 307 of Gilman Hall. This form of the element was known as plutonium-238.

"Almost concurrent with this work was our successful attempt to synthesize and determine the essential nuclear properties of the form of major importance, plutonium-239. In an experiment on March 28, 1941, we demonstrated that this undergoes fission with slow neutrons with a large probability, revealing that it had the potential for serving as the explosive ingredient of a nuclear bomb."

Seaborg's research soon became completely related to the Manhattan project and was subject to stringent security measures. The administrators of the project felt that Seaborg and Perlman were needed in the Chicago Metallurgical Laboratory, and on

April 17, 1942, they both left for Chicago. Latimer served as the leader for those of Seaborg's group who remained behind.

In Chicago, Seaborg was in charge of developing the chemical process that would be used for the extraction of plutonium from uranium and the highly radioactive fission products following its synthesis through the nuclear chain reaction. Seaborg expressed the problem thus:[196] "How could any separations process be tested at the concentrations of plutonium that would exist several years later in the production plants when, at this time, there was not even a microgram of plutonium available? This problem was solved through an unprecedented series of experiments encompassing two major objectives. First, it was decided to attempt the production of an actually weighable amount of plutonium by bombarding large amounts of uranium with the neutrons from cyclotrons. It must be remembered that never before had weighable amounts of transmutation products been produced with any particle acceleration machine. Even extending this possibility to the limit, it was not anticipated that more than a few micrograms of plutonium could be produced. The second aspect of the solution of this problem involved the novel idea of attempting to work with only microgram amounts of plutonium but, at the same time, at ordinary concentrations. It was decided to undertake a program of investigation involving volumes of solutions and weighings on a scale of operations much below that of ordinary microchemistry.

"We solved the first problem by bombarding large amounts of uranyl nitrate with neutrons at the cyclotrons at the University of California and Washington University; plutonium concentrates were derived from these sources through the efforts of teams of chemists who used ether extractions to separate the bulk of the uranium and an oxidation-reduction cycle with rare earth fluoride carrier to concentrate the product. I managed to convince chemists trained in the techniques of ultramicrochemistry to join us to solve the second problem - Burris B. Cunningham and Louis B. Werner of the University of California and Michael Cefola from New York University."

The first isolation of plutonium, in the form of the fluoride, was effected in room 405, Jones Laboratory, on August 20, 1942. The first weighing of a pure plutonium compound, in the form of 2.77 micrograms of the oxide, was achieved on September 10, 1942.

Stanley Thompson joined Seaborg's group on October 1, 1942, and he was given the job of determining the process to be used at Clinton Laboratories (in Tennessee) and the Hanford Engineer Works (in the state of Washington) for the separation of plutonium. The process that was ultimately used was the so-called bismuth phosphate process, based on the fact that when a solution containing both Bi^{III} and Pu^{IV} in a 100-to-1 ratio is treated with phosphate, the precipitated bismuth phosphate carries about 98 percent of the plutonium. On the other hand, when the plutonium is in the form of the +6 oxidation state, it is not carried by bismuth phosphate, and thus a chemical separation is possible.[196]

Years later, immediately following the successful Presidential campaign of John F. Kennedy, Sargeant Shriver met with Seaborg ostensibly to get some suggestions for candidates for the chairmanship of the Atomic Energy Commission.[151] On January 9, 1961, Kennedy offered Seaborg the position. Seaborg admired Kennedy and his goals, and he accepted. He remained as chairman until 1971, thus continuing the influence of the Berkeley chemistry department staff on nuclear weapons development in the United States. An important part of the story of Seaborg's years in Washington is told in his book, *Kennedy, Krushchev, and the Test Ban.*[193]

Even twelve years after resigning the AEC Chairmanship, Seaborg played an important role in weapons development. In 1983, he sent to *Chemical and Engineering News* a letter-to-the-editor in which he proposed a comprehensive test ban (CTB) as the simplest and quickest way of moving forward in nuclear arms control. He wrote:[195]

"A CTB would have great benefits to the U.S. in slowing and reversing the nuclear arms race, in strengthening international efforts to prevent further proliferation of nuclear weapons, and in providing new momentum in arms control negotiations. . . .

"As I have described in my book, *Kennedy, Krushchev, and the Test Ban*, negotiations for a CTB in the early 1960s broke down over U.S. insistence that obligatory onsite inspection was needed in order to be sure that the Soviets would not cheat. I think now, in retrospect, that even at that time we were wrong. The likelihood that the Soviets would have risked international censure by trying to cheat was very small when they could not have been sure of what we would detect. What they could have gained from the very small tests they might have sneaked by could not have affected the military balance. With each passing year since then, the ability to monitor compliance with a CTB has become more assured. At this time, tests above one kiloton have a high probability of being detected and identified, whether through seismic or satellite means, or through intelligence sources. . . . Even more than in the 1960s, it seems unlikely today that the Soviets would take large political risks for the chance of making the insignificant military gains they could achieve through clandestine tests under a CTB."

This letter attracted a lot of attention among all kinds of scientists and catalyzed serious discussions of the CTB. Among the questions asked were the following.[73] What would be the ultimate impact of a ban on warhead testing if other weapon developments were left unrestrained? Wouldn't continued development of delivery and defensive systems become increasingly destabilizing?

In August 1986, the House of Representatives responded to public concern over the nuclear weapons problem by voting to impose a one-year moratorium on nuclear tests, contingent on Soviet agreement to on-site monitoring. However, neither the American Association for the Advancement of Science, the American Chemical Society, nor the U.S. Academy of Sciences has yet made any significant pronouncement or official recommendation regarding this important matter. It will be interesting to see to what extent the scientific community supports the CTB proposal and, in turn, to what extent the Administration is influenced by the scientific community.

Forty years after Hiroshima, Seaborg recalled his feelings on hearing about the Hiroshima blast.[19] "I, like every other scientist, was quite satisfied that the bomb had been successful. It was a different world then, remember. There was no ambivalence. We were at war with what everyone thought was a ruthless enemy. I'd gone through Pearl Harbor. I had first cousins out there in the Pacific fighting - and to this day, they credit me with saving their lives.

"Using the bomb probably saved millions of lives. In retrospect I would rather it had been demonstrated, but I don't feel bitter.

"Do I wish I hadn't discovered plutonium? No way. Once God had made a world that made bombs possible, there was no option. Both sides were going to make them. But if you ask me, 'Do I wish the laws of nature were such that you couldn't make an atomic bomb?' God, yes."

Robert E. Connick

Bob Connick is a native Californian from the northern coastal town of Eureka. Fog is almost an everyday phenomenon in that part of California, and when Bob moved with his family to Berkeley at the age of twelve, he found it hard to understand why other newcomers to Berkeley complained about "the Bay Area fog." He thought Berkeley had a very sunny climate. At Berkeley High, Connick was most interested in the science courses. This was during the depression, when young people had to be very practical when choosing a vocation. Bob decided that chemistry was the science that would be most useful to someone looking for a job, so when he graduated from high school in 1935 and entered the University of California, he signed up in the chemistry curriculum.[32]

He did very well as an undergraduate and soon realized that he wanted to do graduate work in chemistry. He applied to Columbia and was offered a teaching assistantship there; however, the salary they offered would barely pay his tuition. Latimer was incensed when he heard about this and suggested that he go to graduate school at Berkeley, where he could live at home. Bob took his advice. As an undergraduate, Bob had of course taken Chem 120 under Professor Bray. In that course he had been assigned a special project on the reaction of hydrogen peroxide with hypochlorous acid, which he had found especially interesting. Unfortunately there had not been enough time to complete the project. So, when he became a graduate student in 1939, he chose to start his research with Bray in order to finish that Chem 120 project - a project that turned out to be so big that it ended up as his entire Ph.D. work.

Connick found, just as Taube had, that Bray was a genius in his field who, when presented with a problem that he did not understand, was not afraid to ask naive yet penetrating questions. He also noted that Bray was a man who had difficulty expressing his basic kindliness toward others - a somewhat pedantic man whom most people found difficult to talk to on first meeting.

When Connick finished his Ph.D. work in the summer of 1942, he was made an instructor, but Latimer assigned him to work on a war project involving the electrolytic production of heavy water at the Stuart Oxygen Company in San Francisco.

This was a full-scale plant study of the effect of lower temperatures on the relative yields of H_2 and D_2. However, this work didn't last long, and soon Latimer put him on the project for studying the chemistry of plutonium and for devising processes for separating it from fission products. Connick found this work very exciting, and he believes that it may be the most important research he has ever done. He is justifiably proud that he and his coworkers were able to characterize the lower oxidation states of plutonium. They established the existence of the +3 and +5 states, and obtained thermodynamic data for equilibria involving the +3, +4, +5, and +6 states.

One of the steps in the separation of plutonium from fission products involved the extraction of an aqueous solution with an ether solution of a chelating agent. Many such operations were carried out by Connick's group in room 301, Gilman Hall. Now, it happened that this room was the only passageway to the department's spectrographic darkroom, and G. N. Lewis often walked through this room in order to get to the darkroom. One of the fellows doing the ether extraction work was scared to death whenever Lewis passed through because Lewis always had a lit cigar in his mouth, and he was afraid that Lewis would blow the place up some day. Finally he screwed up enough courage to ask, "Professor Lewis, don't you think it's not a good idea to smoke in this room with all these ether fumes?" Lewis replied, "Oh yes, I'm sure you're right." Thereafter whenever Lewis walked through the room, he carefully carried the lit cigar behind his back.

Soon after the war, Connick became interested in thenoyl-trifluoroacetone (TTA), one of the chelating agents that Calvin had been studying for the separation of plutonium. Connick used this ligand in equilibrium extraction studies for determining the formulas of species in aqueous solution. Zirconium and ruthenium were particularly bad actors in the plutonium separation scheme, and much of Bob's research involved the study of the hydrolysis and polymerization of ions of these elements, using TTA as the extractant. Later work, begun in the 1950s, involved studies of the hydrolysis and polymerization of the chromic ion, which in some respects is easier to study.

Connick has always been generous in his service to the College and the University. He has served as chairman of the university-wide Academic Senate and on many important committees. He served as chairman of the Department of Chemistry from 1958 to 1960, as dean of the College from 1960 to 1965, and as academic vice chancellor of the Berkeley campus from 1965 to 1971. The last position was not as enjoyable as the others. While reminiscing about the vice chancellorship, Connick said, "It was during the time of the free speech movement. It was sometimes more exciting than I wished. I guess the thing that was always so worrisome was that students, in their frustration about the war, were continually attacking the University because it was so near at hand, although the University had no influence over these events." Connick believes the movement made very little change in the University. "Nothing is terribly different; that is, we teach and interact with the students the way we did before."[172]

This 1938 photograph shows Chem 1 teaching assistants meeting with Professors Hildebrand and Libby in the storeroom of the Freshman Chemistry Laboratory to discuss the quiz they are to give in their respective rooms. Seated, left to right: J. K. Royal, L. V. Coulter, W. F. Libby, T. T. Magel, (?). Standing: A. P. Carrol (in charge of the freshman laboratory), J. H. Hildebrand, J. C. Goodrich, D. C. DeVault, J. W. Kennedy, R. W. Long.

Gilbert N. Lewis, 1946.

William C. Bray, 1936.

Gilbert N. Lewis, 1946.

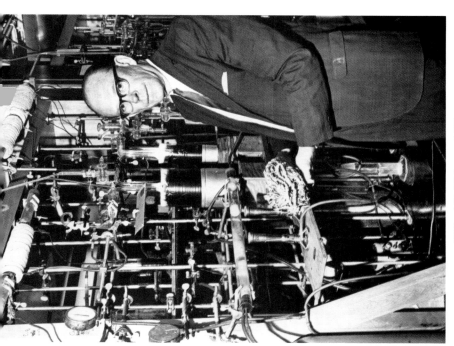

Willard F. Libby, ca 1965.

Wendell M. Latimer (note the cigarette) and Glenn T. Seaborg in room 307 Gilman Hall, ca 1950.

Northeast corner of the Old Radiation Laboratory, ca 1945.

Kenneth S. Pitzer, 1953.

Leo Brewer, 1948.

Wendell M. Latimer, 1952.

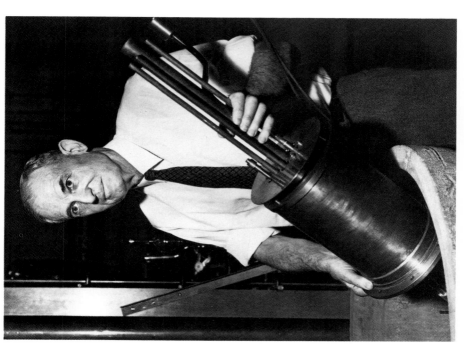

William F. Giauque, ca 1959.

Melvin Calvin, 1961.

Melvin Calvin with coworkers in Laboratory of Chemical Biodynamics, 1966.

In 1960 Berkeley had seven Nobel Laureates: Owen Chamberlain (physics, 1959), Edwin M. McMillan (chemistry, 1951), William F. Giauque (chemistry, 1949), John H. Northrop (chemistry, 1946), Wendell M. Stanley (chemistry, 1946), Emilio G. Segre (physics, 1959), and Glenn T. Seaborg (chemistry, 1951).

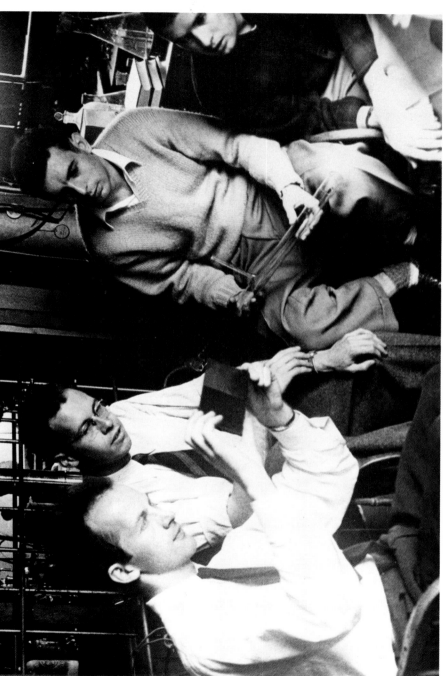

A 1947 spectroscopy laboratory group with Michael Kasha, Donald S. McClure, George C. Pimentel, and William T. Simpson.

The College of Chemistry staff and some of Joel Hildebrand's former research colleagues at the celebration of Hildebrand's 70th birthday, Nov. 16, 1951. Left to right, front row: Latimer, Stewart, Blasdale, Hildebrand, Gibson, Giauque, Branch, and Rollefson. Rear: Gwinn, William H. Clausen, Frank E. Young, F. Campbell Williams, Seaborg (face largely hidden), Connick, George J. Rotariu, Dauben, Powell, Hans A. Benesi, Marshall W. Cronyn, Templeton, Cunningham, Vermeulen, Jura, Cason, Bromley, Tobias, Wilke, Brewer, Rapoport, O'Konski, Hanson, Orlemann, Aaron Wachter, Pimentel, Noyce, Calvin, and Pitzer.

A group posed at the Lawrence Radiation Laboratory on the occasion of President Kennedy's participation in UC Charter Day, March 23, 1962. Left to right: Norris Bradbury, director of Los Alamos Laboratory; John S. Foster, director of Livermore Laboratory; Edwin M. McMillan, director of Lawrence Radiation Laboratory; Glenn T. Seaborg, chairman of Atomic Energy Commission; President John F. Kennedy; Edward Teller, associate director at Livermore; Secretary of Defense Robert McNamara; and Harold Brown, director of defense research and engineering.

The southwest entrance to the Old Chemistry Building, 1961. The foreground is the roof of the Low Temperature Laboratory, now called the Giauque Laboratory.

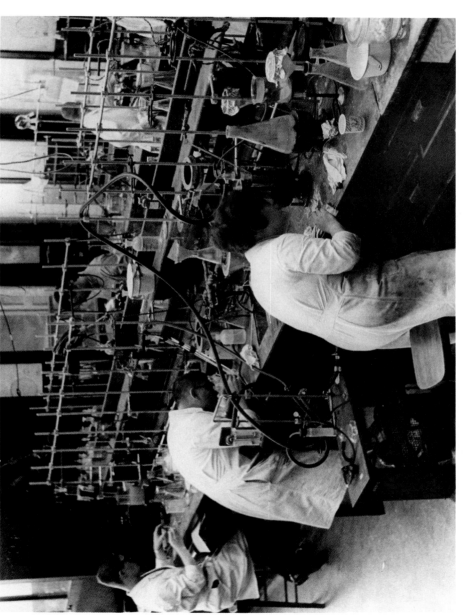

Organic chemistry students slaving away in the Old Chemistry Building, 1961.

A precarious moment for the Old Chemistry Building's cupola, which now adorns the roof of Giauque Laboratory.

Latimer Hall, 1963. The Crocker Laboratory and the construction site for the Physical Sciences Lecture Hall can be seen in the lower right.

Joel H. Hildebrand in front of his hall, 1966.

Post-Lewis Days

CHAPTER
37

James Cason

Jim Cason was born in Tennessee in 1912. He earned his A.B. at Vanderbilt in 1934 and then came to Berkeley to work for a Ph.D. in organic chemistry. But after one year he transferred to Yale University, where he obtained his Ph.D. in 1938. After two years of post-doctoral work at Harvard, a year of teaching at DePauw and four years of teaching at Vanderbilt, he accepted an assistant professorship at Berkeley. Thus he was appointed in 1945, just a year before Lewis died.

One morning in January 1986, I had a nice long chat with Jim.[27] I started off by asking about his early years on the staff at Berkeley, and he was soon going full steam.

"I got this letter from Wendell Latimer about April '45, and the war was still on - the atomic bomb had not been dropped yet, but everybody knew the war couldn't last much longer - see, Germany had already surrendered, oh, quite a little while before, so it was all in the Pacific - and I got this letter from him saying that he'd been looking over the files and noticed that I had a master's degree from here and that I had written a letter as I was finishing my Ph.D. at Yale, inquiring if there was any opportunity of a job here - which there was not at that time - and that he wondered if I was still interested in a job at Berkeley. So I thought a long time - see, I knew what the situation was, and at that time, see, I had a very good job actually at Vanderbilt, and Vanderbilt had a very high endowment. Since I had been there, through the war, I never asked for anything I didn't get. I wanted a high-pressure hydrogenator, so I just put in for it and got it, and so things were fine. So I thought a lot, and I assumed that they had to have somebody around to teach a couple of undergraduate courses - that'd be about the size of it, since that's the way it was when I was here in graduate school - and that's the reason I decided to leave. I worked for Walter Porter because he was the only one of the three - Dale Stewart, Gerry Branch, and Walter Porter were the three in organic - he was the only one who sounded like he was an organic chemist to me. And actually I worked on a very interesting problem - of trying to put a hydrogen and a deuterium on the same carbon to see if that would result in an asymmetric carbon. See, deuterium was pretty new then, and we failed because of all that we didn't know about reaction mechanisms. We tried to do it with the Grignard reagent; it was not known at that time that to form a Grignard reagent from an optically active bromide would give racemization. So we didn't succeed. In fact, it was '44 or '45 that Eliel at Notre Dame then succeeded in doing it, and it was optically active - I just thought of that. Well, anyway, it became apparent to me about half-way through the year that I knew more organic chemistry than Walter Porter did - and I knew I didn't know much - I had had two full years under a guy that graduated from Illinois but I still knew how little I knew about organic chemistry, and Porter just didn't know as much as I did, and I didn't hold it against him - he had no opportunity to learn it. You see, he had no contact with anybody that knew anything about organic chemistry. So I remember a conversation with Glenn Seaborg, who was one of my best friends in graduate school then. And Glenn and I got acquainted registering freshmen together when we first came in, and I was talking with Glenn when I was making up my mind on this business about whether to stay, particularly since, you see, I had met this little blonde at the I-House where I lived that I subsequently married and celebrated our fiftieth wedding anniversary in December. Well, anyway, this was a pretty complicated situation on leaving, and I remember saying to Glenn, 'The trouble with this place is they don't realize that organic chemists are the salt of the earth.' I remember this statement exactly, and Glenn replied, 'My friend, they don't realize the existence of organic chemists.'

"Well, I finally made up my mind I'd have to go away or shift into physics. You see, I had a double major in physics and chemistry as an undergraduate, and with all this business of the little blonde and so on, I almost surely would have stayed - shifted to physics - except I didn't have enough mathematics. I hadn't even taken a course in differential equations. I used differential equations in one of my courses - I got a book and studied it, you know, and found out you look 'em up in the back and so on. And if it hadn't been for that I probably would have taken physics and stayed. And thank God I didn't! I wouldn't have liked the life of a physicist. Well anyhow, I decided to go away, and so I left. And I had known Latimer a little bit at that time because he was one of the people that worked on this thing which later developed into what I think Irving Langmuir called 'pathogenic chemistry' - magneto-optics - and Latimer had published a paper on it, and I did my senior research - if you can call it that - by pushing this trolley along while the physics Professor Slack looked through the eyepiece to see if he could identify things, in that he didn't know either what was in the solution, or where that trolley was. He had his apparatus set up .

Well, to make a long story short, Jim answered Latimer's letter, saying among other things that he would be interested if there would be cooperation in developing organic chemistry at Berkeley. Latimer replied with a letter which began, "I'm so impressed with your letter that I'm offering you a job as an assistant professor."

Jim still wasn't sure about going to Berkeley, so he consulted Homer Adkins at Wisconsin. Adkins said, "Well, most people, I would recommend that they stay away from that den of narrow-minded physical chemists. But you're such a stubborn son of a bitch that I advise you to take the job - I don't think they can budge you." Jim took his advice.

Jim, together with Bill Dauben, who arrived the same year, not only had to start reorganizing the teaching of organic chemistry; they also had to start some good organic research in a department that had never seen anything but physical organic chemistry. "Bill and I both sat down in a very cold-blooded mannner in search of things that we could work on - things that had the greatest probability of producing a paper the quickest - we knew what the ground rules were. So I selected development of this organocadmium reaction, which I published the first paper on, about using it in synthesis. . . . And Bill said, 'What I need is a mechanism that can be solved using carbon-14' - and he picked the Willgerodt reaction, which he got familiar with working with Fieser. [Melvin Calvin had suggested to Dauben that he devise some project utilizing carbon-14 as a tracer.] Bill and I both worked like hell to produce something, because we wanted a job, and we knew what the rules were. At the same time we were doing a great deal of teaching. And we taught in summer session to keep from starving to death, you see."

For many years Jim and his wife Rebecca have owned a house on timberland up in Humboldt county where they spend a lot of vacation time. However, in 1977, Jim figured that he ought to start planning something to do during his retirement, so he bought sixty-five acres of almond orchard ("El Rancho Almendra") near Marysville. Since his retirement in 1982, he and Rebecca have spent about half their time there, where, with the help of a full-time ranch hand, they run the ranch.

Leo Brewer

In 1940, Leo Brewer completed his undergraduate work at Cal Tech, where he carried out senior research with Howard J. Lucas on reactions of unsaturated ketones.[17] Being somewhat naive about graduate schools, he went to Linus Pauling, the chairman of the department, to get some advice. Pauling said that he should go to Berkeley, which he did; he didn't even apply elsewhere. At Berkeley, Brewer did his thesis work under Axel R. Olson on the effect of electrolytes upon the rates of aqueous reactions. When he completed his thesis in December 1942, Latimer asked him to work on an important secret government project. Brewer agreed, and Latimer then told him about the discovery of plutonium, which had not yet been made in macroscopic amounts. Brewer's job was to head up a group that would try to predict a range of possible properties of plutonium metal and to provide materials for casting and fabricating the metal, even if it were to have the worst possible properties. Such prediction required examination of available data for all of the elements and development of models that fit the data and which could be used to extrapolate to plutonium. The problem was difficult because many of the available data were wrong. For example, the then accepted melting point of uranium was 600° too high.

The worst prediction for plutonium indicated that none of the available materials could contain it and that entirely new container materials would be required. From thermodynamic considerations, it was concluded that CeS, a yet undiscovered compound, would provide a crucible material that would be resistant to attack by strongly electropositive metals such as plutonium. Brewer's group succeeded in preparing the compound and in fabricating crucibles that were used for handling molten plutonium.

In that project, Leo worked with Eastman and Latimer, as well as LeRoy Bromley, Norman Lofgren, and Paul Gilles. Gilles described the staggered daily schedule during that project:[64] "Being an early morning riser, I got to the lab about five o'clock; LeRoy would come about eight; Leo would come in at about eleven, and Norman would come in about two. I can remember clearly Leo's sitting in a tiny closet reading *Chemical Abstracts* and eating his lunch out of a jar. During the afternoon he worked at his desk, or sometimes worked with G. H. West in the basement with a surface combustion furnace whose construction caused him to complain about its thermodynamic instability. He would normally go out for dinner briefly, and in the evening was again at his desk usually working on the thermodynamic tables that proved so useful. Then sometime between ten and midnight, he would take over the induction heater from Norman for his analytical endeavors. The following morning when I would come in at five, frequently the induction heater had not yet cooled, and at eleven Leo would come in again. His energy and his dedication were thus apparent very early, and his substantial accomplishments indicate that these are paramount qualities."

Leo is a mild-mannered man who seldom shows anger. Of course, he sometimes shows disappointment. On occasions that would cause most people to have apoplexy - for example once when his vacuum line was completely shattered - he has been heard to say, dejectedly, "Golly!" Leo is also humble. During the war he shared his office with three assistants and, for years thereafter, did the same with graduate students.

One semester around 1951, Leo Brewer was in charge of the weekly physical chemistry seminar, and he played a trick on us. He had one of his graduate students, Guy Elliot, discuss a paper from the literature on the vapor pressure of platinum oxides.[192] After Guy gave the seminar, there was the usual discussion period. A few routine questions were asked, and then Brewer pointed out to us that the experimental data of this paper did not make any sense at all. Brewer, as usual, drew the most charitable conclusion he could. (Brewer hardly ever says anything bad about anyone.) One of the two authors of the paper was a professor, and the other was presumably a student who did the work. The student collected platinum oxide vapor pressure data as a function of the partial pressure of oxygen, and undoubtedly found that a plot of the vapor pressure as a function of the oxygen partial pressure showed a lot of scatter. Brewer postulated that the student *selected* from these points those points which fit the strange (and thermodynamically implausible) theory of the professor. The selected points fell beautifully on a set of zigzag curves. In a sense, the student was not guilty of fabricating data, because the reported points actually corresponded to experimental data. He had merely deleted the apparently "bad" points and had thus provided the professor with data that fit his theory. We in the audience of the seminar were embarrassed that we had not noticed that something was rotten in Denmark. However we were forever impressed with the fact that one should be suspicious of data that are "too good." And we were also impressed with Brewer's teaching skill.

I spent the first half of 1960 in Germany on a sabbatical leave. When I returned, I went to see Miss Kittredge in the College office, and she gave me a shock. She said that Leo was probably going to die of cancer. This was a complete surprise to me. The last time I had seen him was in the fall of 1959, and he had seemed to be in reasonably good health - although I remembered that he had a persistent sore on the right side of his face. Well, it turned out that Leo went to New York to have some radical surgery performed, involving removal of his right eye and much of the right side of his face. Happily, the surgery completely removed the cancer. As far as I know, there has been no recurrence. Although Leo's face was disfigured, it is still obvious that he was a very handsome man. And people who meet him are always charmed by his politeness and his obvious concern for other people. He was a fortunate choice to be head of the Inorganic Materials Research Division of the Radiation Laboratory, a position he held from 1961 to 1975.

Around 1961, Leo became interested in a method for explaining the physical properties of metals and alloys that had been roughly outlined by a Danish scientist named Niels Engel.[50] Since then Leo has greatly elaborated on this method and turned it into a valuable procedure for predicting the various phases which can be formed by mixing various metals. The method has been referred to by others as the Brewer-Engel theory, although it was developed almost entirely by Brewer.

Leo's hobby (or actually, his second expertise) is gardening. He has surrounded his home, which lies on the east slope of the Berkeley hills in Orinda, with native California plants and plants that are adapted to the semi-arid climate of that area. The seriousness with which he approaches this avocation is shown by the fact that, with an importer's license from the U.S. Department of Agriculture, he has imported plants from all over the world. He is familiar with all the plants in his garden, can recall important rainfall data for many past years, and can explain to you the effects of the adiabatic expansion and cooling of the air as it blows over the Berkeley hills.

CHAPTER
39
Burris B. Cunningham

Cunningham was born in Springer, New Mexico, in 1912. After a brief career as assistant postmaster of Springer and a year of study at the University of Southern California, he continued his studies at Berkeley, where he obtained a B.S. in chemistry in 1935. He then switched to biochemistry and obtained a Ph.D. with Paul L. Kirk. (In the 1950s, Kirk became well known for his expert testimony in the famous trial of the murderer Caryle Chessman, whose death in the San Quentin gas chamber was delayed for many years.) Cunningham's Ph.D. project was a study of the metabolism of single cells of Paramecium caudatum. In this research he showed evidence of the experimental skill for which he later became famous. He developed a microrespirometer which for the first time enabled one to follow the "breathing" of an isolated living cell. With this apparatus he could measure gas volumes as small as 5 X 10^{-5} lambda.[213, 230]

Cunningham's field of study changed dramatically in June 1942, when Seaborg, who was in dire need of somebody who knew how to handle microscopic amounts of chemicals, hired him for the Manhattan Project in the Metallurgical Laboratory of the University of Chicago. There Cunningham soon produced amazing results in the chemical characterization of the new synthetic element, plutonium, which was to play a decisive role in ending World War II. In August 1942 he and his coworker, Louis B. Werner, were the first to isolate a visible quantity of plutonium and were thus the first to isolate a visible quantity of any synthetic element. In September 1942 they were the first to weigh a pure compound of plutonium. During the next two years Cunningham and his coworkers carried out, using ultramicrochemical techniques, adequate enough characterization of plutonium to allow its production on a massive scale at Hanford, Washington.[196]

After the war, Seaborg brought Cunningham back to Berkeley with him, where Cunningham worked both in the Radiation Laboratory and the Chemistry Department. Up on "the hill" he and his coworkers were the first to isolate weighable quantities of even heavier synthetic elements - americium, berkelium, californium, einsteinium - and his coworkers were the first to isolate neptunium and curium.

Because of the exacting nature of his research, Cunningham never had very many graduate students, but his laboratory was a kind of Mecca for postdoctoral students from around the world. He was a tireless worker who spent long hours in the laboratory. Visitors seldom found him in his office; he was more often at a glovebox or a glassblowing bench. At a Welch Foundation Conference on Transuranium Chemistry in Houston in 1969, Seaborg gave Cunningham a very fitting honorary title: "The Dean of Actinide Chemists." Cunningham died in 1971 at age 59.

One wonders if Cunningham and some of his coworkers were exposed to excessive radiation while handling the intensely radioactive materials that they studied. At least two of his coworkers, James Wallmann and Stuart Gunn, died of cancer at early ages.

Richard E. Powell

Dick Powell enjoyed solving puzzles. Cryptography and the design of electronic circuits were among his hobbies. Puzzle-solving even extended to his research, which essentially amounted to the solution of a series of fascinating puzzles. Although about one-third of his research problems can be classified as studies on the kinetics and mechanisms of the reactions of aqueous inorganic nitrogen compounds, most of his research did not fit into a unified theme. This lack of emphasis and the fact that he never sought outside support for his research (his students had to be teaching assistants if they didn't have fellowships of their own) may be responsible for the fact that he never had many research students working with him.

However he played an important part in the research of other faculty members, who often consulted him regarding mechanistic or kinetic snarls in their own research problems. Sometimes these consultations led to collaboration and coauthorship, but more commonly he ended up in the acknowledgments section.

Whenever Dick Powell came across an interesting problem, or a clever solution to a problem, he would prowl the halls until he could find someone with whom to share his excitement. In his shirtsleeves, with a bow tie and both belt and wide suspenders, he would often be seen gesticulating with a group of three or four people, his piercing laughter attracting everybody in the vicinity. The topic of discussion might be anything from how to make the five *d* orbitals equivalent to a simple way to test the pH of a sample of paper.

An illustration of how Powell's mind worked is shown by the following item published in the Letters-to-the-Editor section of the *Journal of Chemical Education.*[173]

It was a morning in late May of '75. "Holmes," remarked I, "surely you have noted the article in the *Journal of Chemical Education* by the professor who assigned ever-different teams of pupils for practical work?"

"You mean, Watson," replied he, "the Professor Marron who has never played tournament bridge? And that Journal is edited, if I mistake not, by a Professor Lippincott who has never played tournament bridge, either. Apart from that I know nothing of either professor."

"Holmes!" cried I. "How could you know these things?"
"Elementary, my dear Watson. If either of them were a tournament bridge player, he could not have failed to notice that the good professor's problem is identical with that of conducting a tournament so that no team meets another team twice, and each team plays each board exactly once. So he need only have consulted his neighborhood tournament director, or borrowed a copy of Benyon's book, to find all the procedures he needed. In fact," said Holmes as he warmed to his topic, "the movement used by the good professor, in which half the group only meets the opposite half, is called the Mitchell Movement after John T. Mitchell, who published it in 1891 in *Duplicate Whist* by McClurg of Chicago. The more commonly used movement, in which each team meets all others, is called the Howell Movement after Edwin C. Howell, who worked it out for all numbers of teams from 6 through 46. I do not remember exactly when, but it was about the same time, because he was cited by E. H. Moore in a memoir in the *American Journal of Mathematics* in 1896, volume 18, pages 290-303."

"Remarkable, Holmes! But do you fault the professor's proposal?"

"Not at all, Watson, except that it has been in common use for the better part of a century. In fact the Mitchell Movement which is based on Graeco-Roman squares has a peculiar advantage: if the class is made up half of boys and half of girls, this movement can be set up so every team consists of exactly one boy and one girl. Setting that advantage to one side, the Howell is perhaps better; the teams are more widely mixed, there is a perfectly simple Howell movement for 12 (whereas there is none such Mitchell), and there exists a straightforward method of constructing a Howell for any number of players."

John H. Watson, M.D.
c/o Richard E. Powell

Powell substituted for Joel Hildebrand once when Joel was still lecturing to the freshmen.[40] The afternoon after the lecture, he said, "Joel, I was chagrined this morning because the experiment didn't turn out the way I said it would." Joel said, "Dick, when you are as old as I am you will not say, 'Now I am going to demonstrate - .' You will say, 'What will happen if . . .'" Joel continued, "This is playing safe, of course, but there's a more important reason for doing this. One should create suspense, to get the students to think. One should not give answers before evidence. You should first give evidence and stimulate them to figure out answers."

In 1952, Joel Hildebrand stopped giving the freshman chemistry lectures, and Dick Powell took over. It was a hard act to follow, but he did a tremendous job for almost two decades. Latimer once told him that the real teaching in freshman chemistry was done in the small laboratory sections, and that the lectures for the large groups of over 500 students were as much entertainment as teaching. Powell took him at his word and became a dramatic, energetic, and witty lecturer. He used demonstations to great advantage in his lectures. However, once he went a little too far. He was carrying out the very dangerous reaction of aluminum powder with liquid oxygen (which gives a blinding flash of light), when an enormous explosion blew a big hole in the lecture desk. He almost lost his eyesight that time.

During the 1960s Powell was very busy with University affairs.[94] He was chairman of the Department of Chemistry from 1960 to 1966, during which time two chemistry buildings were constructed (Latimer Hall and Hildebrand Hall) and the campus uprisings occurred. He was chairman of the Berkeley Division of the Academic Senate from 1968-70, during the trying years of the Cambodian War and campus rioting. He familiarized himself with Robert's Rules of Order so well that he needed no Parliamentarian, and therefore the Senate proceedings were greatly expedited. The University is much indebted to him for his astute handling of those turbulent meetings. Dick told me that whenever he went home during those years, he found it necessary to disconnect the bell on his telephone.

In his last years, especially after his wife, Mary Ellen, died, Dick Powell succumbed to alcoholism. Neil Bartlett, Bob Connick and I did our best to get him to take the cure, but he lacked the incentive. He sadly told us that he felt inadequate, that he would never achieve fame for his work, and that therefore he did not want to be active in chemistry any more. In 1979 he died of alcohol poisoning.

CHAPTER
41

Charles R. Wilke

Charles Wilke was born in 1917 in Dayton, Ohio. At an early age, he showed musical ability, with special talent for the piano and trombone. He had dreams of becoming a composer and arranger. Therefore, after graduating from high school, he enrolled in music at Wittenberg College in Springfield, Ohio. He worked part time as a sales organizer for *Colliers* magazine. However, Charles soon discovered that the music world wasn't right for him; he yearned for work of a somewhat more practical nature. So after one year he left Wittenberg, transferred to the University of Dayton, and enrolled in the chemical engineering curriculum.[239]

The time was the late thirties, during the depression. Because it was also the era of the big dance bands, Charles found a way to make money as well as to continue his musical pursuits while going to school. He and a friend organized an eleven-piece dance orchestra for which Charles arranged the music and played trombone. They played seven nights a week in the Van Cleve Hotel in Dayton. Somehow Charles found time to work on his studies during intermissions.

After graduating from Dayton in 1940, Charles gave up the orchestra and accepted a graduate fellowship in physical chemistry at Washington State University in Pullman, where he obtained a Master's degree working with Culbertson. For his Ph.D., he continued graduate work at the University of Wisconsin, where he started out working on the kinetics of explosives with Farrington Daniels. However, he soon found that he was more interested in chemical engineering, so he changed his major and began research with Olaf A. Hougen. He received his Ph.D. in 1944 and accepted a job with Union Oil Company, as a process engineer in the refinery at Rodeo, California.

Still restless, Charles thought that he would enjoy teaching more than the work at the refinery, so he applied for and got an instructorship at Pullman, where he was expected to help develop an expanded program in chemical engineering. However, after a month or two, he became homesick for the Bay Area and Bernice, the girl friend he had met there. So he applied for a job in chemical engineering at UC Berkeley. He was interviewed by the people in the College of Engineering and was offered an assistant professorship. However, soon after he returned to Pullman to finish out his year of work there, he was sent a telegram from the College of Engineering stating that "interdepartmental relations negate the possibility of appointment." This clause was an indirect reference to the friction between Engineering and Chemistry at Berkeley and to the fact that "chemical engineering" had been restricted to the Chemistry Department, as discussed in Chapter 47. Well, Charles soon learned that chemical engineering was starting up in the Chemistry Department, so he wrote to Latimer, asking for a job. Latimer hired him, and thus Wilke joined Schutz and Bromley in the fall of 1946.

Wilke was put in charge of a course in stoichiometry and was asked to develop an undergraduate laboratory course in unit operations. There was very little apparatus on hand for the course, and the required equipment was essentially built by Wilke and his first batch of students.

For the first fifteen years or so of Wilke's career at Berkeley, his research emphasized fundamental studies of diffusion coefficients and mass transfer, often in collaboration with his colleagues in the Department. He achieved world-wide fame for this work. Around 1962, desiring to move into brand new territory, he abruptly shut down that line of research and started work in the budding field of biochemical engineering. He has had great success in that field and has recently shown that the conversion of cellulose to glucose with the fungus Trichoderma viride is a promising process.

For many years Wilke has made a hobby of the stock market - an activity that he has always kept scrupulously separate from his University research. In the early seventies he began developing a computer model for the market that now is sophisticated enough that he can make fairly reliable predictions of stock prices. In the years since he began his phased retirement in 1983 (whereupon he became a 20 percent University appointee), he has devoted considerable time to his investment company, providing advice for the managers of trust accounts. Using information available at the close of business on Friday, he starts up his computer program, and on Saturday or Sunday is able to give his clients advice that they can apply to their portfolios on Monday morning. Quite a nice hobby.

CHAPTER
42

Theodore Vermeulen

Ted Vermeulen was born in 1916 in Los Angeles. At Cal Tech he got a B.S. in Applied Chemistry in 1936 and an M.S. in Chemical Engineering in 1937. After two years as a chemical engineer with Union Oil, he continued his graduate study at UCLA. There he studied the chemistry of ferri-hemoglobin and color theory with Coryell and, in 1942, received the first Ph.D. degree in chemistry awarded by that institution.[72]

Ted then went to work for the Shell Development Company in San Francisco, where he gained experience in catalysis and other areas of applied chemical kinetics. However, he realized that there was a need for teaching and research in this field, and he began to look for academic opportunities in chemical engineering. Indeed, in 1946 he worked part time as an instructor in the Engineering Division of UC Extension, while still employed by Shell Development.[227]

In the late fall of 1946 Philip Schutz, who had been recruited by the Berkeley College of Chemistry to reinstitute a program in chemical engineering, became terminally ill, and Latimer began looking for somebody else to head up the chemical engineering program. On the basis of recommendations from Pitzer (who had known Ted at Cal Tech), Lacey at Cal Tech, and Coryell at UCLA, Latimer and Hildebrand recruited Ted, who joined the Berkeley staff as an associate professor in January of 1947.

Vermeulen immediately began a period of vigorous administrative and teaching activity. The chemical engineering faculty had to be expanded, new courses had to be devised and taught, and graduate research programs had to be started. Ted believed that a professor should be able to teach any undergraduate course in the curriculum and, in these early years, set a good example.

Vermeulen was noted for extreme generosity with his time and effort in his dealings with other people. He probably carried this virtue to the point where it was detrimental to his career. His research covered many fields - more than were optimum for establishing a solid reputation. This excessive variety in his research was due to his willingness to accommodate the wishes of incoming students. Students would come to him and say, "I'd like to work on so and so," and Ted would unhesitatingly say, "O.K."

However there was one field, the chemical engineering of ion exchange, in which Ted was recognized as an early pioneer, if not the founding father. His early papers on ion exchange with Nevin Hiester, who received the first Ph.D. in chemical engineering, are classics. His later review article with LeVan, Hiester and Klein on "Adsorption and Ion Exchange" in Perry's *Chemical Engineer's Handbook* is considered the leading authoritative reference for fixed bed separation processes.

Ted directed his research students rather loosely, thus giving them the valuable experience of running their own research programs. However, he gave good advice to those who would listen. A former student, John H. Shinn, said,[228] "Often in the course of discussing some recent experimental results, Ted would come up with what at first glance would appear to be a crackpot idea on some further experiment to do. Often they would seem to come out of nowhere - I couldn't see how the idea was related to the work we were just discussing. I'd go back to the lab, letting the 'crackpot' idea slide, while I continued the work in what seemed to be more logical steps. After a few months and more of logical steps, I'd have a sudden intuitive leap of a new experiment to do suggested by the most recent discoveries. Then would come the strange realization that I had heard of this idea before. . . . It was the same experiment that Ted had suggested months earlier - one of his crackpot ideas. I never did quite figure out if he had made the same intuitive leap without all the intermediate steps."

Ted was very active in the Academic Senate and served on almost all the major Senate committees. He was deservedly proud of his participation in the Select Committee on Education in 1965-67 during the period of student unrest. He was a friendly and extremely helpful person who genuinely cared for others, sensed their needs, and did his best to help them. His colleagues felt a great loss when he died in 1983.

Charles W. Tobias

Charles Tobias was born in 1920 in Budapest, Hungary.[218] As a boy, he studied music and science with equal fervor, obtaining a diploma in violin performance at the Municipal Conservatory at the same time that he finished his secondary education at the Eotvos Real. However, after deciding to make chemical engineering his vocation and music his avocation, he enrolled at the University of Technical Sciences, where he graduated in 1942. He then took a job in the laboratory of the United Incandescent Lamp and Electrochemical Company (Trade Mark *Tungsram*). Soon thereafter, while continuing his work at the lamp company, he began research for a Ph.D. at the Institute of Physical Chemistry of the Technical University in Budapest.

At that time, the Germans occupied Hungary. It was not until early 1945 that the Soviet army, after months of heavy fighting, drove out the Germans and took over Budapest. Things did not improve much. It took a good deal of skill and luck for young men to avoid deportation to Siberia as "prisoners" and for women of all ages to avoid assault by members of the victorious army. The once beautiful city of Budapest was devastated. Few stores remained among the ruins, and food was scarce. The Russians printed rivers of money, and inflation reached astronomical proportions: eventually more than 10^{20} Hungarian pengos were required for one U.S. dollar, in contrast to four pengos per dollar in 1940.

Tobias recalled that in 1945 and 1946 all kinds of tricks and crazy machinations were required to stay alive. If one didn't steal, one at least had to engage in shady deals or had to provide "services" to those in power in exchange for food. He told me about two occasions when his knowledge of chemistry helped him and his family to survive.

Once the interpreter of a Soviet colonel, the commanding officer of the troops that occupied the lamp factory, paid a visit to Tobias's laboratory and inquired whether someone could provide hair bleach for the colonel's mistress. No such luxuries were available in the devastated city. After unsuccessfully questioning his colleagues, Tobias found in a chemical recipe book that a simple dilute solution of hydrogen peroxide and ammonia would do the job. He then told the colonel's interpreter that at great personal risk and with great ingenuity he had procured the necessary ingredients for one treatment, and that more could be obtained later. The supply of this hair bleach netted Tobias generous supplies of sausages, bread, and chocolate - all great luxuries in those days.

The inventor of the first practical ball-point pen was Laszlo Jozsef Biro, a Hungarian living in Argentina. In early 1946 he sent some of his pens as gifts to his friends in Budapest, including an employee of the lamp company. These men figured that such pens would sell well in Hungary because they were novelties, they were cheap, and they would make nice Christmas presents. The fellows took the pens apart and realized that they would be fairly simple to manufacture. They had the balls (available from bearings) and the metal tubes. But the composition of the ink was a mystery to them, and so they approached Charles Tobias. They offered to pay him a good sum of money if he would determine how to make the ink used in ball-point pens. Charles agreed, but with the stipulation that they pay him one-third of the money first, and then the remaining two-thirds when he finished the project.

Well, it soon became apparent that it was not going to be a simple job. The ink was not just a simple solution of a dye in water or in an organic solvent; such a solution would run out of the pen too easily and would spread all over the paper to which it was applied. Charles figured that the ink must be some kind of chemical combination of an organic dye base with a material such as oleic acid. Soon after he started thinking about this problem, Charles attended a social gathering where he chanced to hear the ex-owner of the Budapest firm that represented I. G. Farbenindustrie (the giant German chemical company) mention that in the ruins of their warehouse there was a stash of some textile dyes. Immediately Charles was excited. He wangled a bottle of Victoria Blue base from the man and started making mixtures of the dye with oleic acid. The work was all done on the sly, after hours, in the laboratory of the lamp factory. He found that it was necessary to grind the two materials together with a ball mill in order to get satisfactorily smooth mixtures. Finally he developed a recipe that gave fairly good results in ball-point pens.

Just about this time, Tobias received his Ph.D. and was desperately making plans to go to California, where he had been offered a fellowship at UC Berkeley. (This offer was obtained with the help of his brother Cornelius, who had gone to Berkeley in 1939, and Professor John Lawrence of the Donner Laboratory.) When he told the ball-point pen fellows that he had found out how to make the ink and that he wanted to be paid, they said that they didn't have the money, but that they would send him the money as soon as they had made money from sales of the pens. Well, Charles didn't fall for that; he refused to give them the ink or the recipe without payment. They then told him that if he didn't give them the recipe, they would put a snag in his efforts to leave the country. Charles then said, "Well, in that case, we would both lose. I wouldn't get out of the country, and you wouldn't get your ink."

Tobias came up with a solution to the impasse. He put a detailed description of the method for making the ink, together with the chemicals and necessary equipment, in the hands of a close friend, an instructor at the university, requesting that he promptly lock them up in the chemistry department's large safe. The friend was to open the safe only after all the money was paid. His friend was to keep half of the money and the rest was to go to Tobias's parents in Budapest. Reluctantly, the ball-point pen fellows agreed to the terms, and, with a sigh of relief, Tobias left for America. (To leave Hungary in 1947 was by no means simple - but that's another story.)

Six months after arriving in Berkeley, Tobias learned that the ink was already in use and that his parents had received the money originally promised. Knowing about the nasty habit of early ball-point pens to leak and ruin clothes, Tobias now hopes that his version of the ink was soon replaced by a more benign concoction.

When he arrived in Berkeley in 1947, he was appointed an instructor in chemical engineering. However, he had a student visa and had to be registered as a student. So Latimer simply arranged for his formal enrollment as a student. He didn't have to take any courses for grades, but he received credits for research, vouched for by Latimer. Obviously Latimer was adept at cutting through red tape.

Tobias had worked on electrochemical problems at the lamp factory in Budapest, and Latimer very much wanted to have electrochemical research in the Chemical Engineering Department, so he encouraged Tobias to go into that area. Tobias soon became a world authority in electrode phenomena and has remained in that field ever since. Much of his work has been carried out in collaboration with his colleagues in the Chemical Engineering Department. He has studied mass transfer in electrochemical systems, current distribution, nonaqueous electrolysis, and electrolytic gas evolution. Thus he initiated and developed the field of electrochemical engineering in the United States. In the 1960s, two more electrochemists - Rolf Muller and John

Newman - joined the staff, and since then there have been three research groups maintaining the fame of the department in electrochemical research.

Tobias prefaces his weekly research group seminars with commentary ranging from music to politics, from physics to food. Once, while discussing the proper tea to serve, he deplored the herbal varieties which "pervade the palate like perfume," and recommended Earl Grey over Darjeeling because "Darjeeling is the tea served by dowagers in damp rooms." He tells his students, "Never be afraid of doing an experiment, even at the risk of finding something new." Nearly half of his doctoral students have gone into the teaching profession, even though he once said, "Do not teach for a living; marry a rich woman. You will be unhappy, but in very pleasant circumstances."[203]

CHAPTER
44

F. Campbell Williams

The Berkeley College of Chemistry has had some really colorful characters on its teaching staff. One of these was Campbell
(Cam) Williams, a Canadian who was hired as an assistant professor of chemical engineering in 1948. He stayed for only four
years, but he made a lasting impression on those who knew him.
He loved the night life of San Francisco and San Pablo Avenue.
Latimer once told me that Williams could easily make more than
his assistant professor's salary at the Albany race track. In fact,
one day both Wendell and Campbell played hooky and went to
watch Citation run against some other horse. It was one of the
all-time great races in the history of horse racing. Wendell bet
with his heart on Citation because he was such a beautiful horse,
and Campbell on the other horse. Campbell's horse won. The
next day Wendell pinned his losing ticket on his office notice
board. He jokingly told Campbell that he was happy that he had
lost because now he had his ticket to remind him of the wonderful race, and all Campbell had was some money. Years later,
Campbell acknowledged that Latimer was right, because he could
remember Citation, but not even the name of his horse.[241]
    In 1952, Campbell was invited to go to Brazil to organize a
graduate course in petroleum refining. It was supposed to be a
temporary job, but he ended up staying in Brazil. One might
have suspected that a fun-loving bachelor like Cam (he is no
longer a bachelor) would be favorably impressed by Latin
America. This was obvious even from the 1952 Christmas letter
that he sent to his friends back in the States and Canada. Here is
a short excerpt from the end of that letter, in which he describes
his experiences on the trip from the United States to Rio de
Janeiro:[241a]

    For me, the hardest country to get into was the U.S. (San
    Juan). It seems that the immigration people in San Francisco
    and those in Miami had different ideas as to whether or not
    I would have to use my U.S. reentry permit in going from
    Cuba to Nassau by way of Miami. To make a long battle
    short I used my reentry permit in Miami and had nothing to
    get me into Puerto Rico, and now I have nothing to get me
    into the U.S. next year. Probably will have to stay here in
    Rio!

Since I had no visa for the U.S. when I landed in San Juan, I was placed in bond. This meant that the airline was responsible for me and my conduct: responsible to see that I got out of the country as arranged on my ticket. All turned out well because it also meant that they were responsible for all of my expenses while in town. I enjoyed myself at the Caribe Hilton and enjoyed some real fine meals that I signed for.

When you register at the Caribe Hilton you are treated like a king and given a card for a free drink at the bar. This drink comes out in a coconut about 12 inches in diameter and 12 inches high, filled with a rum drink which compares favorably with Trader Vic's Scorpion. Casually, on the way down to dinner I stopped off at the casino and made nine straight passes at the crap table - a dream of a lifetime. So you can see that my day which started off so wrong with the immigration people ended quite happily. The Caribe Hilton is the finest hotel that I have ever stayed in, and their swimming pool is one of the finest.

The next day I was kicked out of the U.S. (got my passport back after I was seated on the plane) and took off for Venezuela. Venezuela probably has the worst hotels of any country that I visited, and I hit one of the worst at Maiquetia. I almost missed my plane the next morning since I had not figured on the 50 cycle electricity with my electric clock. However the fleas got me up in time and I reached Maracaibo where I visited some good friends of mine in the oil fields. I spent some interesting days in and around Maracaibo learning first-hand how to get oil out of the ground. The natives here have a fine custom - the man rides the burro while the wife leads it and the children walk behind!

My time was running out as I headed for Trinidad via Barcelona and Maturin. The population of Port of Spain is made up of English, Continental Europeans, Hindus, Chinese, North Americans, and Negros. The sugar plantations and the bamboo groves were very impressive as we drove 15 miles from the airport to the city. The botanical gardens here are very fine, with trees from all over the world. Probably the finest thing about Trinidad was the calypso music. I had dinner at the Trinidad Country Club (acted as if I were a lifetime member as I drove up and passed the guard) and heard this music. There was a steel drum band present. They play on oil drums cut about eight inches deep, 20 inches deep, or the full drum. This music sounded like that of a xylophone and was very fine. But the excellent music was again the calypso trio. I could listen to it for hours, especially one of my favorites, 'Always marry a woman uglier than you.'

Well at last we flew across the equator and landed in Rio. If I started to describe Rio I would never finish this letter, so it must wait until another time. I have made several trips with officials from Conselho Nacional de Petroleo, including a 1000-mile trip to Bahia where the Portuguese first landed in Brazil. I am living on Copacabana Beach and enjoying the sun and bathing beauties to the best of my ability.

Merry Christmas,
Campbell

Who says that chemists lead a dull life? Campbell Williams engaged in both teaching and industrial research until 1967, when he and some of his former students formed the company NATRON, an engineering company dedicated to research and the development of technologies specific for Brazil. Campbell is no longer a playboy. In 1980 he was elected an Honorary Citizen of Rio de Janeiro in recognition of his services, and in 1985 he was named Honorary Canadian Consul in Rio de Janeiro by the Canadian Government.[241]

George C. Pimentel

All four of George Pimentel's grandparents were French.[168] However, when George's father was about seven years old, he was adopted by a Portuguese immigrant named Jose Pimentel who had settled in a rural community near Fresno, California. Grandpa Pimentel was the only grandfather George ever knew, and "he felt just like a blood grandfather." So although George adds to our college's list of Hispanic surnames, he is in fact pure blood French.

George was short in stature for his age, and this shortness was exaggerated in elementary and high school because he was allowed to skip a couple of grades. So he was always the shortest person in his class and was called Peewee - never George. "I remember they used to handle our P.E. classes by lining up all the fellows in the whole class - there might be a hundred or so in a class - according to height. And then we divided into squads, and I was always in the last squad, even when I was in the eleventh or twelfth grade. I was very gung-ho about sports, and it had to do, I guess, with having to prove myself, being so little."

However, while George was at UCLA, he grew six inches and played intramural football, basketball and baseball, and even played on the University's "145-pound" basketball team. "It was a basketball team in which the only restriction was you could not weigh more than 145 pounds. And some of our guys were pretty tall, but they were skinny as hell. . . . Needless to say, our entire style was speed; we would run the hell out of the other team. . . . I lettered in that for two or three years. . . . As I grew, it got to the point where I was not the littlest guy on the team and I was as good as anybody. It turned out to be very gratifying.

"I remember when I was a senior in high school that math and physics interested me, and somebody came to the high school to talk about job opportunities, and he said that there were job opportunities in chemistry but there weren't any jobs in physics and math. Of course this was just at the tail end of the depression; I had been a depression kid, and so I was not about to go into a field in which there was no chance of getting a job. . . . I also had a sentimental career direction, associated with the fact that my father was in construction work and had had no education. I had always thought of going into engineering as sort of a fulfillment of my father's lost opportunity. So I signed up at UCLA as a chem engineer, although they didn't have chem engineering. After I had been there a year or two, I decided 'I don't want to be an engineer - I like chemistry.' I was having too much fun, so I just forgot all about chem engineering and called myself a chemist.

"I got my A.B. degree in February of 1943, and I was very upset because my brother was in the Air Corps risking his life. Our psychological relationship, which was very, very close, was such that I felt that if he was risking his life, I should be risking mine. And so I felt I should be somehow involved in the war effort. In any event, I was not drafted because of the science background, and so I looked around for a job, and there was one job here at Berkeley that I was advised to take by Saul Winstein. He told me that it was important work, but he couldn't tell me anything more than that. That was all. And the other thing that characterized this job was that, of all the job offers I got, it was the lowest salary. But because Winstein spoke so persuasively about it being important work, and because it was at Berkeley, I took this job. I was to come up here and work with a guy whose name I had actually heard once, but had no idea who he was. The guy's name was Seaborg. I arrived, and it turned out that this fellow Seaborg I was supposed to work with had left two weeks before for Chicago. So instead of working for Seaborg, I was put under the supervision of two younger people. . . . One was a real tall slender guy named Bob Connick and the other guy was Jack Gofman. I spent the year working under Bob essentially because Gofman wasn't around very much; he was touring all over the place. . . . Bob really impressed me - I just thought he knew everything; it was marvelous to get to work for him.

"I arrived here not having any idea what I was working on, and for three months I was learning microtechniques - I was precipitating and filtering and doing all these things on a one-drop scale - microliter scale. We were given solutions that contained something called 'copper' and another solution had something called 'silver.' We would go through the chemical manipulations of 'copper' and 'silver.' But it was plain the chemistry wasn't that of copper and silver. But I was just like a kid from the sticks. I was told to do this. I didn't even worry about what copper was, except I knew it wasn't copper and I wasn't supposed to know what it really was. It turned out after three months my F.B.I. check came through, and Latimer called me in and said, 'Well I can tell you now what you're doing; 'copper' is plutonium, and 'silver' is neptunium.' Gradually over the next three to six months it became clear (and we talked about it) what this was to be used for. One of my assignments was to try to investigate why it was that every time you precipitated niobium pentoxide, all the plutonium in solution disappeared [coprecipitated]. . . . It was so effective that they decided we ought to study this thing. So I started working with this, and between Connick and me, we got it to the point where it was an effective separation technique and was proposed actually as a means of purifying plutonium if the phosphate process didn't work. Anyway, after a year on the project and lots of soul-searching, I decided I didn't want to work on the bomb. And so I went in to Latimer one day and told him that I wanted to quit and that I didn't want to work on the bomb and that I was going to join the military and try to get into a role where I could help end the war before the bomb was finished. I liked very much the way he handled the interview; he was very sympathetic and didn't try to persuade me in any direction - he indicated he understood what I was talking about - it was a personal decision - and however I decided, he would help it happen."

So George then joined the Navy and spent nine months in electronics school to become a submarine radar officer and three months of sea duty on a submarine, at which point the war ended. He then wrote to Navy brass in Washington and asked for a job in which he could use his experience on the Manhattan Project. He was almost immediately assigned to the Office of Research and Inventions, which soon became the Office of Naval Research. There he encouraged the Navy to play an active role in the Bikini test and to consider seriously the use of atomic power in such things as nuclear propulsion of submarines. He applied for graduate school in physics at various places, but, because of his lack of specific training in that area, he was not offered a teaching assistantship anywhere. Therefore, when he was discharged from the Navy in 1946, he returned to Berkeley for graduate work in chemistry. Because of his early interest in physics and math, he had done some reading in quantum mechanics while in the Navy. Therefore he chose Ken Pitzer as his research director so he could learn more about quantum mechanics and apply it to chemical bonding.

"What impressed me with Pitzer was his mental quickness in the analytical sense. . . . I remember that I would move along in my research until I got to a point where I felt it was time to go in and tell him how things were getting on. After I had been working for him a year or so, I would stop and think to myself, 'Now I've got to think of every possible question that Pitzer will likely ask me, and what'll be the possible answers. I've got to try to anticipate - to come up with something.' I never could! He'd always see some facet, some insight, that hadn't occurred to me.

"There's one time that was to me a big moment in history. I was in my third year, about to get my Ph.D., and I was to give a seminar on one of the papers that came out of my graduate work, which was about the thermoelectric force of a superconductor. How I got on to that was that Pitzer got interested in superconductors about that time, and I started learning everything I could about superconductors, and I became interested in the Third Law aspect of superconductors and thermal emf. So I presented this seminar, and I felt that whether they were going to hire me as an instructor hinged completely on how I did in the seminar. I had thought very carefully about the dangers of this because I had to talk about the so-called Drude model of metals, and I knew Giauque hated it. Nevertheless, it was built into the understanding of a superconductor. So I started off very gingerly, presenting this the way a physicist would talk. Now Latimer had written some early papers on thermal emfs in terms of entropy, so after I had talked no more than about four or five minutes, Latimer interrupted me and said, 'Would you paraphrase that into what it means about the entropy?' And so I thought for a bit and finally came up with 'Well, it means that the partial molal entropy of the electrons is zero.' So he thought about this for a while. He sat in the Lewis spot at the end of the table, and it turned out that Giauque was catty-corner at the far end. There was dead silence in the room, and I wasn't absolutely certain I had said the right thing, but in any event, I was sitting there hearing the seconds tick off while Latimer thought about this. Finally he leaned and looked down toward Giauque and said, 'What do you think about that, Bill?' I thought, 'Oh my God; the worst possible person to ask!' That was one of the most exciting moments in my life. I figured everything's at stake now; if Giauque says I can't go ahead, I can't proceed with my seminar because there's nothing left, you know. And so Giauque thought for about five or ten seconds that seemed like two hours, and finally he said, 'I guess it's O.K.'"

The high points in Pimentel's research have been his contributions to the understanding of hydrogen bonding, the development of matrix isolation techniques for the study of free radicals, the application of microsecond infrared spectroscopy to the study of gaseous free radicals, the infrared exploration of Mars through the development of spectrometers that were carried on the Mariner 6 and 7 spacecraft, and the discovery and development of the first chemical lasers. George discussed his work as follows:[182]

"I became interested in molecules that were not on the chemical shelf and that consequently fell into an area of unknown - both concerning what molecular structures one would encounter and concerning the applicability of existing ideas of chemical bonding.

"So I set out to try to find ways to study such molecules - free radicals and other transient species - and that led me, along with my graduate and postdoctoral students, to develop the matrix isolation technique. This technique has been extremely successful and it's very widely used now.

"Another contribution evolved from the interest just described. To investigate these transient species, we were continually seeking new approaches. This caused us to develop, alongside the matrix method, what we call 'rapid scan infrared spectroscopy.' As we did this, we built up a set of experimental conditions that were optimum for exploring what is now the field of chemical lasers. As we developed the rapid scan spectrometer, more or less by accident and luck we were ready to do just the right kind of experiment to be the first people to discover chemical lasers. So the matrix isolation technique, with all of the new knowledge it has given us on molecular structure and bonding of transient molecules, plus the chemical laser work, with its implications for chemical kinetics, are two areas in which I've worked that I think are noteworthy.

"There's no question that the chemical laser offers an exciting and opening frontier. Furthermore, there are lots of possibilities if you are interested in applications. The one I see as quite novel is that the chemical laser provides information about intimate aspects of chemical reaction dynamics. I think that we've learned a lot already, and one can expect new things that one can only guess about right now. We are at a turning point because of new instrumental techniques that are made possible by the availability of all types of lasers. The laser provides us with a light source that changes the accessible level of energy input by some three orders of magnitude. Also, the time scale on which you can conduct a chemical experiment is shorter by three orders of magnitude. Nowadays one talks about nanoseconds without the slightest bit of eyebrow raising, and we are approaching the picosecond (10^{-12} second) time scale. The implication of such advances is that brand new phenomena are going to be discovered."

George has always been a little suspicious of theoreticians. He expressed this feeling in an interview with David Ridgway as follows:[182] "There is one trend in chemistry about which I feel some uncertainty. There is a tendency in chemistry now to segregate the activities that are called theoretical from those that are termed experimental. This follows the patterns set by physics over the last three or four decades. One physicist does theory and another does experiments. That has not been the situation that has existed in chemistry. Particulary here at Berkeley, every experimentalist has been expected to be cognizant of, actively using, and trying to advance the theory. Only recently have we succumbed to the vogue that one would hire a scientist who is identified as a theoretician by the negative qualities of unwillingness and/or inability to conduct experimental work. I feel that physics has suffered because of this type of classification and that it is undesirable for people just starting in science to think that theory and experiment are separable. So I am unhappy seeing it come into chemistry. I'd like to minimize the change and try to preserve the image that the best scientist is one who understands and advances theory and also does important experiments that challenge and guide these advances. This type of person maintains perspective about the relationship between theory and experiment."

From 1982 to 1985, George was chairman of a twenty-six-member committee appointed by the Board on Chemical Sciences and Technology of the National Research Council. The committee's charge was to describe:

(1) the contemporary research frontiers of chemistry,

(2) the opportunities for the chemical sciences to address society's needs, and

(3) the resources needed to explore these frontiers to advance human knowledge and to exploit chemistry's opportunities to enhance the well-being of humankind.

The committee's report was issued in 1985 in the form of a 344-page book, entitled *Opportunities in Chemistry*, commonly referred to as "The Pimentel Report."[147a] The primary intended audience for the report were those responsible for guiding science policy in Congress and the Administration, although the report is of importance and interest to all chemists. The conclusions of the report are summarized by the following excerpt:

"The current federal investment in chemical research is still historically rooted in a funding pattern appropriate to a test-tube and Bunsen burner era, an era long since eclipsed. The sophistication of a modern chemistry laboratory requires a much more vigorous and sustained financial commitment of both capital and supporting services. The cost is miniscule when weighed against the potential returns. We must encourage a scientific field brimming with opportunities for discovery that will advance human knowledge and strengthen the underpinnings of a critical industry, and we must attract a substantial share of our brightest young scientists to this rewarding task."

The committee made numerous recommendations, including the following:

"New mechanisms and new incentives should be sought for strengthening links between industrial and academic research.

"Industry should increase its support for university fundamental research in the chemical sciences. Tax incentives to encourage such gains should be explored.

"It is recommended that universities raise their postdoctoral salaries for chemists to bring them into the range established by National Laboratory and industrial postdoctoral programs.

"Whether they are taught to nonscientists, science majors, or chemistry majors, foundational courses in chemistry at the college level must include a substantial component of significant laboratory work.

"Both research universities and industrial laboratories should welcome summer or sabbatical visiting researchers from nearby college faculties.

"Industries should consider passing on serviceable but less than state-of-the-art instrumentation to college departments for both educational and research use. Federal tax incentives would provide impetus to such industrial equipment gift . . . programs.

"The Federal research-funding agencies, in particular, the National Science Foundation, should play an active role by providing competitively awarded research grants of appropriate size and number for research-active faculty at 4-year colleges."

Pimentel is optimistic about the future of chemistry. He says,[171] "All kinds of horizons are opening up that have to do to a great extent with extremely sophisticated techniques. I feel that chemistry is in a real renaissance period, mainly due to technology."

The information explosion is a serious problem, however. "When I was an instructor," he says, "I used to browse through *Chemical Abstracts* every month. I also read almost every article in the *Journal of Chemical Physics* and one or two other journals.

"Now, in one month, the *Journal of Chemical Physics* is as thick as a year's worth when I was an instructor. In one month, *Chemical Abstracts* has gotten to the point where I can't lift it, let alone browse through it. The question of how to keep track of the literature is an entirely different ball game."

CHAPTER
46

Organic Chemistry

The only course Lewis ever flunked was a course in organic chemistry.[101] He probably felt there was too much detail to account for. This experience may have something to do with the fact that organic chemistry at Berkeley never flourished under Lewis. However, his theory of chemical bonding was an important contribution to chemical structural theory and hence to organic chemistry.[190] The shared electron pair concept was the foundation of physical organic chemistry. In fact, the first words in the preface of H. B. Watson's 1937 text on *Modern Theories of Organic Chemistry* are, in conspicuous capitals, PROFESSOR G. N. LEWIS, followed by complimentary remarks indicating the debt which organic and physical chemists owed to Lewis.[229]

When Lewis relinquished his deanship in 1941, the only organic faculty members were Branch, Calvin, and Stewart (who had received their Ph.D.s in physical chemistry) and Porter (who had received his Ph.D. in organic kinetics). Calvin expressed the situation thus:[152] "The three or four organic chemists they had here were really renegade physical chemists for the most part and didn't really have much of a standing in the classical organic chemical world. They were all right, but, you know, they were just average types."

In spite of Branch's research in physical organic chemistry and the publication, in 1941, of Branch and Calvin's *The Theory of Organic Chemistry*, Berkeley did not have much of a reputation in physical organic chemistry in the forties. At an ACS symposium on the history of physical organic chemistry in 1983, Leon Gortler[68] claimed that the early development of this field in the United States took place primarily at Harvard, Columbia, Chicago, and Cal Tech-UCLA. He did acknowledge, however, that the ideas of Lewis had given birth to the British school of physical organic chemistry. He said that "Lewis, a physical chemist, so dominated the intellectual climate at Berkeley that things organic could not grow."

In the middle forties, Latimer and Calvin were looking all around for talent in organic chemistry, but, according to Calvin, they were not very adept at it.[152] Latimer didn't know organic chemists very well, and Calvin was too young and inexperienced to have much influence in such matters. Calvin wrote to Paul D. Bartlett at Harvard, explaining the situation. Bartlett said that he had a pretty good organic chemist there named Bob Woodward and suggested that they come and meet him. Well, Latimer and Calvin did go to Harvard and talked with Woodward for two hours. However, Latimer was unimpressed; he didn't think Woodward would fit into the Berkeley environment. So that was that.

Classical organic chemistry essentially started at Berkeley with the arrival of Jim Cason and Bill Dauben in 1945 and Henry Rapoport in 1946. The main problem facing these pioneers was finding graduate students. For a while they used Berkeley graduates. However, it was recognized that some kind of exchange with other schools would have to be set up, and Cason and Dauben spent a lot of time making contacts with the bigwigs of organic chemistry, such as Homer Adkins at Wisconsin, Art Cope at MIT, and Roger Adams and Carl (Speed) Marvel at Illinois. Illinois presented a special problem; one of their famous organic chemists, R. C. Fuson, had flunked out of Berkeley. Once, at an ACS meeting, Cason asked Speed Marvel, "Speed, how did you like those graduate students we sent you?" Speed said, "Great. Best we've had in a long time." Jim responded, "But we haven't gotten any back from you." Speed said, "If you think I'm going to send any graduate students to that damn den of physical chemistry, you're crazy!" Jim knew he was hearing Fuson speak, and that he had good reason for speaking that way. So he said, "Well, I'm really sorry about that, because we can't keep on sending out our graduates unless we get some back or we'll never get off the ground in organic chemistry. Why don't you talk to some of these students we've sent to Illinois and see what they think of the situation *as of now*, not when they kicked Fuson out." Speed said, "O.K." and the next year, Illinois sent two organic students to Berkeley.[27]

One of the first things that had to be done was to reorganize the undergraduate course of study in organic chemistry. So Latimer appointed a committee, composed of Branch, Calvin and Cason, to make recommendations for changes. They soon came up with a course structure that was quite similar to that found at most of the major universities in the country. Latimer then appointed a departmental committee to review these recommendations. He appointed himself, Axel Olson, and Rollefson. Cason claims that he picked the only people in the department who would approve what had been recommended. "Axel and Rollie were always rebels against the idea that there was nothing in the world but thermodynamics. . . . Olson kind of liked to complain about everything anyhow. . . . Well, so we had this department meeting to discuss it. And boy, the din was deafening! Joel Hildebrand was really put out about this business of putting all these hours of the curriculum into organic chemistry. And Ernest Gibson at one point said, 'Gilbert Lewis would never have tolerated anything like this.'. . . So after this had gone on for quite a while, say like an hour and a half, Wendell said, 'Gentlemen, I really appreciate receiving all of your frank opinions about this matter, and I will certainly take them into consideration when I make up my mind what to do.'" All the recommendations of the organic chemists were accepted, and, except for a few modifications, they represent the structure of the organic courses even today. Thus Latimer played the main role in the establishment of organic chemistry at Berkeley.[27]

In those early days of organic chemistry, the research funding for beginning faculty was handled entirely differently from the way it is today. There was absolutely no pressure to seek funding. Graduate students started out as teaching assistants and later obtained fellowships that were available from the university. Everything in the stockrooms was free, and the shop work, including analytical work, was completely free. It is Rapoport's view that there has been a great deterioration in the research environment since then.[179] In the forties and fifties, the campus was the main source of research funding for the faculty. Now much of the campus administration sort of lives off the faculty by means of the overhead charges on federal research grants. Rapoport says, "I think this has led to a tremendous amount of difficulty and dissatisfaction. At that time, I think, there was much greater institutional loyalty than there is now. And the reason for that was that the institution had a stake in you, and they showed it, and they supported you."

When Latimer Hall was being planned in the late '50s and early '60s, Bill Dauben was the main liaison between the faculty and the architects with respect to the design of the research laboratories. He spent many hours on this planning and on the ordering of equipment and seeing that it was properly installed. The entire department, as well as the organic chemists, are indebted to Dauben for his careful work on this project.

Physical organic chemistry was augmented and modernized by the arrival of Don Noyce in 1948, Andy Streitwieser in 1952, and Fritz Jensen in 1955. The appointment of Clayton Heathcock in 1964, Paul A. Bartlett in 1973, Peter Vollhardt in 1974 and Bob Bergman in 1978 broadened the scope of the organic group in natural product chemistry, bioorganic chemistry, and organometallic chemistry. Organic chemistry at Berkeley is now as good as anywhere and is highly regarded throughout the world.

CHAPTER
47

Chemical Engineering

Although chemical engineering by that name did not start at Berkeley until the 1940s, research and teaching in that field actually began in the first part of the century. O'Neill emphasized technological applications in his teaching and, in that sense, was teaching chemical engineering at the turn of the century. Cottrell's work on the electrostatic precipitation of dusts and mists, which he started in 1905, constituted true chemical engineering research. In 1912, Lewis instituted a "chemical technology" major, subsequently directed by Randall.[207] Thus, the 1917 *Announcement of Courses* lists lecture and laboratory courses in chemical technology, a course in the chemistry of the silicate industries, and a course in applied electrochemistry.[223]

However, while the College under Lewis was achieving fame in physical chemistry, its program in chemical engineering was neglected. It was not until 1940 that Llewellyn M. K. Boelter of the Department of Mechanical Engineering, Latimer, Randall, and others formed a "graduate group" to offer the M.S. in Chemical Engineering.[207] Unfortunately, this program was ill-conceived; it was unrealistic to think that the subject matter could be split between the Colleges of Engineering and Chemistry. There was considerable bickering as to how to divide the program between the colleges. In 1945, the University administration decided that the subject matter should be split into "Process Engineering," administered by the College of Engineering, and "Chemical Engineering," administered by the College of Chemistry.[41] Morrough O'Brien, dean of the College of Engineering, didn't like these names; he wanted both curricula to be called "Chemical Engineering."[156] Latimer, however, insisted on these names because he felt that differentiation was necessary to avoid confusion among the students.[144] It is ironic that this decision was made at a time when practically no students were studying chemical engineering in either college. In fact, after the retirement of Randall, the program was temporarily discontinued. Latimer realized this was a bad situation and, in his 1944-46 biennial report to President Sproul,[115] he enumerated all the important industries in which chemical engineers are important and then stated, "There is today a shortage of many thousands of research chemists and chemical engineers and this shortage will increase in the next ten years if the capacities of the American

Universities for training in these fields is not greatly expanded. In addition it may be noted that the operation of great atomic power industries which will surely come in the next 10-20 years is very largely chemical engineering in nature."

In 1946, Philip Schutz arrived from Columbia University, where he had helped organize a program in chemical engineering. Schutz, of course, was not new to the Department - he had obtained his Ph.D. with Latimer and had served as a research associate with Lewis. When he arrived in Berkeley as an associate professor that fall, he had only two instructors as his colleagues in chemical engineering: Charles Wilke, fresh from a one-year teaching experience at Washington State in Pullman, and LeRoy Bromley, who had not yet completed his Ph.D. research. Unfortunately Schutz contracted cancer of the kidney soon after he arrived, and he died in March of 1947. As soon as it became clear that Schutz was dying, he was replaced by Theodore Vermeulen, who arrived in February of 1947.[239]

At first, working conditions were fairly primitive. Wilke and Bromley shared an office on the second floor of Gilman Hall. They had no telephone. Calls would come in to Miss Kittredge on the first floor, and she would sound a buzzer in their office so that they could dash down to answer the call. However, as the administrative head, Vermeulen enjoyed his private phone. There were no secretaries, and he hated to miss a call. So he always left his office door open and got so that he could detect his phone ringing from almost anywhere on the floor in time to run and answer it.[240]

Meanwhile, O'Brien in Engineering bootlegged a curriculum in the "process engineering" course which covered the same material taught in the College of Chemistry.[239] The mechanical engineering faculty involved in this program included Israel I. Cornet, Robert V. Dunkle, Leonard Farbar, Richard G. Folsom, Lawrence M. Grossman, and Nathan W. Snyder. Thus, in the period 1949-51, there were two separate curricula, in different colleges, which were accredited by the American Institute of Chemical Engineers.[98, 239] The chairman of the AIChE accreditation committee believed that chemical engineering should only be in the College of Engineering and tried to influence the administration in that direction. However, several other factors had more influence in determining the eventual home for chemical engineering.

One factor was a simple matter of nomenclature. In 1949, the Department of Chemistry was officially changed to the Department of Chemistry and Chemical Engineering, and the chemical engineering program in the College of Engineering continued to be called process engineering. Students who wanted to study "chemical engineering" naturally tended to sign up for the program with those words in the name. Hence a lot more students joined the College of Chemistry program than the College of Engineering program. A second factor was the availability of teaching assistantships in freshman chemistry for the incoming graduate students. A third factor was the support and cooperation of Glenn Seaborg in providing research funding in the Radiation Laboratory.

In 1951, when Chancellor Clark Kerr learned of the duplication of effort in these colleges, he set up a committee headed by Francis A. Jenkins of the Physics Department to resolve the conflict. Earl Parker represented the College of Engineering on the committee, and Charles Wilke represented the College of Chemistry. The committee hemmed and hawed for several years. Finally Parker said, in effect, "Look, this is ridiculous; let's end this impasse. To save face for the College of Engineering, let's say that it will be allowed to teach courses emphasizing the mechanical engineering aspects of process engineering, whereas the College of Chemistry will be concerned with all other aspects of chemical engineering." This idea was agreed upon. As expected, after a few years, the College of Engineering discontinued all effort in "process engineering." In 1957, a separate Department of Chemical Engineering, with Wilke as chairman, was created within the College of Chemistry. To a large extent, the ease of conversion from a competitive two-college program to the present one-college program in chemical engineering was due to the good will and cooperative attitude of Earl Parker.[239]

In almost every American university with a department of chemical engineering, that department is separate from the department of chemistry and is a subdivision of the college of engineering. The only exceptions I know of are UC Berkeley, Cal Tech, and Illinois at Urbana.[47] However, there are good reasons for believing that the situation at the latter schools, where chemical engineering is closely affiliated with chemistry, is preferable. Chemistry and chemical engineering are much closer in character than are other sciences and the corresponding engineering disciplines. At the undergraduate level there should be a strong chemistry component in the chemical engineering curriculum, and the Berkeley-type administrative structure makes it easy to serve the needs of both the chemistry and chemical engineering students. At the graduate research level, there is considerable overlap of interest, and the Berkeley-type structure fosters interdepartmental collaboration. Finally, there are obvious advantages in the sharing of facilities such as the college library, shops, storerooms, and business office.

CHAPTER
48

Inorganic Chemistry

Bray and Latimer established what became known during the '30s and '40s as the Berkeley school of inorganic chemistry. Berkeley inorganic chemistry was firmly based on kinetics and thermodynamics. These disciplines were, and still are, a good foundation for studying chemical reactions. Connick and Powell continued in the Bray tradition of studying kinetics and equilibria in aqueous solutions; Brewer expanded the thermodynamic approach to high-temperature systems, and Cunningham applied thermodynamics to the actinide elements. However, even with this powerhouse of researchers, most of the knowledgeable chemists in the rest of the world did not consider Berkeley to be a strong school in inorganic chemistry. In other schools, inorganic chemistry was mainly synthetic inorganic chemistry, with very little activity in kinetic-thermodynamic research. At Berkeley it was just the opposite, and Latimer was well aware of the problem. In 1950, near the end of a talk on the teaching of inorganic chemistry at Berkeley, he said,[113] "On the negative side, we give no organized work in inorganic preparation, although we do have a few students each term doing special problems in this field. I regard this as unfortunate. In my early days I took a course in inorganic preparations from Professor Harkins at Chicago, and I have always regarded this training as highly valuable."

When Latimer sent me off to Livermore in 1952, I said that I hoped I could come back some day. He said, "Well, we have a great need for work in inorganic synthesis." I took the hint, and while at Livermore I learned the technique of vacuum-line manipulation of volatile compounds - the technique that Schlesinger, Brown, and Burg used so successfully in studying the chemistry of the boron hydrides during World War II. Thus when I returned to the Department in 1955, I was able to start a research program in the synthesis of volatile hydrides.

The undergraduate teaching curriculum in inorganic chemistry needed reorganization in 1955. My first teaching assignment was Chem 104, a course that Latimer had started in 1936, based on his book, *Oxidation Potentials.* I appreciated the value of oxidation potentials in the interpretation of the inorganic chemistry of solutions, and I intended to include such interpretation in the course. However, there is a lot more to inorganic chemistry than its thermodynamics, and I wanted to present a balanced view. So when it came time to submit my choice of textbook on the form that was routinely sent to the bookstores through the department office, I specified the best available general textbook on inorganic chemistry, Moeller's *Inorganic Chemistry*. All hell broke loose when Miss Kittredge saw this. You see, Wendell had just died a few months earlier, and she felt it would be sacrilegious to change the textbook so soon after his death. Pitzer called me in, explained the situation, and we came to a rather poor compromise: Latimer was the assigned textbook, but six copies of Moeller were put on reserve in the library for the students to read. Fortunately I had my own choice of textbook in succeeding years. In 1957 I organized the first formal course in inorganic synthesis and soon thereafter wrote the first modern textbook for such a course.

When a few more "classical" inorganic chemists (that is, inorganic chemists who worked in areas other than kinetics or thermodynamics) were hired, the department began to acquire a good reputation in inorganic chemistry among outsiders. I was particularly pleased to play a part in the first appointment of a tenure-level inorganic chemist, namely Neil Bartlett, who had recently shown that the noble gases are not chemically inert. That appointment in 1969 was an important step in the upgrading of inorganic chemistry in the Department.

CHAPTER
49

Biophysical Chemistry

The first members of the Chemistry Department to work in the field of biophysical chemistry were Bruno Zimm (appointed in 1946) and Chester O'Konski (appointed in 1948). However, Zimm left in 1952 to accept a position at General Electric, and O'Konski's research has not been exclusively in biophysical chemistry. The first full-fledged, permanent biochemist in the department was Ignacio Tinoco, Jr. (appointed in 1956). The biophysical group developed slowly, however. It was not until 1962 that John Hearst arrived, followed by Kenneth Sauer (1963) and James Wang (1966). Later arrivals were Wayne Hubbell (who left for UCLA in 1983), Richard Mathies, Judith Klinman, and Sung-Hou Kim.

At present, there are about nine faculty members (both non-tenure and tenure) in the biophysical group. Such a concentration of biochemically oriented people within a chemistry department is unique in America, if not the world. There are, of course, departments of biochemistry in dozens of universities. And several chemistry departments in America have perhaps two or three faculty members interested in biochemistry. The remarkable fact is that Berkeley has not only a Department of Biochemistry, but also a large biophysical group within its chemistry department.

Until 1948, biochemistry was taught at Berkeley mainly in the Department of Biochemistry of the Medical School, which moved to San Francisco in 1958. In 1948, a new Department of Biochemistry was organized in the College of Letters and Science, with Wendell M. Stanley as chairman. There has always been a difference in emphasis between the Biochemistry Department and the biophysical group of the Chemistry Department. The research problems are similar, but the methods used are different. The biochemists often use genetics or bacteria in their studies, whereas the biophysical chemists tend to use physical chemical methods, such as fluorescence spectroscopy, circular dichroism spectroscopy, resonance Raman spectroscopy, x-ray diffraction, and NMR. Undoubtedly this emphasis on physical methods in the biophysical group is derived from the G. N. Lewis tradition. Zimm, O'Konski and Tinoco were hired mainly because of their physical chemical approach to research. Only as the group of researchers grew in size was the research emphasis allowed to shift slightly toward biology.[217]

There is no antagonism between the two departments. It has been claimed that most of the biochemists teach only one course per year, whereas most of the chemists teach two courses per year. To rationalize this difference, the biochemists argue that teaching in biochemistry is more taxing because of the relatively rapid developments in biochemistry compared to subjects such as freshman chemistry and thermodynamics.

CHAPTER
50

Conclusions

The farther backward you look, the farther forward you can see. I hope that our brief look at the early years of the Berkeley College of Chemistry can help us chart the future course of academic chemistry. This chapter consists mainly of my personal conclusions, based on my experiences as a professor and on this historical study. For example, I believe that, because chemistry at Berkeley prospered under Wheeler and Lewis, it is reasonable to conclude that benevolent dictatorship can, with suitable precautions, be both tolerated and encouraged. That is, as long as faculty members have a say in the appointment and recall of their deans and chairmen, these leaders should be empowered to make certain kinds of decisions and to act on them without obtaining the approval of the faculty. With suitable checks and balances, this procedure can be quite democratic. Indeed, most faculty members would welcome a system that relieved them of the chores that have little to do with teaching or research and would prefer to have wise decisions made by appointed individuals than to serve on committees charged with making the same decisions. Of course, if this policy is followed, great care must be taken when making executive appointments.

Great care must also be taken when appointing new faculty members. Throughout the tenure of Lewis, all initial staff appointments were to non-tenure positions. In recent years, the Department of Chemistry has had some unfortunate experiences in attempts to recruit faculty at the tenure level. We have aimed at world fame in all the main categories of chemistry - physical, inorganic, organic, nuclear, biophysical, and analytical (yes, even analytical chemistry, which has never had an important place in our research program). We have attempted to expand or to improve our images in several of these fields by attracting highly respected, well established chemists from wherever they might be. These efforts have usually required the promise of facilities such as specially-equipped laboratories, expensive instrumentation, and luxurious offices, as well as high salaries and help in finding suitable housing (not a minor consideration in today's Bay Area real estate market). In several cases we have been successful in such recruiting and have been rewarded with good colleagues who have raised the prestige of the Department. However, much of our tenure-level recruiting has been an enormous waste of time, as far as the benefits to our department are concerned. Several deals have fallen through at the last minute. In some cases, our efforts have merely served to raise the stock of the sought individual in his home department, where he has been rewarded with a special promotion or appointment. Our recent attempts to hire a famous chemist from a prestigious midwestern university were particularly frustrating. This professor led us on for several years, giving his colleagues at home the impression that he would probably never leave, while giving us the impression that he would probably come to Berkeley. Finally we just gave up.

I find that many of my colleagues now have serious doubts about the wisdom of hiring at the tenure level. Aside from the difficulty of successfully recruiting such people and the likelihood that such efforts will be in vain, there are other points to be considered. Whereas a faculty member who has risen through the ranks generally acquires a colleagueship and *esprit de corps* that leads to true department loyalty, such loyalty is less likely to develop in a tenured recruit. A second point was made by George Pimentel in a conversation we had in 1986.[168] He said, "I think the major reason the Department is in good health is because one thing that has survived from the Lewis days has been a conviction on the part of everybody that the future of the department rests on young people - bringing in hot young people. There are things that give me cause for alarm, and one is this seemingly accelerating tendency to look to developing the future of the department through tenured appointments rather than through bringing up our young people. . . . I have a great belief in the desirability of having a good spectrum of insights and ranges of experience. The young people don't know enough to be conservative yet, and they're apt to think thoughts that the rest of us think are crazy - and that's good. They'll try things that other people know aren't going to work, and once in a while they do work! So it's very desirable for everybody to have this continual infusion of young people. When you bring in somebody at the top, inevitably you reach out and get somebody who has a real sparkling career and, these days, the empire that goes with it. One tends to build up groups of individual empires rather than reinforcing the collegial atmosphere that was the hallmark of the place when you and I were young."

A feature of Lewis's hiring policy that led to a very unbalanced department was his policy of inbreeding - that is, of appointing people who had done their graduate work, if not also their undergraduate work, at Berkeley. This kind of hiring should be done with great caution. It is not necessarily true that one should hire a top-notch person irrespective of his or her field. However, there is more to worry about than appointing faculty. The most important activities in any university are teaching and research. Let us consider the policies in these areas separately.

Teaching

It is well known that there is a crying need for workers with technical competence or with at least an appreciation of the importance of technology. Science and engineering must be made attractive to young people, and the best place to do this is in elementary and high schools. Unfortunately, there are not enough qualified science teachers. That's where universities can help. Undergraduates should learn, by observation of their professors, that teaching young people can be a pleasurable and satisfying experience. The best professors should teach the freshman courses. If professors avoid teaching freshmen, and if those who do teach freshmen do so reluctantly, students will get the impression that such teaching is considered a second-class occupation relative to research and to the teaching of advanced topics close to the research interests of the professor.

Another way university faculty can help is by actively encouraging undergraduates to go into high school or elementary school teaching. Such careers should not be looked upon as last resorts for scientists, in spite of the low salary scales of such teaching jobs. The satisfactions associated with teaching that compensate for low salaries should be pointed out. After all, professors of science and engineering know all about this - they are all underpaid when compared with their counterparts in industry!

Probably the most important thing we can teach freshman chemistry students (most of whom will not follow careers in chemistry) is that chemistry is important to everybody and that there is a great need for chemical research. These students will soon have an influence on public opinion, and the better the public image of chemistry, the more likely it will be that young people choose careers in chemistry. Of course, the same reasoning applies to other sciences as well.

The policy that Lewis started in 1912 of involving the entire College of Chemistry staff in the freshman chemistry course was a good one, and should be continued as far as possible. It is important that the course have input from all sectors of the College because all the upperclassmen of the College, no matter what their specialties, have the freshman course as a common basis for their studies. The administration should reward professors who are good at encouraging freshmen to enter careers in science or science teaching, just as professors who are brilliant at research are rewarded. Our best and most experienced graduate students should be encouraged to be teaching assistants in freshman chemistry, where they can act as role models for the students. Surely, when Latimer gave the lectures in freshman chemistry as a graduate student in 1918, he must have been an inspiration to his students! New, inexperienced graduate students can be assigned as teaching assistants in second-, third-, and fourth-year courses in accord with their interests and abilities.

What about teaching evaluation? It has become common practice, at the end of each course, to poll students regarding their opinions of the instructor. These student opinions are summarized quantitatively and are often the only data used by promotion committees when determining the teaching effectiveness of the instructor. There is even an agency on the campus with the purpose of aiding professors in raising their student teaching evaluations. No matter how carefully these evaluations are carried out, they are essentially popularity polls, because many students have difficulty identifying good and bad teaching. Consider Calvin's remarks about Carson, one of his early chemistry teachers:[152] "He taught a course in physical chemistry and thermodynamics which I took, both in succession. He was a very methodical kind of guy. I used to work hard during the term, taking notes and doing the exercises, and when final examination time came I relaxed because he organized so well that I didn't have anything to do for the final examination week. I just took the exam. It was no problem, he had it so well organized. That had merit and it also had demerit. Had merit in that it makes it easy. On the other hand, if it's easy you don't remember it too well after a while, you know. . . . It didn't produce the long term learning that it should have, or could have, had it been a little more difficult for me."

Also consider Bray, who "irritated students into learning." Forty-five years after being taught by Bray, Taube publicly acknowledged his own, and inorganic chemistry's, debt to Bray's teaching ability.[212]

Teaching ability is best measured by the ability of the teacher to motivate students to learn. The duty of promotion committees should be to measure that motivational ability.

In the old days, the Lewis-style research conferences provided an opportunity for the faculty to discuss half-baked research ideas with their colleagues. These discussions were not for the bashful or those easily embarrassed by mistakes, but they

were invaluable for those who wanted to test out their ideas
before proclaiming them to the harsh outside world. The
discussions also allowed graduate students to see first-hand the
thought processes involved in imaginative research. Our present
seminar system seldom provides the opportunity for such
discussion. Now seminars are restricted to particular disciplines
and, whether given by visiting speakers or our own faculty, are
usually presentations of completed work which is ready for
publication, if not already published. The graduate student
research conferences, given by graduate students at the beginning
of their second year, in conjunction with their prelims, are no
substitute. And even the "group" research conferences held by
professors with relatively large research groups are poor
substitutes because such groups usually have only one senior
member and the discussions are highly restricted as to topic.
Both graduate teaching and research would benefit if we could
find a way to reinstitute something like the old-time research
seminar.

Pimentel expressed it thus: "We don't talk to each other in our
seminars the way we should. . . . We are tending to lose the
cohesiveness that is always a problem with size. . . . I'd like to see
our seminars return to the place where you and I talk to our
other faculty colleagues and tell them what's on our minds - not
what was finished and published two months ago."

Research

Lewis made the Department a wonderful place for research
in physical chemistry. By his definition, physical chemistry was
anything that was interesting. The faculty were free to work on
just about anything they pleased. Research was relatively cheap
in those days, and the Department usually could provide funds
for any special equipment needed.

Things are different now. The College consists of two
departments - Chemical Engineering, encompassing electrochemical engineering, biochemical engineering, polymers, molecular
thermodynamics, separations, catalysis, plasma processing, solid
state electronics, and semiconductor device manufacturing, and
Chemistry, encompassing physical, nuclear, inorganic, organic,
and biophysical chemistry. Research is expensive; as much as
$200 thousand in equipment funds may be required just to set up
a new assistant professor so that he or she can start research.

And now chemists cannot work on anything they please.[201]
Funds are provided by research grants that sometimes have
unrealistically short terms. The awarding of a research grant is
subject to current fashions in research and to the whims of

anonymous peer reviewers and government bureaus. Professors have to spend more time getting the next grant and worrying about personnel than they have available to think about chemistry itself. The research environment is a kind of Darwinian jungle in which the fittest survive. A chemist who does not survive may be poor only at administration - he may be the kind of person who works all night in the lab and forgets about his paperwork until it is too late - and yet he may be the kind of person who will make a dazzling contribution to chemistry.

Many professors find that, in order to get research funds, they must apply to mission-oriented agencies. Unfortunately, those who fashion United States science policy don't yet realize that the funding of basic research is a kind of tithe to be paid by any nation with a high standard of living. I am not suggesting that all research in a college of chemistry should be basic research. Although Cottrell's research at the beginning of the century was certainly basic - it involved rather esoteric phenomena associated with galvanic cells - that didn't prevent him from inventing the electrostatic precipitator. Seaborg wasn't thinking about atom bombs when he first synthesized plutonium, but he led the groups that characterized its chemistry and metallurgy during World War II. Much of Calvin's research has involved theoretical aspects of photosynthesis, but in recent years he has been trying to find a practical method for getting gasoline directly from plants. I believe that professors should be free to engage in either basic or applied research according to their individual preferences. Graduate students should not be given any reason for thinking that one kind of research is better than the other.

An alternative to peer-review grants and grants from mission-oriented agencies is the block grant. In this system, a block of money is awarded to a department which then distributes the funds, as it sees fit, to its individual members. The state of California does this on a small scale: it provides blocks of research money, with essentially no strings attached, to university departments. Perhaps the federal government should distribute some of its research money in a similar way, with the size of each departmental grant determined by the recent performance and promise of the department as a whole.

Alphabetical List of References

1. Allison, F., *Phys. Rev.*, **1927**, *29*, 370.
2. "Alpha Chi Sigma Fraternity, Its Origins," 14th ed., Issued by the Office of the Grand Master of Ceremonies, no date.
3. "Alpha Chi Sigma Fraternity, Today," Issued by the Office of the Grand Master of Ceremonies, 1984.
4. Alpha Chi Sigma publication, "The Bear," Berkeley, California, 1922.
5. Alpha Chi Sigma, Sigma Chapter, History Book. Berkeley, California.
6. Alpha Chi Sigma, Sigma Chapter, Archives. Berkeley, California.
7. Arrhenius, S. A., to Wheeler, B. I., Apr. 21, 1904. President's Files, UC Archives.
8. Arrhenius, S. A., "Theories of Chemistry," Longmans, Green and Co., London, 1907.
9. Arrhenius, S. A., "Immunochemistry," Macmillan, New York, 1907.
10. Bell, H. H., Master's Thesis, UC Berkeley, 1947, "George C. Pardee and the Oakland Water Supply."
11. Berger, C. R.; Knopoff, L.; McMillan, W. G., "In Memoriam," Univ. of Calif., 1980. "Willard Frank Libby."
12. Berger, R.; Libby, L. M., eds., "Willard F. Libby; Collected Papers," Geo Science Analytical, Santa Monica, and UCLA, 1981.
13. Biddle, H. C., UC bio-bibliographical file, UC Archives.
14. Birge, R. T., *Science*, **1940**, *91*, 323.
15. *Blue and Gold* Yearbooks, UC Berkeley, 1927, 1928, 1929, 1931.
16. Bode, W., *Dimensions* (Publication of the Department of Chemistry), **1979**, *2*(19), Aug. 20, 1979 (Interview with A. G. Loomis).
17. Brewer, L., *J. Chem. Education*, **1984**, *61*, 101.
18. Bush, V., *Natl. Acad. Sci. Biogr. Memoirs*, Vol. 27, p. 1. "Frederick Gardner Cottrell."
19. Butler, K., *San Francisco Chronicle*, Aug. 2, 1985, p. 4. Article on Hiroshima.
20. Cady, H. P., Autobiographical address given at ACS dinner in his honor in 1936.
21. *California Monthly*, Nov. **1933**, p. 13, obituary on Eddie O'Neill.
22. Calvin, M., Chapter VIII in The Robert A. Welch Foundation Conferences on Chemical Research. XX. American Chemistry - Bicentennial. Nov. 8-10, 1976, 116.
23. Calvin, M., *J. Chem. Education*, **1984**, *61*, 14.
24. Calvin, M.; Bailes, R. H.; Wilmarth, W. K., *J. Am. Chem. Soc.*, **1946**, *68*, 2254.
25. Cameron, F., "Cottrell, Samaritan of Science," Doubleday, Garden City, New York, 1952.
26. Campbell, W. W., to Nobel Committee, Dec. 5, 1930. Nobel Committee Archives.
27. Cason, J., Conversation, Jan. 13, 1986.
28. Castlewood Country Club brochures, 1985.
29. Cattell, J. M., "American Men of Science," The Science Press, New

York, 1927. "George A. Hulett."
30. Cloud, R. W., "Education in California," Stanford Univ. Press, 1952, 61-62.
31. Compton, A. H., *J. Franklin Inst.*, **1928**, *205*, 156.
32. Connick, R. E., Conversation, Dec. 17, 1985.
33. Cottrell, F. G., to O'Neill, E., Sept. 4, 1908. Bancroft Library.
34. Cottrell, F. G., *Calif. J. Technol.*, **1905**, *6*, 3.
35. Cottrell, Frederick G., biographical sketch on, College of Chem. files.
36. *Daily Californian*, April 15, 1913, p. 3.
37. *Daily Californian*, March 31, 1914, p. 1.
38. *Daily Californian*, Sept. 30, 1936. Article: "Student Dies in Accidental Rifle Shooting."
39. *Daily Californian*, Dec. 9, 1983, p. 17. Article about Mrs. E. O. Lawrence. Also see *San Francisco Chronicle*, Sep. 7, 1985, p. 2.
40. Daniel, E. T., Transcription of interview of Joel H. Hildeband, Bancroft Library, Regional Cultural History Project, 1960.
41. Deutsch, M. E., to Latimer, W. M., Dec. 11, 1945. Copy courtesy of C. R. Wilke.
42. *Dimensions* (Publication of the College of Chemistry), **1980**, *3*(10), 1; **1984**, *7*(10), 1.
43. Donnan, F. G., to Lewis, G. N., Nov. 17, 1929. UC Archives.
44. Dupras, D., *Calif. Geology*, **1986**, *39*, 3.
45. Egan, C. E., *New York Times* article, Oct. 16, 1953.
46. Einstein, A., to Lewis, G. N., Aug. 22, 1926. UC Archives. Translation by R. H. Stuewer (ref. 211).
47. Ekerdt, J. G., "Chemical Engineering Faculties, 1984-1985," Vol. 33, Am. Inst. Chem. Eng., New York.
48. Emmett, P. H., in "The Physical Basis for Heterogeneous Catalysis," Drauglis, E., and Jaffee, R. T., eds., Plenum, New York, 1975, p. xiv.
49. *Encyclopaedia Britannica*, Vol. 2, Univ. of Chicago, 1969. "Arrhenius, Svante August."
50. Engel, N., See citations in ref 17.
51. Eyring, H., *Chem. Eng. News*, **1976**, *54*, April 6, 88.
52. Fairbanks, Morse and Co. to O'Neill, E., May 11, 1906. Author's files.
53. Federation of American Scientists, Information Bulletin No. 27, Oct. 19, 1953. "Kelly Report on Functions and Operations of the Bureau of Standards."
54. Fisher, R. A., to Haight, H. H., Nov. 1, 1870. UC Archives.
55. Fitzgibbon, R. H., "The Academic Senate of the University of California," University of California, 1968.
56. Franklin, F., "Life of Daniel Coit Gilman," Dodd, Mead, New York, 1910.
57. Geiger, H.; Mueller, W., *Naturwiss.*, **1928**, *16*, 617.
58. Giauque, W. F., to La Mer, V. K., Mar. 1, 1955. College Files.
59. Giauque, W. F.; Hildebrand, J. H.; Seaborg, G. T., "In Memoriam," Univ. of Calif., 1961. "George Ernest Gibson."
60. Giauque, W. F.; Hildebrand, J. H.; Lenzene, V. F., "In Memoriam,"

Univ. of Calif. "Walter Charles Blasdale."
61. Giauque, W. F., *Nature*, **1939**, *143*, 623.
62. Giauque, W. F., *Year Book of the Am. Phil. Soc.*, **1946**, p. 317, "Gilbert Newton Lewis."
63. Gibson, G. E.; Calvin, M.; Hildebrand, J. H.; Tippett, J. E., "In Memoriam," Univ. of Calif., 1957. "Gerald E. K. Branch."
64. Gilles, P. W., *J. Electrochem. Soc.*, **1972**, *119*, 5C.
65. Gilman Hall Fund, Declaration of Trust, Feb. 19, 1937, and related records. College Files.
66. Goodstein, J. R., in "Dictionary of American Biography, Supplement Four, 1946-1950," Garraty, J. A.; James, E. T., eds., Scribner's, New York, 1974, 837-840.
67. Goodstein, J. R., Conversation, Nov. 1985, and Letter, Dec. 2, 1985.
68. Gortler, L., *J. Chem. Education*, **1985**, *62*, 753.
69. Gwinn, W. D., Conversation, July 31, 1985.
70. Hahn, O.; Meitner, L.; Strassmann, F., *Z. Phys.*, **1937**, *106*, 249.
71. Halley, W., "The Centennial Year Book of Alameda County, California," Publ. by W. Halley, Oakland, Calif., 1876, p. 543.
72. Hanson, D.; Pitzer, K. S.; Tobias, C. W.; Wilke, C. R., "In Memoriam," Univ. of Calif., 1985. "Theodore Vermeulen."
73. Heylin, M., *Chem. Eng. News*, **1985**, *63*, July 17, 5.
74. Hildebrand, J. H.; Pitzer, K. S.; Powell, R. E., "In Memoriam," Univ. of Calif., 1958. "Wendell Mitchell Latimer."
75. Hildebrand, J. H., Chapter 1 in "Going Light with Backpack or Burro," Sierra Club, San Francisco, 1951.
76. Hildebrand, J. H., in "Symposium on the Physical and Earth Sciences," University of California, 1958, pp. 1-11.
77. Hildebrand, J. H., "Principles of Chemistry," Macmillan, New York, 1918.
78. Hildebrand, J. H., *Chem. Eng. News*, **1945**, *23*, 2317.
79. Hildebrand, J. H., *Obituary Notices of Fellows of the Royal Society*, **1947**, *5*, 491. "Gilbert Newton Lewis."
80. Hildebrand, J. H., *Int. Sci. Technology*, July, **1967**, 68.
81. Hildebrand, J. H., *Perspectives Biol. Med.*, **1972**, *16*, 88.
82. Hildebrand, J. H., *Chem. Eng. News*, **1976**, *54*, Sept. 13, 26.
83. Hildebrand, J. H., *Natl. Acad. Sci. Biogr. Memoirs*, **1958**, *32*, 221. "Wendell Mitchell Latimer."
84. Hildebrand, J. H., *Natl. Acad. Sci. Biogr. Memoirs*, *26*, 13. "William Crowell Bray."
85. Hillinger, C., *Los Angeles Times*, Part V, p. 2, Dec. 8, 1983.
86. Hitchcock Lecture Records, President's Files, UC Archives.
87. Hulett, G. A., to Wheeler, B. I., Aug. 9, 1911. President's Files, UC Archives.
88. Hulett, G. A., to Wheeler, B. I., Sept. 1, 1911. President's Files, UC Archives.
89. Hulett, G. A., to Wheeler, B. I., Sept. 19, 1911. President's Files, UC Archives.
90. Jensen, W. B., "The Lewis Acid-Base Concepts: An Overview," Wiley, New York, 1980.

91. Jensen, W. B., *J. Chem. Education*, **1984**, *61*, 191.
92. Jewett, F. S., to Latimer, W. M., Sept. 11, 1946. College Files.
93. Jones, W. C., "Illustrated History of the University of California," Students' Cooperative, Berkeley, 1901.
94. Jura, G.; Connick, R. E.; Hutson, A. E.; Somorjai, G. A., "In Memoriam," Univ. of Calif., 1980. "Richard Edward Powell."
95. Kamen, M. D., "Radiant Science, Dark Politics," U. of Calif. Press, Berkeley, 1985.
96. Kasha, M., *J. Chem. Education*, **1984**, *61*, 204.
97. Kaya, G. S., to Jolly, W. L., Feb. 13, 1986.
98. King, C. J., Remarks to Chemical Engineering Advisory Board, Oct. 27, 1978.
99. Kirkwood, J. G.; Wulf, O. R.; Epstein, P. S., *Natl. Acad. Sci. Biogr. Memoirs*, **1952**, *27*, 139. "Richard Chase Tolman."
99a. Koenig, F. O., *Isis*, **1942**, *34*, 142. Biography of Stillman.
100. Kohler, R. E., *Historical Studies in the Physical Sciences*, **1971**, *3*, 343; **1974**, *4*, 39; **1975**, *6*, 431.
101. Lachman, A., "Borderland of the Unknown - The Life Story of Gilbert Newton Lewis," Pageant Press, N.Y., 1955.
102. Lage, A. and R., Transcription of interviews with Joel H. Hildebrand. Sierra Club History Committee.
103. Langmuir, I., to Lewis, G. N., Apr. 3, 1920. UC Archives.
104. Langmuir, I., "Pathological Science," Colloquium at the Knolls Research Laboratory of the General Electric Co., December 18, 1953. From a recording in the Manuscript Division of the Library of Congress.
105. Latimer, W. M., to Jewett, F. S., Sept. 18, 1946. College Files.
106. Latimer, W. M., to Smith, G. F., Mar. 10, 1947. College Files.
107. Latimer, W. M., to newspaper reporter, Feb. 25, 1955. College Files.
108. Latimer, W. M.; Calvin, M.; Hoagland, D. R., "In Memoriam," Univ. of Calif., 1943. "Samuel Ruben."
109. Latimer, W. M., "The Oxidation States of the Elements and their Potentials in Aqueous Solutions," Prentice Hall, New York, 1938 and 1952.
110. Latimer, W. M., Short autobiography, reproduced in toto in ref. 83.
111. Latimer, W. M.; Rodebush, W. H. *J. Am. Chem. Soc.*, **1920**, *42*, 1419. Polarity and Ionization from the Standpoint of the Lewis Theory of Valence.
112. Latimer, W. M.; Young, H. A., *Phys. Rev.*, **1939**, *56*, 963.
113. Latimer, W. M., *J. Chem. Education*, **1950**, *27*, 451.
114. Latimer, W. M.; Jolly, W. L., *J. Am. Chem. Soc.*, **1953**, *75*, 4147. Absolute Entropies in Liquid Ammonia.
115. Latimer, W. M., Report of the Department of Chemistry for the Biennium July 1, 1944 to June 30, 1946. President's Files, UC Archives.
116. Le Bel, J. A., *Bull. Soc. Chim.*, **1874**, *22*, 337.
117. Lewis, E. S., Conversation, Aug. 1, 1985.
118. Lewis, G. N., to Einstein, A., July 27, 1926. UC Archives.
119. Lewis, G. N., to Hart, W. M., Mar. 28, 1924. UC Archives.

120. Lewis, G. N., to Fischer, C., May 6, 1930. UC Archives.
121. Lewis, G. N. to Wheeler, B. I., July 26, 1916. UC Archives.
122. Lewis, G. N. to Wheeler, B. I., March 13, 1912. UC Archives.
123. Lewis, G. N. to Wheeler, B. I., Dec. 9, 1911. UC Archives.
124. Lewis, G. N. to Millikan, R. A., Oct. 28, 1919. UC Archives.
125. Lewis, G. N. to Soule, L. P., Mar. 1, 1927. UC Archives.
126. Lewis, G. N. to Partington, J. R., Dec. 7, 1928. UC Archives.
127. Lewis, G. N. to Noyes, W. A., July 13, 1926. UC Archives.
128. Lewis, G. N., "Valence and the Structure of Atoms and Molecules," Chemical Catalog Co., 1923, p. 109.
129. Lewis, G. N.; Randall, M., "Thermodynamics and the Free Energy of Chemical Substances," McGraw-Hill, New York, 1923.
130. Lewis, G. N., "The Anatomy of Science," Yale Univ. Press, New Haven, 1926.
131. Lewis, G. N., *Proc. Nat. Acad. Sci.*, **1925**, *11*, 179.
132. Lewis, G. N., *Proc. Nat. Acad. Sci.*, **1926**, *12*, 22.
132a. Lewis, G. N., *Nature*, **1926**, *118*, 874.
133. Lewis, G. N., *J. Franklin Inst.*, **1938**, *226*, 297.
134. Lewis, G. N.; Adams, E. Q., *Phys. Rev.*, **1914**, *3*, 92.
135. Lewis, G. N., *Phil. Mag.*, **1925**, *49*, 739.
136. Lewis, R. N., *J. Chem. Education*, **1984**, *61*, 3.
137. Libby, W. F., Eulogy to Wendell Latimer on the occasion of the dedication of Latimer Hall, May 3, 1963. College Files. (Also see *Ann. Rev. Phys. Chem.*, **1964**, *15*, 1.)
138. Lipkin, David, Private communication, July 16, 1985.
139. Louderback, G. D.; Blasdale, W. C., *Univ. Calif. Publicns, Bull. Dept. Geology*, **1907**, *5*(9), 149; **1909**, *5*(23), 331.
140. Luder, W. F.; Zuffanti, S., "The Electronic Theory of Acids and Bases," Wiley, New York, 1946.
141. Lyon, D., Quotations in an article on W. F. Giauque in *Dimensions*, **1982**, *5*(8), April 14, 1982. (Publication of the Department of Chemistry.)
142. Mendeleev, D., *J. Russ. Chem. Soc.*, **1869**, *1*, 60; *Z. Chem.*, **1869**, *5*, 405.
143. Miller, C., *Cornell Alumni News*, Sept. 1979, p. 30. "Benny Ide."
144. MLH to Deutsch, undated (ca 1945), President's files, UC Archives.
145. Moe, L. H., Conversation, Feb. 5, 1986.
146. Moore, T. S.; Winmill, T. F., *J. Chem. Soc.*, **1912**, *101*, 1635.
147. National Academy of Sciences, Report of the Committee on Battery Additives. Oct. 30, 1953.
147a. National Research Council, "Opportunities in Chemistry," National Academy Press, Washington, D.C., 1985.
148. Nobel Committee Archives, courtesy of Prof. A. Magneli, Secretary of the Committee for Chemistry.
149. Norberg, A. L., *Chem. Eng. News*, **1976**, *54*, Aug. 30, 26.
150. Norberg, A. L., Transcription of interviews with Joel H. Hildebrand, Bancroft Library, History of Science and Technology Program, 1980.
151. Norberg, A. L., Transcription of interviews with Glenn T. Seaborg,

Bancroft Library, History of Science and Technology Program, 1984.

152. Norberg, A. L., "Melvin Calvin: Chemistry and Chemical Biodynamics at Berkeley, 1937-1980," Transcription of interviews, Bancroft Library, History of Science and Technology Program, 1984.

153. *Oakland Daily Transcript*, Oct. 4, 1870, p. 3, and Nov. 4, 1870, p. 3. Reports of actions of the UC Board of Regents.

153a. *Oakland Daily Transcript*, Oct. 6 and 26, 1870. Articles about E. S. Carr's lectures.

154. *Oakland Times*, July 16, 1895, p. 1 and July 23, 1895, p. 5. Royal Baking Powder advertisements.

155. *Oakland Tribune*, Aug. 28, 1917. Obituary for Edward Booth.

156. O'Brien, M. P. to Sproul, R. G., Feb. 22, 1946. UC Archives.

157. O'Neill, E., to Hulett, G. A., Aug. 3, 1911. President's Files, UC Archives.

158. O'Neill, E., to Wheeler, B. I., Nov. 22, 1903. President's Files, UC Archives.

159. O'Neill, E., *Calif. Engineer*, 1923, *2*(1), 3.

160. O'Neill, E., *J. Ind. Eng. Chem.*, 1918, *10*(5), 391.

161. O'Neill, Edmond, Biographical sketch on. College of Chem. files.

162. O'Neill, Edmond, Memorial Resolution on, to President and Academic Senate, Feb. 28, 1934. UC Archives.

163. Ostwald, W., "Lebenslinien," Vol. 2, Klasing & Co., Berlin, 1927.

164. Pardee, G. C., to O'Neill, E., Apr. 7, 1890. Author's files.

165. Pauling, L., Chapter VI in the Robert A. Welch Foundation Conferences on Chemical Research. XX. American Chemistry - Bicentennial. Nov. 8-10, 1976, p. 88.

166. Petersen, W., *Vortex*, Sept. 1976, *37*, 40.

167. Pfaff, T., *Calif. Monthly*, Nov. 1985, p. 10; also see Seaborg, G. T., *New York Times*, July 16, 1985, p. C6.

168. Pimentel, G., Conversation, Jan. 9, 1986.

169. Pitzer, K. S., Biographical Memoirs, *Am. Phil. Soc.*, "William Francis Giauque, 1895-1982."

170. Pitzer, K. S., Conversation, Oct. 7, 1985.

171. *Potentials* (Publicn. of the Department of Chemistry), 1983, *5*(1), 1.

172. *Potentials* (Publicn. of the Department of Chemistry), 1986, *8*(1), 6.

173. Powell, R. E., *J. Chem. Education*, 1975, *52*, 820.

174. Powell, R. E., "History of the Department and College of Chemistry, University of California," Chemistry Dept. Files.

175. Ramsay, W., to Wheeler, B. I., Nov. 16, 1903. President's Files, UC Archives.

176. Ramsay, W., to Wheeler, B. I., Apr. 26, 1904. President's Files, UC Archives.

177. Randall, M., and Giauque, W. F., to Provost Deutsch, Oct. 25, 1937. UC Archives.

178. Randall, M.; Young, L. E., "Elementary Physical Chemistry," Randall & Sons, Berkeley, 1942.

179. Rapoport, H., Conversation, Feb., 1986.

180. Regents of UC as trustee of the O'Neill Trust, petitioner, vs. T. C. Lynch, Attorney General of California, respondent: Findings of Fact, Conclusions of Law, and Judgment Applying Cy Pres Doctrine. May 17, 1966, Alameda County Superior Court.
181. Research Corpn., "Science, Invention, and Society," 1972.
182. Ridgway, D., *J. Chem. Education*, **1974**, *51*, 224. "Interview with George Pimentel."
183. Ridgway, D., *J. Chem. Education*, **1975**, *52*, 219. "Interview with Kenneth Pitzer."
183a. Rising, W. B., to Cottrell, F. G., Sept., 1895. Also see Rising, W. B., to Kellogg, M., Aug. 30, 1895. Regents' Files, UC Archives.
184. Rising, W. B., to Ramsay, W., Sept. 22, 1903. President's Files, UC Archives.
185. Ritchie, J. M. (as told to H. Kursh), Reprint from an article in *Cars*, 1952. "My Battle for Battery AD-X2."
186. Rodebush, W. H.; Rodebush, E. K., "An Introductory Course in Physical Chemistry," Van Nostrand, N.Y., 1932.
187. Rollefson, G. K.; Branch, G. E. K.; Gibson, G. E., "In Memoriam," Univ. of Calif. "Merle Randall."
188. Royal School of Mines, Register of Old Students 1851-1920, London, p. 173. Courtesy College Archivist, Imperial College of Science and Technology.
189. Ruben, S.; Randall, M.; Kamen, M.; Hyde, J. L., *J. Am. Chem. Soc.*, **1941**, *63*, 877. "Heavy Oxygen (O^{18}) as a Tracer in the Study of Photosynthesis."
190. Saltzman, M. D., *Chem. in Britain*, **1986**, *22*, 543.
191. Sanders, J. W., "Peddlers of Crisis," South End Press, Boston, 1983.
191a. *San Francisco Chronicle*, May 19, 1986, p. 2, and Oct. 26, 1986, p. 4 in "This World" section. Articles referring to Willard F. Libby.
192. Schneider, A.; Esch, U., *Z. Elektrochem.*, **1943**, *49*, 55.
193. Seaborg, G. T., "Kennedy, Krushchev, and the Test Ban," Univ. of Calif. Press, Berkeley, 1981.
194. Seaborg, G. T., *J. Chem. Education*, **1984**, *61*, 93.
195. Seaborg, G. T., *Chem. Eng. News*, **1983**, *61*, June 13, 2.
196. Seaborg, G. T., Talk presented at the 184th National Meeting of the ACS, Kansas City, Sept. 13, 1982, at the Symposium on the Chemistry of Plutonium. (LBL Oct. 11, 1982.)
197. Seaborg, G. T., "Journal of Glenn T. Seaborg," Two volumes, Aug. 11, 1934 - June 30, 1939 and July 1, 1939 - Apr. 17, 1942. Privately published Oct., 1982.
198. Seidel, R. W., Transcription of interview with Kenneth S. Pitzer, Bancroft Library, History of Science and Technology Project, 1985.
199. Selbin, J., *Chem. Eng. News*, **1985**, *63*, Aug. 26, 3.
200. Servos, J. W., *J. Chem. Education*, **1984**, *61*, 5.
201. Shapley, D.; Roy, R., "Lost at the Frontier," ISI Press, Philadelphia, 1985.
202. Shiffler, W. H., Conversation, April 2, 1986.
203. Sides, P. J., Hanson, K. J., Prentice, G. A., *Chem. Eng. Commun.*, **1985**, *38*, 85.

204. Sinclair, U., "The Goose-Step," Published by author, Pasadena, 1923, 261-263.

205. Smith, G. F., to Latimer, W. M., Mar. 1, 1947. College Files.

206. Spreer, L. O.; Maliyackel, A. C.; Holbrook, S.; Otvos, J. W.; Calvin, M., *J. Am. Chem. Soc.*, **1986**, *108*, 1949.

207. Stadtman, V. A., Editor, "The Centennial Record of the University of California," Univ. of Calif., Berkeley, 1967.

208. Stillman, J. M., *J. Ind. Eng. Chem.*, **1918**, *10*, 392.

208a. Stillman, J. M. *Am. Chem. J.*, **1880**, *2*, 38.

208b. Stillman, J. M. "The Story of Early Chemistry," Appleton, New York, 1924.

209. Stillman, John, eulogies: "In Memory of John M. Stillman," Stanford Univ., 1924.

210. Stranges, A. N., *J. Chem. Education*, **1984**, *61*, 185.

211. Stuewer, R. H., *Historical Studies in the Physical Sciences*, **1975**, *6*, 469.

212. Taube, H., *Chem. Eng. News*, **1985**, *63*, May 6, 40. (Priestly Medal Address)

213. Templeton, D. H.; Perlman, I.; Seaborg, G. T., "In Memoriam," Univ. of Calif. "Burris Bell Cunningham."

214. Terrall, M., Transcription of interviews with Willard F. Libby. Oral History Program of UCLA, Copyright UC, 1983.

215. Thompson, S. P., "The Life of William Thomson," Macmillan, London, 1910, Vol. 2, 1125.

216. *Time*, **1954**, *63*(15), 21, 72.

217. Tinoco, I., Conversation, October 15, 1985.

218. Tobias, C. W., Conversations, Sept. 1985.

219. Tolman, R. C.; Karrer, S.; Guernsey, E. W., *Phys. Rev.*, **1923**, *21*, 525.

220. U.S. Atomic Energy Commission, "In the Matter of J. Robert Oppenheimer. Transcript of Hearing before Personnel Security Board," U.S.G.P.O., Washington, D.C., 1954.

221. U.S. Dept. of Commerce Press Release G-394, Aug. 22, 1953.

222. U.S. Dept. of Commerce Press Release G-411, Oct. 16, 1953.

222a. University of California Archives.

223. University of California Bulletin, Announcement of Courses, 1917-18.

224. University of California Bulletin, 1904.

225. University of California Registers, Publ. by Regents of the University, 1885-1900.

226. van't Hoff, J. H., *Arch. Neerl. Sci. Exactes Natur.*, **1874**, *9*, 445.

227. Vermeulen, T., UC Biobibliographical File, Chem. Eng. Files.

228. Vermeulen, Theodore, Eulogies for, at Convocation, Nov. 20, 1983.

229. Watson, H. B., "Modern Theories of Organic Chemistry," The Clarendon Press, Oxford, 1937.

230. Weigel, F., *Radiochim. Acta*, **1971**, *16*, 1.

231. Wells, A. F., "Structural Inorganic Chemistry," 4th ed., Clarendon Press, Oxford, 1975, 815.

232. Wheeler, B. I., to Arrhenius, S. A., Feb. 16, 1904. President's Files, UC Archives.

233. Wheeler, B. I., to Hulett, G. A., Aug. 4, 1911. President's Files, UC Archives.
234. Wheeler, B. I., to Hulett, G. A., Aug. 17, 1911. President's Files, UC Archives.
235. Wheeler, B. I., to Lewis, G. N., Jan. 16, 1912, UC Archives.
236. Wheeler, B. I., to Ramsay, W., Dec. 3, 1903. President's Files, UC Archives.
237. Wheeler, B. I., to Ramsay, W., Apr. 9, 1904. President's Files, UC Archives.
237a. Wheeler, B. I., to Regents, June 24, 1899. UC Archives.
238. Wheeler, B. I., essay on "America's Debt to German Education" in German Relief Bazaar brochure, May 19-May 24, 1916.
239. Wilke, C. R., Conversation, Oct. 25, 1985.
240. Wilke, C. R., Eulogy for T. Vermeulen, Nov. 20, 1983.
241. Williams, F. C., Private communication, 1985.
241a. Williams, F. C., to his friends, December, 1952. Dept. of Chemical Engineering Files.
242. Wilson, E. B. to Lewis, G. N., June 10, 1924. UC Archives.
243. Wilson, E. B., to Lewis, G. N., Feb. 18, 1935. UC Archives.
244. Wilson, Mrs. M. K., Conversation, Feb. 23, 1986.
245. Yost, D. M.; Russell, H., "Systematic Inorganic Chemistry," Prentice-Hall, 1946.
246. Young, S. W., Foreword to ref. 208b.

Acknowledgments. We are grateful to the following organizations and individuals for granting permission to reproduce copyrighted material or other material in their possession. Quotations are identified as such in the text, and detailed citations are given in the preceding Alphabetical List of References.
American Association for the Advancement of Science, Washington, D.C.; American Chemical Society, Washington, D.C.; Annual Reviews, Inc., Palo Alto, California; California Alumni Association, UC Berkeley Campus; College of Chemistry, UC Berkeley; The Daily Californian, Berkeley, California; Delius, Klasing and Co., Bielefeld, West Germany; Department of Chemical Engineering, UC Berkeley; Department of Chemistry, UC Berkeley; Franklin Institute Press, Philadelphia, Pennsylvania; General Electric Company, Schenectady, New York; Gordon and Breach Science Publishers, New York, New York; Journal of Chemical Education, University of Texas, Austin, Texas; Journal of the Electrochemical Society, Pennington, New Jersey; Macmillan Journals, Ltd., London, England; Macmillan Publishing Company, New York, New York; McGraw-Hill Book Co., New York, New York; National Academy Press, Washington, D.C.; Nobel Committee for Chemistry, Stockholm, Sweden; San Francisco Chronicle, San Francisco, California; Glenn T. Seaborg, Chemistry Department, UC Berkeley; The Sierra Club, San Francisco, California; Henry Taube, Chemistry Department, Stanford University, Stanford, California; UC Press, Berkeley; University of Chicago Press, Chicago, Illinois; The Robert A. Welch Foundation, Houston, Texas.

APPENDIX **1**

Chronological List of Tenured Faculty

Faculty Members Who Achieved Tenure in Chemistry or Who Served in Chemistry for a Significant Period, With the Date of Their First Tenure-Track Appointment (Instructor or Higher)

1868	Fisher, Robert A.	1946	Zimm, Bruno Hasbrouck
1869	Carr, Ezra Slocum	1947	Hanson, Donald Norman
1872	Rising, Willard Bradley	1947	Templeton, David Henry
1875	Christy, Samuel Benedict	1947	Tobias, Charles William
1876	Stillman, John Maxson	1947	Vermeulen, Theodore
1878	Booth, Edward	1948	Noyce, Donald Sterling
1879	O'Neill, Edmond C.	1948	O'Konski, Chester Thomas
1890	Gray, John Hatfield	1948	Williams, (Ford) Campbell
1892	Sharwood, William John	1949	Pimentel, George Claude
1895	Blasdale, Walter Charles	1949	Street, Kenneth, Jr.
1901	Biddle, Henry Chalmers	1951	Myers, Rollie John
1901	Morgan, William Conger	1952	Jolly, William Lee
1902	Cottrell, Frederick Gardner	1952	Rasmussen, John Oscar, Jr.
1912	Bray, William Crowell	1952	Streitwieser, Andrew, Jr.
1912	Lewis, Gilbert Newton	1953	Petersen, Eugene Edward
1912	Tolman, Richard Chace	1954	Acrivos, Andreas
1913	Gibson, (George) Ernest	1954	Lyon, David Nathaniel
1913	Hildebrand, Joel Henry	1955	Jensen, Frederick Richard
1915	Branch, Gerald E. K.	1955	Phillips, Norman Edgar
1917	Eastman, Ermon Dwight	1955	Prausnitz, John Michael
1917	Randall, Merle	1956	Mahan, Bruce Herbert
1918	Porter, Charles Walter	1956	Tinoco, Ignacio, Jr.
1918	Stewart, (Thomas) Dale	1957	Johnston, Harold Sledge
1919	Latimer, Wendell Mitchell	1958	Markowitz, Samuel S.
1919	Olson, Axel Ragnar	1958	Olander, Donald Raymond
1921	Hogness, Thorfin Rusten	1959	Herschbach, Dudley Robert
1922	Giauque, William Francis	1960	Shirley, David Arthur
1923	Rollefson, Gerhard Krohn	1961	Boudart, Michel
1933	Libby, Willard Frank	1961	Cerny, Joseph
1933	Schutz, Philip William	1961	Foss, Alan Stuart
1937	Calvin, Melvin	1961	Strauss, Herbert Leopold
1937	Pitzer, Kenneth Sanborn	1962	Goren, Simon Land
1939	Ruben, Samuel	1962	Grens, Edward Anthony, II
1939	Seaborg, Glenn Theodore	1962	Hearst, John Eugene
1941	Orlemann, Edwin Franklyn	1962	Newman, John Scott
1942	Connick, Robert Elwell	1963	Harris, Robert Arthur
1942	Gwinn, William Dulaney	1963	King, (Cary) Judson, III
1945	Cason, James	1963	Moore, (Charles) Bradley
1945	Dauben, William Garfield	1963	Sauer, Kenneth
1946	Brewer, Leo	1964	Heathcock, Clayton Howell
1946	Bromley, LeRoy Alton	1964	Merrill, Robert Perkins
1946	Cunningham, Burris Bell	1964	Somorjai, Gabor Arpad
1946	Jura, George	1965	Williams, Michael Charles
1946	Perlman, Isadore	1966	Wang, James C.
1946	Powell, Richard Edward	1967	Bell, Alexis Tarassov
1946	Rapoport, Henry	1967	Lynn, Scott
1946	Wilke, Charles Robert	1968	Harris, Charles Bonner

1968	Raymond, Kenneth Norman	1976	Radke, Clayton John
1969	Bartlett, Neil	1977	Hess, Dennis William
1969	Miller, William Hughes	1978	Bergman, Robert George
1969	Schaefer, H. Frederick, III	1978	Blanch, Harvey Warren
1969	Shen, Mitchel Ming-Chi	1978	Cairns, Elton James
1970	Hubbell, Wayne Lester	1978	Kim, Sung-Hou
1970	Klinman, Judith Pollock	1978	Muetterties, Earl Leonard
1971	Moretto, Luciano Giuseppe	1979	Saykally, Richard James
1972	Pines, Alexander	1979	Soong, David Syhlih
1973	Bartlett, Paul Allan	1980	Denn, Morton Mace
1974	Lee, Yuan Tseh	1981	Lester, William A., Jr.
1974	Vollhardt, (Kurt) Peter C.	1984	Hoffman, Darleane C.
1976	Andersen, Richard Allan	1986	Chandler, David
1976	Mathies, Richard Alfred		

APPENDIX **2**

Alphabetical List of Tenured Faculty, with Professional Data

Acrivos, Andreas (b. 13 Jun 1928)
B.Ch.E. 1950, Syracuse.
M.S., 1951; Ph.D. 1954, Minnesota, with Amundson on "A Theoretical Discussion of Steady and Unsteady State Multicomponent Rectification Including a Treatment of Mixtures with an Indefinite Number of Components."
Appointed 1954. Research on fluid mechanics and applied mechanics. Teaching in chemical engineering.
Resigned 1963 to join faculty at Stanford.
Some significant publications:
Acrivos, A.; Taylor, T. D. *Phys. Fluids* **1962**, *5*, 387. "Heat and Mass Transfer from Single Spheres in Stokes Flows."
Pan, F.; Acrivos, A. *J. Fluid Mech.* **1967**, *28*, 643. "Steady Flow in Rectangular Cavities."
Acrivos, A.; Lo, T. S. *J. Fluid Mech.* **1978**, *86*, 641. "Deformation and Breakup of a Single Slender Drop in an Extensional Flow."
Acrivos, A.; Herbolzheimer, E. *J. Fluid Mech.* **1979**, *92*, 435. "Enhanced Sedimentation in Settling Tanks with Inclined Walls."

Andersen, Richard Allan (b. 16 Nov 1942)
B.A. 1965, South Dakota.
Ph.D. 1973, Wyoming, with Coates on "Sterically Hindered Beryllium Alkoxides and Some of their Derivatives."
Postdoctoral positions, Univ. of Oslo (1973-74); Imperial College, London (1974-76).
Appointed 1976. Research in synthetic inorganic and organometallic chemistry, especially with respect to compounds with metal-to-carbon, -oxygen, -nitrogen, and -hydrogen bonds. Teaching in inorganic chemistry.
Some significant publications:
Girolami, G. S.; Mainz, V. V.; Andersen, R. A.; Vollmer, S. H.; Day, V. W. *J. Am. Chem. Soc.* **1981**, *103*, 3953. "Quadruply Bonded Tetramethyl-Tetrakis(Trialkylphosphine) Dimolybdenum Compounds: Phosphine Exchange Kinetics, Acetone Formation with Carbon Monoxide and Crystal Structure of $Me_4Mo_2(PMe_3)_4$."
Edwards, P. G.; Andersen, R. A.; Zalkin, A. *J. Am. Chem. Soc.* **1981**, *103*, 7792. "Tertiary Phosphine Derivatives of the f-Block Metals. Preparation of $X_4M(Me_2PCH_2CH_2PMe_2)_2$, where X is Halide, Methyl, or Phenoxo and M is Thorium or Uranium. Crystal Structure of Tetra-(Phenoxo)Bis[bis(1,2-dimethylphosphino)ethane]Uranium(IV)."
Planalp, R. P.; Andersen, R. A. *J. Am. Chem. Soc.* **1983**, *105*, 7774. "Cleavage of Carbon Monoxide by Mononuclear Zirconium Dialkyls:

Formation of a (μ-Oxo)dialkyl and an Enolate."
Brennan, J. G.; Andersen, R. A. *J. Am. Chem. Soc.* **1985**, *107*, 514.
"Electron-Transfer Reactions of Trivalent Uranium. Preparation and
Structure of $(MeC_5H_4)_3U=NPh$ and $[(MeC_5H_4)_3U]_2[\mu - \eta^1, \eta^2-PhNCO]$."

Bartlett, Neil (b. 15 Sep 1932)
B.Sc. 1954; Ph.D. 1958, Durham, with Robinson on "Tetrafluorides of the
Sulphur Sub Group; Their Properties and Compounds and Studies in
Sulphate and Phosphate Melts."
Faculty positions at British Columbia (1958-66) and Princeton (1966-69).
Appointed 1969. Research in inorganic fluorine, solid state and noble
gas chemistry, with particular interest in the structural aspects of
compounds of elements in unusual oxidation states. Teaching in
inorganic chemistry.
Some significant publications:
  Bartlett, N.; Lohmann, D. H. *J. Chem. Soc.* **1962**, 5253. "Fluorides of
the Noble Metals. Part II. Dioxygenyl Hexafluoroplatinate(V), $O_2[PtF_6]$."
  Bartlett, N.; Sladky, F. O. In "Comprehensive Inorganic Chemistry";
Pergamon Press: Oxford and New York, 1973; Vol 1, pp. 213-330."The
Chemistry of Krypton, Xenon and Radon,"
  Bartlett, N. In "The Chemical Industry"; Sharp, D. H.; West, T. S.,
Eds.; Ellis Horwood: Chichester, 1982; pp. 292-305. "Electron-Oxidation
of Aromatic Molecules, Layer-Form Boron Nitride and Graphite."
  Mallouk, T.; Hawkins, B. L.; Conrad, M. P.; Zilm, K.; Maciel, G. E.;
Bartlett, N. *Phil. Trans. Roy. Soc.* **1985**, *A314*, 179. "Raman, Infrared and
NMR Studies of the Graphite Hydrofluorides $C_xF_{1-\delta}(HF)_\delta (2 \leqslant x \leqslant 5)$."

Bartlett, Paul Allan (b. 5 Jan 1948)
A.B. 1969; A.M. 1969, Harvard
Ph.D. 1972, Stanford, with Johnson on "An Improved Reagent for the O-
Alkyl Cleavage of Methyl Esters by Nucleophilic Displacement; The
Total Synthesis of Estrone via a Cationic Cyclization."
N.I.H. Fellow, UC San Diego (1972-73).
Appointed 1973. Research in synthetic organic and bioorganic chemistry,
the development of methodology for stereocontrolled synthesis of acyclic
and oxacyclic natural products, and the synthesis and evaluation of
enzyme inhibitors and other biologically active molecules. Teaching in
organic chemistry.
Some significant publications:
  Bartlett, P. A. *Tetrahedron* **1980**, *36*, 2. "Stereocontrol in the Synthesis
of Acyclic Systems: Applications to Natural Product Synthesis."
  Bartlett, P. A.; Marlowe, C. K. *Biochemistry* **1983**, *22*, 4618. "Phos-
phonamidates as Transition State Analog Inhibitors of Thermolysin."
  Bartlett, P. A.; Meadows, J. D.; Ottow, E. *J. Am. Chem. Soc.* **1984**, *106*,
5304. "Enantiodivergent Syntheses of (+)- and (-)-Nonactic Acid and the
Total Synthesis of Nonactin."
  Ashley, G. W.; Bartlett, P. A. *J. Biol. Chem.* **1984**, *259*, 13621.

"Inhibition of Escherichia coli Cytidine Deaminase by a Phosphapyrimidine Nucleoside."

Bell, Alexis Tarassov (b. 10 Oct 1942)
B.S. 1964; Sc.D. 1967, MIT, with Baddour on "Chemical Reactions in a Radiofrequency Discharge. The Oxidation of Hydrogen Chloride."
Appointed 1967. Research on chemical reactions in electric discharges coal liquefaction, heterogeneous catalysis, and reaction engineering. Teaching in chemical engineering.
Some significant publications:
Brown, L.; Bell, A. T. *I&EC Fund.* **1974**, *13*, 203. "Kinetics of the Oxidation of Carbon Monoxide and the Decomposition of Carbon Dioxide in a Radiofrequency Electric Discharge: I. Experimental Results."
Jensen, R. J.; Bell, A. T.; Soong, D. S. *Plasma Chem. Plasma Proc.* **1983**, *3*, 163. "Plasma Polymerization of Ethane. II. Theoretical Analysis of Effluent Gas Composition and Polymer Deposition Rates."
Winslow, P.; Bell, A. T. *J. Catal.* **1984**, *86*, 158. "Application of Transient Response Techniques for Quantitative Determination of Adsorbed Carbon Monoxide and Carbon Present on the Surface of a Ruthenium Catalyst during Fischer-Tropsch Synthesis."
Duncan, T. M.; Winslow, P.; Bell, A. T. *J. Catal.* **1985**, *93*, 1. "The Characterization of Carbonaceous Species on Ruthenium Catalysts with Carbon-13 Nuclear Magnetic Resonance Spectroscopy."

Bergman, Robert George (b. 23 May 1942)
B.A. 1963, Carleton.
Ph.D. 1966, Wisconsin, with Berson on "Reactions of Methylnorbornyl Cations and Reactions of the Nortricyclyl-3-carbinyl Cation."
NATO Postdoctoral Fellow, Columbia (1966-67); faculty appointment at Cal Tech (1967-78).
Appointed 1978. Research on carbonium ion rearrangements, reactions controlled by orbital symmetry, reactive non-benzenoid aromatic compounds, organometallic complexes and processes, and applications of organometallic reagents in organic synthesis.
Some significant publications:
Jones, R. R.; Bergman, R. G. *J. Am. Chem. Soc.* **1972**, *94*, 660. "Para-Benzyne. Generation as an Intermediate in a Thermal Isomerization Reaction and Trapping Evidence for the 1,4-Benzenediyl Structure."
Schore, N. E.; Ilenda, C.; Bergman, R. G. *J. Am. Chem. Soc.* **1976**, *98*, 7436. "Synthesis of a Doubly Alkylated Binuclear Cobalt Carbonyl Complex. Generation of Acetone, a Process Involving the Formation of Two New Carbon-Carbon Bonds in its Thermal Decomposition."
Becker, P. N.; Bergman, R. G. *J. Am. Chem. Soc.* **1983**, *105*, 2985. "Reversible Exchange of (η^5-Cyclopentadienyl)(dinitrosoalkane)cobalt Complexes with Alkenes. Kinetic and Spectroscopic Evidence for $C_5H_5Co(NO)_2$ as a Reactive Intermediate."
Janowicz, A. H.; Bergman, R. G. *J. Am. Chem. Soc.* **1983**, *105*, 3929.

"Activation of C-H Bonds in Saturated Hydrocarbons on Photolysis of (η^5-C$_5$Me$_5$)(PMe$_3$)IrH$_2$. Relative Rates of Reaction of the Intermediate with Different Types of C-H Bonds and Functionalization of the Metal-Bound Alkyl Groups."

Biddle, Henry Chalmers (4 Oct 1869 - 1 Sep 1935)
B.S. 1891, Monmouth College.
Ph.D. 1900, Chicago, with Nef "Ueber Derivate des Insuretins und der Formhydroamsaeure und ihre Beziehungen zur Knallsaeure."
Appointed 1901. Research in biochemistry; teaching in organic chemistry.
Resigned in 1918 to practice chemical engineering. In 1925 joined faculty of California College of Pharmacy (later the School of Pharmacy of UC).
Some significant publications:
Pictet, A. "The Vegetable Alkaloids," 2nd French Ed.; Wiley: New York, 1904. Translation by H. C. Biddle.
Robertson, T. B.; Biddle, H. C. *J. Biol. Chem.* **1911**, *9*, 295. "On the Composition of Certain Substances Produced by the Action of Pepsin upon the Products of the Complete Peptic Hydrolysis of Casein."
Biddle, H. C. *J. Am. Chem. Soc.* **1913**, *35*, 273. "Color Changes among Dyes of the Triphenylmethane Series as Influenced by the Hydrogen Ion Concentration of Acids of Different Dissociation Constants."
Biddle, H. C.; Watson, T. *J. Am. Chem. Soc.* **1917**, *39*, 968. "The Influence of Varying Concentration of Hydrogen Ion on the Optical Rotation of the Isomeric Alkaloids, Cinchonine, Cinchonidine and Cinchotoxine."

Blanch, Harvey Warren (b. 17 Jan 1947)
B.Sc. 1968, Sydney.
Ph.D. 1971, New South Wales, with Rogers on "Production of Gramicidin S in Batch and Continuous Cultures."
Post doctoral, ETH (1971-73); Squibb & Sons (1973-74); Chem. Eng. faculty, Delaware (1974-78).
Appointed 1978. Research on biochemical engineering, cultivation of yeast, bacteria, mammalian and plant cells, mass transfer in biological systems, and biological separation processes. Teaching in chemical engineering.
Some significant publications:
Bhavaraju, S. M.; Russell, T. W. F.; Blanch, H. W. *AIChE Journal* **1978**, *24*, 754. "The Design of Gas Sparged Devices for Various Liquid Systems."
Blanch, H. W.; Wilke, C. R. *Rev. Chem. Eng.* **1982**, *1*, 71. "Sugars and Chemicals from Cellulose."
Maiorella, B. L.; Blanch, H. W.; Wilke, C. R. *Biotechnol. Bioeng.* **1984**, *26*, 1155. "Feed Component Inhibition in Ethanolic Fermentation by Saccharomyces Cerevisiae."

Arnold, F. H.; Blanch, H. W.; Wilke, C. R. *Chem. Eng. J.* **1985**, *30*, B9. "Analysis of Affinity Separations. I. Predicting the Performance of Affinity Adsorbers."

Blasdale, Walter Charles (10 Jan 1871 - 23 May 1960)
B.S. 1892; M.S. 1896; Ph.D. 1900, UC Berkeley, on "A Chemical Study of the Indument Found on the Fronds of Gymnogramme Triangularis."
Appointed 1895. Research on botany and equilibria involving mixtures of salts. Teaching in analytical chemistry. Retired in 1941.
Some significant publications:
Blasdale, W. C. *J. Am. Chem. Soc.* **1895**, *17*, 935. "On the Physical and Chemical Properties of Some California Oils."
Blasdale, W. C. "Principles of Quantitative Analysis"; Van Nostrand: New York, 1914.
Blasdale, W. C. "Equilibria in Saturated Salt Solutions"; Chemical Catalog: New York, 1927.
Blasdale, W. C. "The Cultivated Species of Primula"; UC Press: Berkeley, 1948.

Booth, Edward (27 Jul 1857 - 23 Aug 1917)
B.S. 1877, UC Berkeley.
Appointed 1878. Teaching in analytical chemistry.
Some significant publications:
Booth, E. *Chem. News*, May **1901**. "Prout's Hypothesis with Reference to the Radio-Active Elements."
Booth, E. *Med. News*, Dec. **1901**. "Possible Curative Effects of the New Element Radium."
Booth, E. *Mining & Sci. Press*, Dec. **1901**. "Can Gold be Made Artificially?"
Booth, E. *Cal. J. Techn.*, *3*, No. 2. "Radium."

Boudart, Michel (b. 18 Jun 1924)
B.Sc. 1944; M.Sc. 1947, Louvain, Belgium.
Ph.D. 1950, Princeton, with Taylor on "The Nature of Active Centers."
Forrestal Res. Center, Princeton (1950-54); Chem. Eng. Faculty, Princeton (1954-61).
Appointed 1961. Research on surface chemistry and heterogeneous catalysis. Teaching in chemical engineering.
Resigned 1964 to join faculty at Stanford.
Some significant publications:
Boudart, M. *J. Am. Chem. Soc.* **1950**, *72*, 1040. "Pauling's Theory of Metals in Catalysis."
Boudart, M.; Ozaki, A.; Taylor, H. S. *Proc. Roy. Soc.* **1960**, *A258*, 47. "Kinetics and Mechanism of the Ammonia Synthesis."
Boudart, M.; Delbouille, A.; Derouane, E. G.; Indovina, V.; Walters, A. B. *J. Am. Chem. Soc.* **1972**, *94*, 6622. "Activation of Hydrogen at 78°K on

Paramagnetic Centers of Magnesium Oxide."
Boudart, M.; Topsoe, H.; Dumesic, J. A. In "The Physical Basis for Heterogeneous Catalysis"; Drauglis, E.; Jaffee, R. I., Eds.; Plenum Press: New York, 1975; p. 337. "Catalytic and Magnetic Anisotropy of Iron Surfaces."

Branch, Gerald Eyre Kirkwood (16 Apr 1886 - 14 Apr 1954)
B.Sc. 1911; M.S. 1912, Liverpool.
Ph.D. 1915, UC Berkeley, with Lewis on "The Free Energy of Formation of Formic Acid."
Appointed 1915. Research on physical organic chemistry. Teaching in organic chemistry.
Some significant publications:
Bettman, B.; Branch, G. E. K.; Yabroff, D. L. *J. Am. Chem. Soc.* 1934, *56*, 1865. "Dissociation Constants of Organic Boric Acids."
Branch, G. E. K.; Calvin, M. "The Theory of Organic Chemistry. An Advanced Course"; Prentice-Hall: New York, 1941.
Ferguson, L. N.; Branch, G. E. K. *J. Am. Chem. Soc.* 1944, *66*, 1467. "Absorption Spectra of Some Linear Conjugated Systems."
Thomas, J. F.; Branch, G. E. K. *J. Am. Chem. Soc.* 1953, *75*, 4793. "The Principal Electronic Absorption Bands of the Vinylogous Series Derived from Benzylaldehyde and Benzophenone."

Bray, William Crowell (2 Sep 1879 - 24 Feb 1946)
B.S. 1902, Toronto.
Ph.D. 1905, Leipzig, with Luther on "Beitraege zur Kenntnis der Halogensauerstoffverbindungen."
On MIT staff (1905-12).
Appointed 1912. Research in the kinetics and mechanism of inorganic reactions in aqueous solutions. Teaching in inorganic chemistry.
Some significant publications:
Bray, W. C.; Noyes, A. A.; Spear, E. B. *J. Am. Chem. Soc.* 1907, *29*, 137; 1908, *30*, 481; 1909, *31*, 611. "A System of Qualitative Analysis for the Common Elements."
Bray, W. C.; Kraus, C. A. *J. Am. Chem. Soc.* 1913, *35*, 1315. "A General Relation between the Concentration and the Conductance of Ionized Substances in Various Solvents."
Bray, W. C.; Branch, G. E. K. *J. Am. Chem. Soc.* 1913, *35*, 1440. "Valence and Tautomerism."
Bray, W. C. *J. Am. Chem. Soc.* 1921, *43*, 1262. "A Periodic Reaction in Homogeneous Solution and its Relation to Catalysis."
Bray, W. C.; Livingston, R. S. *J. Am. Chem. Soc.* 1923, *45*, 1251. "The Catalytic Decomposition of Hydrogen Peroxide in a Bromine-Bromide Solution, and a Study of the Steady State."
Latimer, W. M.; Bray, W. C. "A Course in General Chemistry"; Macmillan: New York, 1923.
Bray, W. C.; Hershey, A. V. *J. Am. Chem. Soc.* 1936, *58*, 1760. "Kinetic

and Equilibrium Measurements of the Reaction $2Fe^{+++} + 2I^- = 2Fe^{++} + I_2$."

Brewer, Leo (b. 13 Jun 1919)
B.S. 1940, Cal Tech.
Ph.D. 1943, UC Berkeley, with Olson on "The Iodination of Mesityl Oxide."
Research Associate, Manhattan Project, UC Berkeley (1943-46).
Appointed 1946. Research in high temperature thermodynamics, studies of metallic phases, and development of metallic bonding theory. Teaching in physical and inorganic chemistry.
Some significant publications:
Brewer, L.; Gilles, P. W.; Jenkins, F. A. *J. Chem. Phys.* **1948**, *16*, 797. "The Vapor Pressure and Heat of Sublimation of Graphite."
Brewer, L., In "High Strength Materials"; Zackay, V. F., Ed.; Wiley: New York, 1965; Chapter 2. "Prediction of High Temperature Metallic Phase Diagrams."
Brewer, L. *J. Opt. Soc. Amer.* **1971**, *61*, 1101. "Energies of the Electronic Configurations of the Lanthanide and Actinide Neutral Atoms."
Brewer, L.; Wengert, P. R. *Met. Trans.* **1973**, *4*, 83. "Transition Metal Alloys of Extraordinary Stability: An Example of Generalized Lewis Acid-Base Interactions in Metallic Systems."

Bromley, LeRoy Alton (b. 30 Sept 1919)
B.S. 1941, UC Berkeley.
M.S. 1943, Ill. Inst. Tech.
Ph.D. 1948, UC Berkeley, with Latimer on "Heat Transfer in Stable Film Boiling."
Appointed 1946. Research on heat transfer in condensation and boiling, thermodynamics, high vacuum, properties of gases, sea water conversion, and the SO_2-sea water system. Teaching in chemical engineering. Visiting Prof. Univ. of Philippines (1954-56); head Sea Water Test Facility, Scripps (1962-64). Retired in 1976.
Some significant publications:
Bromley, L. A. *Chem. Eng. Prog.* **1950**, *46*, 221. "Heat Transfer in Stable Film Boiling."
Bromley, L. A.; Read, S. M. *Desalination* **1970**, *7*, 343. "Multiple Effect Flash (MEF) Evaporator."
Bromley, L. A. *Int. J. Sulfur Chem. Part B* **1972**, *7*, 77. "Use of Sea Water to Scrub Sulfur Dioxide from Stack Gases."
Bromley, L. A. *AIChE J.* **1973**, *19*, 313. "Thermodynamic Properties of Strong Electrolytes in Aqueous Solution."

Cairns, Elton James (b. 7 Nov 1932)
B.S. 1955, Mich. Tech. Univ.

Ph.D. 1959, UC Berkeley, with Prausnitz on "Mixing Properties and Chemical Kinetics in Chemical Flow Reactors."
G.E. Res. Lab., Schenectady (1959-66); Argonne Natl. Lab. (1966-73); Gen. Motors Res. Labs., Warren, MI (1973-78).
Appointed 1978. Research on fundamentals of electrode behavior, with emphasis on metal electrodes in aqueous electrolytes, solid electrodes in molten salts, and liquid electrodes with solid electrolytes. Teaching in chemical engineering.
Some significant publications:
Cairns, E. J.; Liebhafsky, H. A. "Fuel Cells and Fuel Batteries; A Guide to their Research and Development"; Wiley: New York, 1968.
Cairns, E. J.; Shimotake, H. *Science* 1969, *164*, 1347. "High-Temperature Batteries."
Cairns, E. J. In "Advances in Electrochemistry and Electrochemical Engineering"; Tobias, C. W., Ed.; Wiley-Interscience: New York, 1971; Vol. 8, p. 337. "The Anodic Oxidation of Hydrocarbons and the Hydrocarbon Fuel Cell."
Cairns, E. J.; McBreen, J. In "Advances in Electrochemistry and Electrochemical Engineering"; Tobias, C. W., Ed.; Wiley-Interscience: New York, 1978; Vol. 11. "The Zinc Electrode."

Calvin, Melvin (b. 8 Apr 1911)
B.S. 1931, Mich. Coll. Mining & Tech.
Ph.D. 1935, Minnesota, with Glockler on "The Electron Affinity of Iodine and Bromine."
Postdoctoral Fellow, Manchester (1935-37).
Appointed 1937. Research on metal complexes with organic ligands, chemical evolution, photosynthesis, photochemistry, chemical carcinogenesis, and solar energy conversion. Teaching in organic chemistry.
Some significant publications:
Lewis, G. N.; Calvin, M. *J. Am. Chem. Soc.* 1945, *67*, 1232. "Paramagnetism of the Phosphorescent State."
Calvin, M. *Science* 1962, *135*, 879. "The Path of Carbon in Photosynthesis."
Calvin, M. "Chemical Evolution: Molecular Evolution Towards the Origin of Living Systems on the Earth and Elsewhere"; Oxford Univ. Press; Clarendon Press: Oxford, 1969.
Calvin, M. *Acc. Chem. Res.* 1978, *11*, 369. "Simulating Photosynthetic Quantum Conversion."

Carr, Ezra Slocum (1819 - 1894)
B.S. ca 1840, Rensselaer.
M.D. 1842, Castleton Med. Coll., Vermont.
Misc. academic posts (1842-68).
Appointed 1869. Dismissed by Regents in 1874. Elected State Superintendent of Public Instruction, 1875.
Some significant publications:

Carr, E. S. "An introductory lecture, delivered in the Castleton Medical College, at the opening of the fall session, 1843," C. Van Benthuysen: Albany, 1843.

Carr, E. S. "Patrons of Husbandry of the Pacific Coast," A. L. Bancroft: San Francisco, 1875.

Carr, E. S. "Child Culture; an address delivered before the State Agricultural Society of California at Sacramento, Sept. 23, 1875," E. Steiger: New York, 1877.

Carr, E. S. "The University of California and its Relations to Industrial Education as Shown by Professor Carr's Reply to the Grangers and Mechanics"; B. Dore: San Francisco, 1874.

Cason, James (b. 30 Aug 1912)
A.B. 1934, Vanderbilt
M.S. 1935, UC Berkeley
Ph.D. 1938, Yale, with Anderson on "The Chemistry of the Lipids of Tubercle Bacilli."
Res. Assoc., Harvard (1938-40); taught at DePauw (1940-41) and Vanderbilt (1941-45).
Appointed 1945. Research on branched-chain fatty acids, structure of natural products, synthetic methods, reaction mechanisms, and mass spectrometry. Teaching in organic chemistry. Retired 1983.
Some significant publications:
Cason, J. *Chem. Rev.* **1947**, *40*, 15. "The Use of Organocadmium Reagents for the Preparation of Ketones."
Cason, J.; Smith, R. D. *J. Org. Chem.* **1953**, *18*, 1201. "Concerning the Mechanism of the Ester Acid Chloride Rearrangement."
Cason, J.; Kraus, K. W. *J. Org. Chem.* **1961**, *26*, 1772. "Mechanism of the Reactions of Grignard Reagents and of Organocadmium Reagents with Acid Chlorides in Presence of Ferric Chloride."
Cason, J.; Koch C. W.; Fisher R. P.; Kow R.; Kutas M. G.; Teranishi A. Y.; Walba D. M. *J. Org. Chem.* **1972**, *37*, 2573. "Products from Cyanoethylation of 2-Octanone."

Cerny, Joseph (b. 24 Apr 1936)
B.S. 1957, Mississippi.
Ph.D. 1961, UC Berkeley, with Perlman on "Two-Nucleon Transfer Reactions in the Light Elements."
Appointed 1961. Research on in-beam nuclear reactions at intermediate energies, studies of nuclei far from stability, and new modes of radioactivity. Teaching in nuclear and physical chemistry.
Some significant publications:
Cerny, J.; Cosper, S. W.; Butler, G. W.; Pehl, R. H.; Goulding, F. S.; Landis, D. A.; Detraz, C. *Phys. Rev. Lett.* **1966**, *16*, 469. "The Mass of ^{8}He from the Four-Neutron Transfer Reaction $^{26}Mg(\alpha, ^8He)^{22}Mg$."
Cerny, J. *Ann. Rev. Nucl. Sci.* **1968**, *18*, 27. "High Isospin Nuclei and Multiplets in the Light Elements."

Cerny, J.; Hardy, J. C. *Ann. Rev. Nucl. Sci.* **1977**, *27*, 333. "Delayed Proton Radioactivities."

Cable, M. D.; Honkanen, J.; Schloemer, E. C.; Ahmed, M.; Reiff, J. E.; Zhou, Z. Y.; Cerny, J. *Phys. Rev.* **1984**, *C30*, 1276. "Beta-Delayed Two-Proton Decays of ^{22}Al and ^{26}P."

Chandler, David   (b. 15 Oct 1944)
B.S. 1966, MIT.
Ph.D. 1969, Harvard, with Gordon on "The Mode Expansion, A New Method in Statistical Mechanics."
Faculty positions at UC San Diego (1969-70), Illinois (1970-77), Columbia (1977-78), Illinois (1978-83), Pennsylvania (1983-86).
Appointed 1986. Research in statistical mechanics of amphiphiles in solution. Teaching in physical chemistry.
Some significant publications:
Chandler, D.; Weeks, J. D. *Phys. Rev. Lett.* **1970**, *25*, 149. "Equilibrium Structure of Simple Liquids."
Lowden, L. J.; Chandler, D. *J. Chem. Phys.* **1974**, *61*, 5228. "Theory of Intermolecular Pair Correlations for Molecular Liquids. Applications to the Liquids Carbon Tetrachloride, Carbon Disulfide, Carbon Diselenide, and Benzene."
Pratt, L. R.; Chandler, D. *J. Chem. Phys.* **1977**, *67*, 3683. "Theory of the Hydrophobic Effect."
Chandler, D.; Wolynes, P. G. *J. Chem. Phys.* **1981**, *74*, 4078. "Exploiting the Isomorphism Between Quantum Theory and Classical Statistical Mechanics of Polyatomic Fluids."

Christy, Samuel Benedict   (8 Aug 1853 - 30 Nov 1914)
Ph.B. 1874, UC Berkeley.
Honorary Sc.D., Columbia, 1902.
Appointed 1875. Research in mining and metallurgical chemistry.
Transferred to Dept. of Mining and Metallurgy, 1879.
Some significant publications:
Christy, S. B. *Am. J. Science and Arts* **1879**, *17*, 453. "On the Genesis of Cinnabar Deposits."
Christy, S. B. *Trans. Am. Inst. Mining Eng.* **1888**, *17*, 3. "On the Losses in Roasting Gold-Ores, and the Volatility of Gold."
Christy, S. B. *Trans. Am. Inst. Mining Eng.* **1896**, *26*, 735. "The Solution and Precipitation of The Cyanide of Gold."
Christy, S. B. *Proc. Cal. Miners Assoc.*, 11th Annual Convention, Nov. 18, 1902, p. 85. "The Concentration of Sulphuret Ores by Means of Petroleum."

Connick, Robert Elwell   (b. 29 Jul 1917)
B.S. 1939; Ph.D. 1942, UC Berkeley, with Bray on "The Interaction of Hydrogen Peroxide and Hypochlorous Acid in Acidic Solutions Contain-

ing Chloride Ion."
Appointed 1942. From 1943-46 on leave to work on the chemistry of plutonium. Research on NMR, reaction kinetics, ligand exchange reactions, hydrolytic oligomerization, ruthenium chemistry, sulfur chemistry, and computer modeling of exchange reactions. Teaching in inorganic and physical chemistry.
Some significant publications:
Connick, R. E. *J. Chem. Soc.* **1949**, *Suppl. Issue No. 2*, S235. "Oxidation States of the Rare Earth and Actinide Elements."
Connick, R. E.; Hugus, Z Z. *J. Am. Chem. Soc.* **1952**, *74*, 6012. "The Participation of f Orbitals in Bonding in Uranium and the Transuranium Elements."
Swift, T. J.; Connick, R. E. *J. Chem. Phys.* **1962**, *37*, 307. "NMR-Relaxation Mechanisms of O^{17} in Aqueous Solutions of Paramagnetic Cations and the Lifetime of Water Molecules in the First Coordination Sphere."
Connick, R. E.; Alder, B. J. *J. Phys. Chem.* **1983**, *87*, 2764. "Computer Modeling of Rare Solvent Exchange."

Cottrell, Frederick Gardner (10 Jan 1877 - 16 Nov 1948)
B.S. 1896, UC Berkeley.
Ph.D. 1902, Leipzig, with Ostwald on "Der Reststrom bei Galvanischer Polarisation, Betrachtet als ein Diffusions Problem."
Appointed 1902. Research in physical chemistry and chemical engineering. Teaching in physical chemistry.
Resigned in 1911 to become physical chemist for the Bureau of Mines.
Some significant publications:
Cottrell, F. G. *J. Phys. Chem.* **1906**, *10*, 264. "On Air Liquefiers."
Cottrell, F. G. *J. Ind. Eng. Chem.* **1911**, *3*, 542. "The Electrical Precipitation of Suspended Particles."
Cottrell, F. G. *J. Ind. Eng. Chem.* **1912**, *4*, 864. "The Research Corporation, an Experiment in Public Administration of Patent Rights."
Cottrell, F. G. *Chem. Age* **1924**, *11*, 282, 310, 342. "The Problem of Nitrogen Fixation. I, II, III."

Cunningham, Burris Bell (16 Feb 1912 - 28 Mar 1971)
B.Sc. 1935; Ph.D. 1940, UC Berkeley, with Kirk on "The Metabolism of Paramecium caudatum."
Chicago Metallurgical Laboratory (1942-46).
Appointed 1946. Research on crystal structures and physical properties of the actinide elements, fluorescence spectra of actinide compounds, and thermochemistry of the actinide elements. Teaching in analytical chemistry.
Some significant publications:
Cunningham, B. B.; Werner, L. B. *J. Am. Chem. Soc.* **1949**, *71*, 1521. "The First Isolation of Plutonium."
Thompson, S. G.; Cunningham, B. B.; Seaborg, G. T. *J. Am. Chem. Soc.*

234   *Professional Data of Tenured Faculty*

1950, *72*, 2798. "Chemical Properties of Berkelium."
Cunningham, B. B. *Ann. Rev. Nuclear Sci.* **1964**, *14*, 323. "Chemistry of the Actinide Elements."
Cunningham, B. B.; Peterson, J. R.; Baybarz, R. D.; Parsons, T. C. *Inorg. Nucl. Chem. Letters* **1967**, *3*, 519. "The Absorption Spectrum of Es^{3+} in Hydrochloric Acid Solutions."

Dauben, William Garfield (b. 6 Nov 1919)
B.A. 1941, Ohio State.
A.M. 1942; Ph.D. 1944, Harvard, with Linstead and Fieser on "(1) Naphthalene Models of the Cardiac Aglycones. (2) Delousing Agents."
Appointed 1945. Research on synthetic, structural and mechanistic aspects of fused ring systems, natural products, and photochemistry. Teaching in organic chemistry.
Some significant publications:
Dauben, W. G.; Hutton, T. W. *J. Am. Chem. Soc.* **1956**, *78*, 2647. "The Biosynthesis of Steroids and Triterpenes. The Origin of Carbons 11 and 12 of Ergosterol."
Dauben, W. G.; Thiessen, W. E.; Resnick, P. R. *J. Org. Chem.* **1965**, *30*, 1693. "Cembrene, a Fourteen-Membered Ring Diterpene Hydrocarbon."
Dauben, W. G.; Kessel, C. R.; Takemura, K. H. *J. Am. Chem. Soc.* **1980**, *102*, 6893. "Simple, Efficient Total Synthesis of Cantharidin via a High-Pressure Diels-Alder Reaction."
Dauben, W. G.; Phillips, R. B. *J. Am. Chem. Soc.* **1982**, *104*, 5780. "Effects of Wavelength on the Photochemistry of Provitamin D$_3$."

Denn, Morton Mace (b. 7 July 1939)
B.S.E. 1961, Princeton.
Ph.D. 1964, Minnesota, with Aris on "The Optimization of Complex Systems."
Postdoctoral Fellow, Delaware (1964-65); Faculty, Delaware (1965-81).
Appointed 1980. Research on polymer processing and chemical process analysis. Teaching in chemical engineering.
Some significant publications:
Denn, M. M. "Optimization by Variational Methods"; McGraw-Hill: New York, 1969.
Russell, T. W. F.; Denn, M. M. "Introduction to Chemical Engineering Analysis"; Wiley: New York, 1972.
Denn, M. M. "Stability of Reaction and Transport Processes"; Prentice-Hall: Englewood Cliffs, NJ, 1975.
Denn, M. M. "Process Fluid Mechanics"; Prentice-Hall: Englewood Cliffs, NJ, 1980.

Eastman, Ermon Dwight (30 Nov 1891 - 19 May 1945)
B.S. 1913; M.S. 1914; Ph.D. 1917, UC Berkeley, with Lewis on "The Measurement of Low Temperatures and the measurement of Specific

Heats between 60 Degrees and 300 Degrees Absolute."
Appointed 1917. Research on chemical thermodynamics. Teaching in physical chemistry.
Some significant publications:
Eastman, E. D. *J. Am. Chem. Soc.* 1926, *48*, 552. "Thermo-Electric Effects and the Heat Capacity of Electrons in Metals."
Eastman, E. D. *J. Am. Chem. Soc.* 1928, *50*, 292. "Electromotive Force of Electrolytic Thermocouples and Thermocells and the Entropy of Transfer and Absolute Entropy of Ions."
Cornish, R. E.; Eastman, E. D. *J. Am. Chem. Soc.* 1928, *50*, 627. "The Specific Heat of Hydrogen Gas at Low Temperatures from the Velocity of Sound; and a Precision Method of Measuring the Frequency of an Oscillating Circuit."
Eastman, E. D.; Rollefson, G. K. "Physical Chemistry"; McGraw-Hill: New York, 1947.

Fisher, Robert A.
Sheffield Scientific School, Yale (ca 1860); Prof. at Vassar (1861); Study at Heidelberg, Goettingen, Paris (1863-64).
Appointed 1868. Research and teaching in chemistry, mining and metallurgy.
His professorship abolished by Regents 1870.

Foss, Alan Stuart (b. 9 Sep 1929)
B.S. 1952, Worcester Polytech Inst.
M.Ch.E. 1954; Ph.D. 1957, Delaware, with Gerster on "The Effect of Liquid Mixing on Plate Efficiencies."
Research engineer, duPont (1956-61).
Appointed 1961. Research on chemical process dynamics and control, computer control, and heat storage systems. Teaching in chemical engineering.
Some significant publications:
Hoiberg, J. A.; Lyche, B. C.; Foss, A. S. *AIChE Journal* 1971, *17*, 1434. "Experimental Evaluation of Dynamic Models for a Fixed-Bed Catalytic Reactor."
Foss, A. S. *AIChE Journal* 1973, *19*, 209. "Critique of Chemical Process Control Theory."
Vakil, H. B.; Michelsen, M. L.; Foss, A. S. *Ind. Engr. Chem. Fundam.* 1973, *12*, 328. "Fixed-Bed Reactor Control with State Estimation."
Silva, J. M.; Wallman, P. H.; Foss, A. S. *Ind. Engr. Chem. Fundam.* 1979, *18*, 383. "Multi Bed Catalytic Reactor Control Systems: Configuration, Development and Experimental Testing."

Giauque, William Francis (12 May 1895 - 28 Mar 1982)
B.S. 1920; Ph.D. 1922, UC Berkeley, with Gibson on "The Third Law of Thermodynamics."

Appointed 1922. Research on experiments designed to test the third law of thermodynamics and the calculation of the thermodynamic properties of gases from spectroscopic data by the methods of statistical mechanics. Teaching in physical chemistry.

Some significant publications:

Giauque, W. F.; Johnston, H. L. *J. Am. Chem. Soc.* **1929**, *51*, 1436. "An Isotope of Oxygen, Mass 18. Interpretation of the Atmospheric Absorption Bands."

Giauque, W. F., MacDougall, D. P. *Phys. Rev.* **1933**, *43*, 768. "Attainment of Temperatures Below 1° Absolute by Demagnetization of $Gd_2(SO_4)_3 \cdot 8H_2O$."

Giauque, W. F. *Nature* **1939**, *143*, 623. "A Proposal to Redefine the Thermodynamic Temperature Scale. A Parable of Measures to Improve Weights."

Giauque, W. F. *Phys. Rev.* **1953**, *92*, 1339. "Determination of Thermodynamic Temperatures near 0°K without Introducing Heat below 1°."

Gibson, (George) Ernest (9 Nov 1884 - 26 Aug 1959)
B.Sc. 1906, Edinburgh.
Ph.D. 1911, Breslau, with Lummer on "Ueber eine Monochromatische Temperaturstrahlung des Thalliumdampfes."
On staffs of Breslau (1911-12) and Edinburgh (1912-13).
Appointed 1913. Research in physical chemistry. Teaching in physical chemistry. Retired 1954.

Some significant publications:

Gibson, G. E. *Phys. Zeit.* **1911**, *12*, 1145. "Ueber eine Monochromatische Temperaturstrahlung des Thalliumdampfes."

Gibson, G. E.; Argo, W. L. *Phys. Rev.* **1916**, *7*, 33. "The Absorption Spectra of the Blue Solutions of Sodium and Magnesium in Liquid Ammonia."

Lewis, G. N.; Gibson, G. E. *J. Am. Chem. Soc.* **1920**, *42*, 1529. "The Third Law of Thermodynamics and the Entropy of Solutions and of Liquids."

Gibson, G. E.; Noyes, W. A., Jr. *J. Am. Chem. Soc.* **1922**, *44*, 2091. "A Study of the Luminous Discharge in Hydrogen and in Mercury and a New Method of Measuring Ionization Potentials."

Goren, Simon Land (b. 31 Aug 1936)
B.S. 1958; D.Eng. 1961, Johns Hopkins, with Gavis on "Hydrodynamic Stability of Stagnant and Flowing Films."
Esso Research and Engineering (1961-62).
Appointed 1962. On leave, NSF (1977-78). Research on formation, dynamics, transport, and separation of aerosols, colloids, and emulsions. Teaching in chemical engineering.

Some significant publications:

Krantz, W. B.; Goren, S. L. *I&EC Fund.* **1971**, *10*, 91. "Stability of Thin Liquid Films Flowing Down a Plane."

Spielman, L. A.; Goren, S. L. *I&EC Fund.* 1972, *11*, 66, 73. "Coalescence by Flow Through Porous Media." Goren, S. L.; Gottlieb, M. *J. Fluid Mech.* 1982, *120*, 245. "Surface-Tension-Driven Breakup of Viscoelastic Liquid Threads." D'Ottavio, T.; Goren, S. L. *Aerosol Sci. & Tech.* 1983, *2*, 91. "Aerosol Capture in Granular Beds in the Impaction Dominated Regime."

Gray, John Hatfield (26 Aug 1866 - ?)
B.S. 1887, UC Berkeley.
Appointed 1890. Instructor 1890-92 and 1896-1900. Research in analytical chemistry.

Grens, Edward Anthony, II (b. 14 May 1931)
B.S. 1953; M.S. 1960; Ph.D. 1963, UC Berkeley, with Tobias on "Dynamic Analysis of a One Dimensional Porous Electrode Model."
Appointed 1962. Research on computer implemented process design and simulation, electrochemical energy conversion, and the gasification and liquefaction of coal. Teaching in chemical engineering.
Some significant publications:
Grens, E. A. *Electrochim. Acta* 1970, *15*, 1047. "On the Assumptions Underlying Theoretical Models for Flooded Porous Electrodes." Upadhye, R. S.; Grens, E. A. *AIChE J.* 1975, *21*, 136. "Selection of Decompositions for Chemical Process Simulation." Anderson, T. F.; Abrams, D. S.; Grens, E. A. *AIChE J.* 1978, *24*, 20. "Evaluation of Parameters for Nonlinear Thermodynamic Models." Grens, E. A.; Hershkowitz, F.; Holten, R. R.; Shinn, J. H.; Vermeulen, T. *I&EC Proc. Des. Dev.* 1980, *19*, 396. "Coal Liquefaction Catalysis by Zinc Chloride Melts in Combination with Organic Solvents."

Gwinn, William Dulaney (b. 28 Sep 1916)
B.S. 1937; M.A. 1939, Missouri.
Ph.D. 1942, UC Berkeley, with Pitzer on "Rotation Within Molecules, Including Dichloro- and Dibromoethane."
Appointed 1942. Research on dipole moments of vapors, infrared and Raman spectra, and the role of imprisonment on resonant radiation in photochemical reactions, microwave spectroscopy, forces within molecules, and symmetry of electronic distributions in chemical bonds. Teaching in physical chemistry. Retired 1979.
Some Significant Publications:
Gwinn, W. D.; Harris, D. O.; Harrington, H. W.; Luntz, A. C. *J. Chem. Phys.* 1966, *44*, 3467. "Microwave Spectrum, Vibration-Rotation Interaction, and Potential Function for the Ring Puckering of Trimethylene Sulfide." Gwinn, W. D.; Flygare, W. H.; Narath, A. *J. Chem. Phys.* 1962, *36*, 200. "Microwave Spectrum, Structure, Quadrupole Interaction, Dipole Moment, and Bent C-Cl Bonds in 1,1-Dichlorocyclopropane."

Gwinn, W. D. *J. Chem. Phys.* 1971, *55*, 477. "Normal Coordinates: General Theory, Redundant Coordinates, and General Analysis Using Electronic Computers."
Gwinn, W. D.; Turner, B. E.; Goss, W. M.; Blackman, G. L. *Astrophys. J.* 1979, *179*, 789. "Excitation of Interstellar OH by the Collisional Dissociation of Water."

Hanson, Donald Norman (b. 3 Aug 1918)
B.S. 1940, Illinois.
M.S. 1941; Ph.D. 1943, Wisconsin, with Kowalke on "Rates of Esterification in the Vapor Phase."
Staff, Wisconsin (1943-44); Shell Dev. Co., San Francisco (1944-46; 1947); Kansas State Coll. (1946-47).
Appointed 1947. Research on separation processes, computation, design, development, and electrostatic processes. Teaching in chemical engineering.
Some significant publications:
Duffin, J. H.; Hanson D. N.; Somerville, G. F. "Computation of Multistage Separation Processes"; Reinhold: New York, 1962.
Hanson, D. N.; Schweizer, J. W. *J. Colloid Interf. Sci.* 1971, *35*, 417. "Stability Limit of Charged Drops."
Barnes, F. J.; Hanson, D. N.; King, C. J. *I&EC Proc. Des. Dev.* 1972, *11*, 136. "Calculation of Minimum Reflux for Distillation Columns with Multiple Feeds."
Hanson, D. N.; Rasquin, E. A.; Lynn, S. *I&EC Fund.* 1978, *17*, 170. "Vacuum Stream Stripping of Volatile, Sparingly Soluble Organic Compounds from Water Streams."

Harris, Charles Bonner (b. 24 Apr 1940)
B.S. 1963, Michigan.
Ph.D. 1966, MIT, with Cotton on "The Structure and Theory of Metal-Ligand and Metal-Metal Bonds in Third-Row Transition Metal Complexes."
AEC Postdoctoral Fellow, MIT (1967-68).
Appointed 1968. Research in coherent properties of matter and radiation, electronic properties of solids and surfaces, dynamics of energy transfer in solids, and fundamental studies on the picosecond time scale of chemical reactions in the condensed phase. Teaching in physical chemistry.
Some significant publications:
Francis, A. H.; Harris, C. B. *Chem. Phys. Lett.* 1971, *9*, 188. "The Observation of Coherent Triplet Excitons and Density of States Functions in Molecular Crystals."
Breiland, W. G.; Brenner, H. C.; Harris, C. B. *J. Chem. Phys.* 1975, *62*, 3458. "Coherence in Multilevel Systems. I. The Optical Detection of Coherence in Excited States and its Application to Phosphorescent Triplet States in Zero Field."

Shelby, R. M.; Harris, C. B.; Cornelius, P. A. *J. Chem. Phys.* 1979, *70*, 34. "The Origin of Vibrational Dephasing of Polyatomic Molecules in Condensed Phases."

Berg, M.; Harris, A. L.; Harris, C. B. *Phys. Rev. Lett.* 1985, *54*, 951. "Rapid Solvent-Induced Recombination and Slow Energy Relaxation in a Simple Chemical Reaction: Picosecond Studies of Iodine Photodissociation in CCl_4."

Harris, Robert Arthur (b. 9 Aug 1936)
B.S. 1957, Illinois.
M.S. 1959, Ph.D. 1960, Chicago, with Rice on "Nonequilibrium Statistical Mechanics."
Junior Fellow, Harvard (1960-63).
Appointed 1963. Research in theoretical chemistry. Teaching in physical chemistry, quantum mechanics, statistical mechanics.
Some significant publications:
Harris, R. A. *J. Chem. Phys.* 1963, *39*, 978. "Predissociation."
Heller, D. F.; Harris, R. A.; Gelbart, W. M. *J. Chem. Phys.* 1975, *62*, 1947. "Density Functional Formulation of Collisional Polarizabilities: Application to Homonuclear Noble Gas Diatoms."
Harris, R. A.; Stodolsky, L. *J. Chem. Phys.* 1981, *73*, 2145. "On the Time Dependence of Optical Activity."
Harris, R. A.; Silbey, R. *J. Chem. Phys.* 1983, *78*, 7330. "On the Stabilization of Optical Isomers Through Tunneling Friction."

Hearst, John Eugene (b. 2 Jul 1935)
B.E. 1957, Yale.
Ph.D. 1961, Cal Tech, with Vinograd on "A Quantitative Examination of the Buoyant Behavior of Macromolecules of Known Molecular Weight in a Density Gradient at Equilibrium in the Ultracentrifuge."
Postdoctoral Fellow, Dartmouth (1961-62).
Appointed 1962. Research on the structure of nucleic acids in ribosomes, the photochemistry of psoralens with nucleic acids, the kinetics of propagation of enzymes, and the molecular genetics of photosynthesis. Teaching in physical chemistry and general chemistry.
Some significant publications:
Harris, R. A.; Hearst, J. E. *J. Chem. Phys.* 1966, *44*, 2595. "On Polymer Dynamics."
Gamper, H. B.; Hearst, J. E. *Cell* 1982, *29*, 81. "A Topological Model for Transcription Based on Unwinding Angle Analysis of E. coli RNA Polymerase Binary, Initiation and Ternary Complexes."
Zsebo, K.; Hearst, J. E. *Cell* 1984, *37*, 937. "Genetic-Physical Mapping of a Photosynthetic Gene Cluster from R. capsulata."
Cimino, G. D.; Gamper, H. B.; Isaacs, S. T.; Hearst, J. E. *Ann. Rev. Biochem.* 1985, *54*, 1151. "Psoralens as Photoactive Probes of Nucleic Acid Structure and Function: Organic Chemistry, Photochemistry, and Biochemistry."

Heathcock, Clayton Howell (b. 21 Jul 1936)
B.S. 1958, Abilene Christian.
Ph.D. 1963, Colorado, with Hassner on "Synthesis and Stereochemistry of Some Steroidal Nitrogen Compounds."
NSF Fellow, Columbia (1963-64).
Appointed 1964. Research in the total synthesis of natural products, particularly terpenes and alkaloids, and the stereoselective synthesis of acyclic molecules having many stereocenters. Teaching in organic chemistry.
Some significant publications:
Heathcock, C. H.; Badger, R. A.; Patterson, J. W., Jr. *J. Am. Chem. Soc.* **1967**, *89*, 4133. "Total Synthesis of (+-)-Copaene and (+-)-Ylangene. A General Method for the Synthesis of Tricyclo[4.4.0.0^{2,7}]decanes."
Heathcock, C. H. *Science* 1981, 214, 395. "Acyclic Stereocontrol Through the Aldol Condensation."
Heathcock, C. H.; Kleinman, E. F.; Binkley, E. S. *J. Am. Chem. Soc.* **1982**, *104*, 1054. "Total Synthesis of Lycopodium alkaloids: (+-)-Lycopodine, (+-)-Lycodine and (+-)-Lycodoline."
Rosen, T.; Heathcock, C. H. *J. Am. Chem. Soc.* **1985**, *107*, 3731. "Synthetic and Biological Studies of Compactin and Related Compounds. 4. Total Synthesis of (+)-Compactin.

Herschbach, Dudley Robert (b. 18 Jun 1932)
B.S. 1954; M.S. 1955, Stanford.
A.M. 1956; Ph.D. 1958, Harvard, with Wilson on "Internal Rotation and Microwave Spectroscopy."
Appointed 1959. Research on molecular dynamics of chemical reactions and energy transfer processes, van der Waals clusters, solvation of molecules and electrons, and mechanisms of surface reactions and catalysis. Teaching in physical chemistry.
Resigned 1963 to join faculty at Harvard.
Some significant publications:
Herschbach, D. R.; Johnston, H. S.; Rapp, D. *J. Chem. Phys.* **1959**, *31*, 1652. "Molecular Partition Functions in Terms of Local Properties."
Herschbach, D. R. *Adv. Chem. Phys.* **1966**, *10*, 319. "Reactive Scattering in Molecular Beams."
Herschbach, D. R. *Pure Appl. Chem.* **1976**, *47*, 61. "Molecular Dynamics of Chemical Reactions."
Loeser, J. G.; Herschbach, D. R. *J. Phys. Chem.* **1985**, *89*, 3444. "Dimensional Interpolation of Correlation Energy for Two-Electron Atoms."

Hess, Dennis William (b. 1 Mar 1947)
B.S. 1968, Albright Coll.
M.S. 1970; Ph.D. 1973, Lehigh, with Fowkes on "Oxygen Vacancies in Thin Films of SiO_2 on Si."
Fairchild Semiconductor (1973-77).

Appointed 1977. Research on the chemistry of thin films and of thin film technology for microelectronic and optical applications. Teaching in chemical engineering.
Some significant publications:
 Hess, D. W.; Deal, B. E. *J. Electrochem. Soc.* 1977, *124*, 735. "Kinetics of the Thermal Oxidation of Silicon in O_2/HCl Mixtures."
 Szeto, R.; Hess, D. W. *J. Polym. Sci., Lett. Ed.* 1981, *19*, 119. "Phase Separation in Plasma-Deposited Polysiloxane Films."
 Tang, C. C.; Hess, D. W. *Appl. Phys. Lett.* 1984, *45*, 633. "Plasma-Enhanced Chemical Vapor Deposition of beta-Tungsten, a Metastable Phase."
 Blair, C. S.; Hess, D. W. *J. Electrochem. Soc.* 1984, *131*, 932. "Capacitance-Voltage Technique for the Determination of Carrier Concentrations in Thin Film Photoanodes."

Hildebrand, Joel Henry (16 Nov 1881 - 30 Apr 1983)
B.S. 1903; Ph.D. 1906, Pennsylvania, with Smith on "The Determination of Anions in the Electrolytic Way."
Postdoctoral position, Berlin (1906-07); On faculty at Pennsylvania (1907-13).
Appointed 1913. Research on the theory of solutions. Teaching in general chemistry. Retired 1954.
Some significant publications:
 Hildebrand, J. H. *J. Am. Chem. Soc.* 1915, *37*, 970. "The Entropy of Vaporization as a Means of Distinguishing Normal Liquids."
 Hildebrand, J. H. "Principles of Chemistry"; Macmillan: New York, 1918.
 Hildebrand, J. H. "Is Intelligence Important?"; Macmillan: New York, 1963.
 Hildebrand, J. H., Prausnitz, J. M., Scott, R. L. "Regular and Related Solutions: The Solubility of Gases, Liquids, and Solids"; Van Nostrand Reinhold: New York, 1970.

Hoffman, Darleane Christian (b. 8 Nov 1926)
B.S. 1948; Ph.D. 1951, Iowa State, with Martin on "High Specific Radioactivities of Cobalt, Platinum and Iridium from Photonuclear Reactions.
Oak Ridge Natl. Lab., 1952; Los Alamos Natl. Lab. (1953-84).
Appointed 1984. Research in separation chemistry of lanthanide and actinide elements, nuclear structure, transuranium element research, search for heavy elements in nature, studies of the fission process, heavy ion reactions, production of new neutron-rich heavy element isotopes. Teaching in nuclear chemistry.
Some significant publications:
 Hoffman, D. C.; Lawrence, F. O.; Mewherter, J. L.; Rourke, F. M. *Nature* 1971, *234*, 132. "Detection of Plutonium-244 in Nature."
 Hoffman, D. C.; Hoffman, M. M. *Ann. Rev. Nucl. Sci.* 1974, *24*, 151.

"Post-Fission Phenomena."
Hoffman, D. C.; Wilhelmy, J. B.; Weber, J.; Daniels, W. R.; Hulet, E. K.; Lougheed, R. W.; Landrum, J. H.; Wild, J. F.; Dupzyk, R. J. *Phys. Rev.* **1980**, *C21*, 972. "12.3-min ^{256}Cf and 43-min ^{258}Md and Systematics of the Spontaneous Fission Properties of Heavy Nuclides."
Hoffman, D. C. *Acc. Chem. Res.* **1984**, *17*, 235. "Spontaneous-Fission Properties and Production of Heavy-Element Isotopes."

Hogness, Thorfin Rusten (9 Dec 1894 - 14 Feb 1976)
B.S. 1918, Minnesota.
Ph.D. 1921, UC Berkeley, with Hildebrand on "The Surface Tensions and Densities of Liquid Mercury, Cadmium, Zinc, Lead, Tin, and Bismuth."
Appointed 1921. Research on ionization of gases by electron impact, photochemistry, chemical kinetics, spectroscopy and physical chemistry applied to biological systems, and the respiratory enzymes. Teaching in physical chemistry.
Resigned in 1930 to join faculty at Chicago.
Some significant publications:
Hogness, T. R.; Franck, J. *Z. Physik* **1927**, *44*, 26. "Relative Velocity of the Decomposition Product in Optical Dissociations."
Hogness, T. R.; Zscheile, F. P., Jr.; Sidwell, A. E., Jr. *J. Phys. Chem.* **1937**, *41*, 379. "Photoelectric Spectrophotometry - An Apparatus for the Ultraviolet and Visible Spectral Regions: Its Construction, Calibration and Application to Chemical Problems."
Hogness, T. R.; Sidwell, A. E., Jr.; Munch, R. H.; Barron, E. S. Guzman *J. Biol. Chem.* **1938**, *123*, 335. "The Salt Effect on the Hemoglobin-Oxygen Equilibrium."
Hogness, T. R.; Haas, E.; Horecker, B. L. *J. Biol. Chem.* **1940**, *136*, 747. "Enzymic Reduction of Cytochrome C. Cytochrome C Reductase."

Hubbell, Wayne Lester (b. 24 Mar 1943)
B.S. 1965, Oregon State
Ph.D. 1970, Stanford, with McConnell on "Spin Label Studies of Biological Membranes."
AFOSR-NRC postdoctoral fellow, Stanford (1969-70).
Appointed 1970. Research on biomembrane structure and dynamics and the molecular basis of membrane excitation. Teaching in biophysical and general chemistry.
Left in 1983 to accept endowed chair at UCLA.
Some significant publications:
Hubbell, W. L.; McConnell, H. M. *J. Am. Chem. Soc.* **1971**, *93*, 314. "Molecular Motion in Spin-Labeled Phospholipids and Membranes."
Castle, J. D.; Hubbell, W. L. *Biochem.* **1976**, *15*, 4818. "Estimation of Membrane Surface Potential and Charge Density from the Phase Equilibrium of a Paramagnetic Amphiphile."
Fung, B. K. K.; Hubbell, W. L. *Biochem.* **1978**, *17*, 4403. "Organization of Rhodopsin in Photoreceptor Membranes. 2. Transmembrane Organ-

ization of Bovine Rhodopsin: Evidence from Proteolysis and Lactoper-oxidase Catalyzed Iodination of Native and Reconstituted Membranes." Cafiso, D. C.; Hubbell, W. L. *Biochem.* **1978**, *17*, 187. "Estimation of Transmembrane Potentials from Phase Equilibria of Hydrophobic Paramagnetic Ions."

Jensen, Frederick Richard (8 Dec 1925 - 14 Feb 1987)
B.S. 1951, M.S. 1952, Nevada.
Ph.D. 1955, Purdue, with Brown on "A Study of the Friedel-Crafts Acylation and Sulfonylation Reactions."
Appointed 1955. Research on electrophilic aliphatic substitution, the chemistry of organometallic compounds, and the measurement of fast reaction rates by NMR. Teaching in organic chemistry. Retired 1987.
Some significant publications:
Jensen, F. R.; Noyce, D.; Sederholm, C.; Berlin, A. *J. Am. Chem. Soc.* **1960**, *82*, 1256. "The Energy Barrier for the Chair-Chair Interconversion of Cyclohexane."
Jensen, F. R.; Rickborn, B. "Electrophilic Substitution of Organomercurials"; McGraw-Hill: New York, 1968.
Jensen, F. R.; Davis, D. *J. Am. Chem. Soc.* **1971**, *93*, 4048. "Stereochemistry and Mechanism of the Bromine Cleavage of Organotin Compounds."
Fukuto, J. M.; Jensen, F. R. *Acc. Chem. Res.* **1983**, *16*, 177. "Mechanism of S_E2 Reactions: Emphasis on Organotin Compounds."

Johnston, Harold Sledge (b. 11 Oct 1920)
A.B. 1941, Emory.
Ph.D. 1948, Cal Tech, with Yost on "Kinetics of the Fast Reaction Between Nitrogen Dioxide and Ozone."
On Stanford staff (1947-56); at Cal Tech (1956-57).
Appointed 1957. Research on the kinetics and photochemistry of homogeneous gaseous reactions, oxides of nitrogen, ozone, chemistry in the atmosphere, and the spectra of free radical intermediates. Teaching in physical chemistry.
Some significant publications.:
Johnston, H. S.; Sharp, T. *J. Chem. Phys.* **1962**, *37*, 1541. "Hydrogen-Deuterium Kinetic Isotope Effect, an Experimental and Theoretical Study over a Wide Range of Temperature."
Johnston, H. S. "Gas Phase Reaction Rate Theory"; Ronald Press: New York, 1966.
Johnston, H. S. *Science* **1971**, *173*, 517. "Reduction of Stratospheric Ozone by Nitrogen Oxide Catalysts from Supersonic Transport Exhaust."
Johnston, H. S.; Marinelli, W. J. *J. Chem. Phys.* **1982**, *77*, 1225. "Reaction Rates of Hydroxyl Radical with Nitric Acid and with Hydrogen Peroxide."

Jolly, William Lee (b. 27 Dec 1927)
B.S. 1948; M.S. 1949, Illinois.
Ph.D. 1952, UC Berkeley, with Latimer on "Some Problems in the Chemistry of Germanium."
Appointed 1952. Group leader, Livermore Radiation Laboratory, (1953-5). Research on synthetic inorganic chemistry of volatile hydrides and sulfur-nitrogen compounds, liquid ammonia chemistry, hydroborate hydrolysis, and the photoelectron spectroscopy of inorganic and organometallic compounds. Teaching in inorganic and freshman chemistry.
Some significant publications:
　　Jolly, W. L. *Chem. Revs.* **1952**, *50*, 351. "Heats, Free Energies and Entropies in Liquid Ammonia."
　　Jolly, W. L. "Synthetic Inorganic Chemistry"; Prentice-Hall: Englewood Cliffs, NJ, 1960.
　　Hollander, J. M.; Jolly, W.L. *Acc. Chem. Res.* **1970**, *3*, 193. "X-Ray Photoelectron Spectroscopy."
　　Jolly, W. L. *Acc. Chem. Res.* **1983**, *16*, 370. "The Partnership of Gas-Phase Core and Valence Photoelectron Spectroscopy."

Jura, George (b. 18 Nov 1911)
B.S. 1939, Ill. Inst. Tech.
Ph.D. 1942, Chicago, with Harkins on "The Energy Relations of the Surfaces of Solids."
On staff at Chicago (1942-46).
Appointed 1946. Research in surface phenomena and high pressure effects on solids. Teaching in physical chemistry. Retired 1979.
Some significant publications:
　　Jura, G.; Harkins, W. D. *J. Am. Chem. Soc.* **1944**, *66*, 1362. "Surfaces of Solids. XII. An Absolute Method for the Determination of the Area of a Finely Divided Crystalline Solid."
　　Jura, G.; Pitzer, K. S. *J. Am. Chem. Soc.* **1952**, *74*, 6030. "The Specific Heat of Small Particles at Low Temperatures."
　　Jura, G.; Stark, W. A., Jr. *Rev. Sci. Inst.* **1969**, *40*, 656. "A Technique for Measurement of the Heat Capacity of Metals Under Pressure."
　　Burton, J. J.; Jura, G. *Phys. Rev.* **1968**, *171*, 699. "Fermi Momentum of Aluminum from 0 to 100 kbar."

Kim, Sung-Hou (b. 12 Dec 1937)
B.S. 1960; M.S. 1962, Seoul National Univ.
Ph.D. 1966, Pittsburgh, with Jeffrey on "X-Ray Crystallographic Studies on Carbohydrate Compounds."
Research Associate, MIT (1966-70); Senior Scientist, MIT (1970-72); on staff, Dept. of Biochem., Duke (1972-78).
Appointed 1978. Research on structures of abnormal base pairs in RNA and DNA, transfer RNA structure, protein-nucleic acid interaction, and taste-receptor binding proteins. Teaching in physical chemistry.

Some significant publications:

Kim, S.-H.; Suddath, F. L.; Quigley, G. J.; McPherson, A.; Sussman, J. L.; Wang, A. H. J.; Seeman, N. C.; Rich, A. *Science* 1974, *185*, 435. "Three-Dimensional Tertiary Structure of Yeast Phenylalanine Transfer RNA."

Warrant, R. W.; Kim, S.-H. *Nature* 1978, *271*, 130. "Alpha-Helix-Double Helix Interaction Shown in the Structure of a Protamine-Transfer RNA Complex and a Nucleoprotamine Model."

Kim, R.; Modrich, P.; Kim, S.-H. *Nucleic Acids Res.* 1984, *12*, 7285. "'Interactive' Recognition in EcoRI Restriction Enzyme-DNA Complex."

de Vos, A. M.; Hatada, M.; van der Wel, H.; Krabbendam, H.; Peerdeman, A. F.; Kim, S.-H. *Proc. Nat. Acad. Sci.* 1985, *82*, 1406. "Three-Dimensional Structure of Thaumatin I, an Intensely Sweet Protein."

King, (Cary) Judson, III (b. 27 Sep 1934)
B.E. 1956, Yale.
S.M. 1958; Sc.D. 1960, MIT, with Vivian on "The Mechanism of Liquid Phase Resistance to Gas Absorption in a Packed Column."
On faculty MIT (1959-62).
Appointed 1963. Research on separation processes, including freeze drying, spray drying, solvent extraction, adsorption, and process synthesis. Teaching in chemical engineering.
Some significant publications:

King, C. J. "Freeze Drying of Foods"; CRC Press: Cleveland, 1971.

King, C. J. "Separation Processes" McGraw-Hill: New York, 1971, 1980.

Ricker, N. L.; Pittman, E. F.; King, C. J. *J. Separ. Proc. Technol.* 1980, *1*, 23. "Solvent Extraction with Amines for Recovery of Acetic Acid from Dilute Aqueous Industrial Streams."

Kieckbusch, T. G.; Greenwald, C. G.; King, C. J. *Advances in Drying* 1984, *3*, 71. "Food Quality Factors in Spray Drying."

Klinman, Judith Pollock (b. 17 Apr 1941)
A.B. 1962; Ph.D. 1966, Pennsylvania, with Thornton on "Imidazole Catalyzed Hydrolysis of Benzoyl Imidazoles."
Postdoctoral Fellow, Weizmann Institute (1966-67); Research Scientist, Institute for Cancer Research, Philadelphia (1968-70).
Appointed 1970. Research on the mechanism of enzyme catalyzed redox reactions and the enzymology of hormone/neurotransmitter biosynthesis and metabolism. Teaching in organic and physical chemistry.
Some significant publications:

Klinman, J. P. *Adv. in Enzymology* 1978, *46*, 415. "Kinetic Isotope Effects in Enzymology."

Klinman, J. P. *CRC Crit. Rev. Biochem.* 1981, *10*, 39. "Probes of Mechanism and Transition-State Structure in the Alcohol Dehydrogenase Reaction."

Klinman, J. P.; Brenner, M.; Krueger, M.; Edmondson, D. *J. Biol. Chem.* 1984, *259*, 3399. "Evidence for Two Copper Atoms per Subunit in

Dopamine β-Monooxygenase Catalysis."
Klinman, J. P.; Matthews, R. S. *J. Am. Chem. Soc.* **1985**, *107*, 1058.
"Calculation of Substrate Dissociation Constants from Steady-State
Isotope Effects in Enzyme-Catalyzed Reactions."

Latimer, Wendell Mitchell   (22 Apr 1893 - 6 Jul 1955)
A.B. 1915; M.A. 1917, Kansas.
Ph.D. 1919, UC Berkeley, with Gibson on "Entropy Changes at Low
Temperatures: Formic Acid and Urea."
Appointed 1919.   Research on low-temperature calorimetry, the entropies
of aqueous ions, oxidation-reduction potentials, and nuclear chemistry.
Teaching in inorganic chemistry.
Some significant publications:
    Latimer, W. M.; Rodebush, W. H. *J. Am. Chem. Soc.* **1920**, *42*, 1419.
"Polarity and Ionization from the Standpoint of the Lewis Theory of
Valence."
    Latimer, W. M.; Hildebrand, J. H. "Reference Book of Inorganic
Chemistry"; Macmillan: New York, 1929, 1940, 1951.
    Latimer, W. M.; Pitzer, K. S.; Smith, W. V. *J. Am. Chem. Soc.* **1938**, *60*,
1829. "The Entropies of Aqueous Ions."
    Latimer, W. M. "The Oxidation States of the Elements and Their
Potentials in Aqueous Solutions"; Prentice-Hall: New York, 1938, 1952.

Lee, Yuan Tseh   (b. 29 Nov 1936)
B.S. 1959, National Taiwan Univ.
M.S. 1961, National Tsinghua Univ.
Ph.D. 1965, UC Berkeley, with Mahan on "Photosensitized Chemi-
ionization of Alkali Atoms."
Research Chemist, UC Berkeley (1965-66); Research Fellow, Harvard
(1966-67); on staff at Chicago (1967-74).
Appointed 1974.   Research in chemical dynamics, photochemistry,
elementary atomic and molecular processes, and crossed molecular beam
chemistry. Teaching in physical chemistry.
Some significant publications:
    Parson, J. M.; Siska, P. E.; Lee, Y. T. *J. Chem. Phys.* **1972**, *56*, 1511.
"Intermolecular Potentials from Crossed Beam Differential Elastic
Scattering Measurements. IV. Ar + Ar."
    Schulz, P. A.; Sudbo, Aa. S.; Grant, E. R.; Shen, Y. R.; Lee, Y. T. *J.
Chem. Phys.* **1980**, *72*, 4985. "Multiphoton Dissociation of SF_6 by a
Molecular Beam Method."
    Buss, R. J.; Baseman, R. J.; He, G.; Lee, Y. T. *J. Photochem.* **1981**, *17*,
389. "Reaction of Oxygen Atoms with Ethylene and Vinyl Bromide."
    Neumark, D. M.; Wodtke, A. M.; Robinson, G. N.; Hayden, C. C.; Lee
Y. T. J. Chem. Phys. 1985, 82, 3045. "Molecular Beam Studies of the F +
H_2 Reaction."

Lester, William Alexander, Jr. (b. 24 Apr 1937)
B.S. 1958; M.S. 1959, Chicago.
Ph.D. 1964, Catholic Univ. of America, with Dooling and Krauss on "A Correlated Molecular Orbital Study of H_3^+."
Positions at Wisconsin (1965-68); IBM Res. Lab. (1968-78); Lawrence Berkeley Lab. (1978-81).
Appointed 1981. Research on theory and computation of molecular collision processes and potential energy surfaces for scattering and reaction pathways. Teaching in physical chemistry.
Some significant publications:

Lester, W. A., Jr. *Methods Comput. Phys.* **1971**, *10*, 211. "Calculation of Cross Sections for Rotational Excitation of Diatomic Molecules by Heavy Particle Impact: Solution of the Close-Coupled Equations."

Schaefer, J.; Lester, W. A., Jr. *J. Chem. Phys.* **1975**, *62*, 1913. "Theoretical Study of Inelastic Scattering of H_2 by Li^+ on SCF and CI Potential Energy Surfaces."

Rebentrost, F.; Lester, W. A., Jr. *J. Chem. Phys.* **1977**, *67*, 3367. "Nonadiabatic Effects in the Collision of $F(^2P)$ with $H_2(1\sigma_g^+)$. III. Scattering Theory and Coupled-Channel Computations."

Reynolds, P. J.; Ceperley, D. M.; Alder, B. J.; Lester, W. A., Jr. *J. Chem. Phys.* **1982**, *77*, 5593. "Fixed-Node Quantum Monte Carlo for Molecules."

Lewis, Gilbert Newton (23 Oct 1875 - 23 Mar 1946)
A.B. 1896; A.M. 1898; Ph.D. 1899, Harvard, with T. W. Richards on "Some Electrochemical and Thermochemical Relations of Zinc and Cadmium Amalgams."
Instructor at Harvard (1898-1900); Postdoctoral scholarship at Leipzig and Goettingen (1900); Instructor at Harvard (1901-03); Supt. Wghts. & Measures, Philippines (1904-05); Faculty at MIT (1905-12).
Appointed 1912. Research on the application of thermodynamics to chemistry, chemical bonding theory, generalized acid-base theory, deuterium chemistry, and the theory of color. Teaching via supervision of research conferences.
On leave 1917-18, Chemical Warfare Service, U.S. Army.
Some significant publications:

Lewis, G. N.; Randall, M. "Thermodynamics and the Free Energy of Chemical Substances"; McGraw-Hill: New York, 1923.

Lewis, G. N. "Valence and the Structure of Atoms and Molecules"; Chem. Catalog: New York, 1923.

Lewis, G. N. *J. Franklin Inst.* **1938**, *226*, 293. "Acids and Bases."

Lewis, G. N.; Calvin, M. *Chem. Revs.* **1939**, *25*, 273. "The Color of Organic Substances."

Libby, Willard Frank (17 Dec 1908 - 8 Sept 1980)
B.S. 1931; Ph.D. 1933, UC Berkeley, with Latimer on "Radioactivity of Ordinary Elements, Especially Samarium and Neodymium, Method of

Detection."
Appointed 1933. Left in 1942 to join Manhattan Project (1942-45); faculty, Chicago (1945-54); Atomic Energy Commissioner (1954-59); faculty, UCLA (1959-80). Research on nuclear chemistry, dating methods based on tritium and radiocarbon, and the chemistry of environmental problems. Teaching in physical chemistry.
Some significant publications:
Libby, W. F. *Ann. Rev. Phys. Chem.* 1950, *1*, 93. "Radioactivity and Nuclear Theory."
Kaufman, S.; Libby, W. F. *Phys. Rev.* 1954, *93*, 1337. "Natural Distribution of Tritium."
Libby, W. F. *Science* 1961, *133*, 621. "Radiocarbon Dating."
Marshall, L.; Libby, W. F. *Nature* 1967, *214*, 126. "Stimulation of Jupiter's Radio Emission by Io."

Lynn, Scott (b. 18 Jun 1928)
B.S. 1950; M.S. 1951; Ph.D. 1954, Cal. Tech., with Corcoran and Mason on "I. Radial Diffusion in a Turbulent Air Stream. II. Absorption of Light by the System Nitric Acid-Nitrogen Dioxide-Water. III. Kinetics of the Decomposition of Sodium Dithionite. IV. Determination of Chromium Oxidation in the Presence of Silver Nitrate."
Res. Fellow, Delft (1953-54); Dow Chemical (1954-66).
Appointed 1967. Research on process synthesis, with emphasis on air pollution abatement, conversion of hydrogen sulfide to sulfur, vacuum stripping of volatiles from water, and extractive crystallization of salts from aqueous solutions. Teaching in chemical engineering.
Some significant publications:
Lynn, S.; Huff, J. E. *AIChE Journal* 1971, *17*, 475. "Polymerization in a Tubular Reactor."
Simpson, S. G.; Lynn, S. *AIChE Journal* 1977, *23*, 666. "Vacuum-Spray Stripping of Sparingly Soluble Gases from Aqueous Solution."
Neumann, D. W.; Lynn, S. *AIChE Journal* 1984, *30*, 62. "Oxidative Absorption of H_2S and O_2 by Iron Chelate Solutions."
Hanson, D. N.; Lynn, S. U.S. Patent No. 4,430,227, 1984. "Method of Concentrating Aqueous Solutions."

Lyon, David Nathaniel (b. 15 Apr 1919)
A.B. 1940; M.A. 1942, Missouri.
Ph.D. 1948, UC Berkeley, with Giauque on "Magnetic and Thermodynamic Properties of $FeSO_4 \cdot 7H_2O$."
Appointed 1954. Lecturer (1954-65); visiting member technical staff, Bell Telephone Labs, (1963-64). Research on applied thermodynamics. Teaching in chemical engineering. Retired 1982.
Some significant publications:
Lyon, D. N. *Adv. Cryog. Eng.* 1965, *10(2)*, 371. "Boiling Heat Transfer and Peak Nucleate Boiling Fluxes in Saturated Liquid Helium Between the λ and Critical Temperatures."

Lyon, D. N.; McWhan, D. B.; Stevens, A. L. *Rev. Sci. Inst.* 1967, *38*, 1234. "Cryostat for Studies at ~100 Kilobars at Liquid Helium Temperatures."

Giauque, W. F.; Lyon, D. N. *Rev. Sci. Inst.* 1960, *31*, 374. "Design of a 100-Kilogauss 4-Inch Core Solenoid for Continuous Operation."

Amin, H.; Lyon, D. N. *Energy Research*, 1983, *7*, 211. "Evaluation of Oxygen as Oxidant in Coal Fired Open Cycle MHD-Steam Power Plants."

Mahan, Bruce Herbert (17 Aug 1930 - 12 Oct 1982)

A.B. 1952; A.M. 1954; Ph.D. 1956, Harvard, with Kistiakowski on "Photolysis of Methylketene."

Appointed 1956. Research on photochemistry in the vacuum ultraviolet, molecular dynamics and kinetics of homogeneous gas phase reactions, ion-molecule reactions, and molecular beams. Teaching in physical chemistry.

Contracted amyotrophic lateral sclerosis around 1977; resigned from department in 1980.

Some significant publications:

Mahan, B. H. "University Chemistry"; Addison-Wesley: Reading, MA, 1965, 1969, 1975.

Gentry, W. R.; Gislason, E. A.; Mahan, B. H.; Tsao, C.-W. *J. Chem. Phys.* 1968, *49*, 3058. "Dynamics of the Reaction of N_2^+ with H_2, D_2, and HD."

Mahan, B. H. *J. Chem. Phys.* 1970, *52*, 5221. "Refined Impulse Approximation for the Collisional Excitation of the Classical Anharmonic Oscillator."

Mahan, B. H.; Ruska, W. E. W.; Winn, J. S. *J. Chem. Phys.* 1976, *65*, 3888. "Sequential Impulse Model of Direct Reactions."

Markowitz, Samuel Solomon (b. 31 Oct 1931)

B.S. 1953, Rensselaer.

M.A. 1955; Ph.D. 1957, Princeton, with Rowland on "(p,pn) Reactions in the Bev Energy Region."

NSF Fellow, Birmingham (1957-58).

Appointed 1958. Research on high energy nuclear reactions, charged particle activation analysis, nuclear reactions for environmental studies of low-Z elements and atmospheric aerosol chemistry. Teaching in nuclear chemistry, general chemistry, and analytical chemistry.

Some significant publications:

Reeder, P.; Markowitz, S. S. *Phys. Rev.* 1964, *133*, B639. "Excitation Fuction for the $C^{12}(\pi^-,\pi^-n)C^{11}$ Reaction."

Lamb, J. F.; Lee, D.; Markowitz, S. S. *Anal. Chem.* 1970, *42*, 212. "Surface Profile Analysis by Helium-3 Activation; Oxygen in Silicon."

Clemenson, M.; Novakov, T.; Markowitz, S. S. *Anal. Chem.* 1980, *52*, 1758. "Determination of Carbon in Atmospheric Aerosols by Deuteron Activation Analysis."

Oblath, S.; Novakov, T.; Chang, S.-G.; Markowitz, S. S. *Inorg. Chem.*

1983, *22*, 579. "Reaction of Nitrite Ion with Hydroxylamine-N-Sulfonate in Aqueous Solution."

Mathies, Richard Alfred (b. 20 Sep 1946)
B.S. 1968, Washington.
M.S. 1970; Ph.D. 1974, Cornell, with Albrecht on "Experimental and Theoretical Studies on the Excited Electronic States of Some Aromatic Hydrocarbons through Electric Field Perturbation and through Chemical Substituents."
Postdoctoral Fellow, Yale (1974-76).
Appointed 1976. Research on the determination of ground and excited state structure and dynamics in chemical and biological systems with resonance Raman spectroscopy, the mechanism of photochemical excitation in rhodopsin and bacteriorhodopsin, and polyene and vitamin A excited state and vibrational structure. Teaching in biophysical chemistry.
Some significant publications:
Eyring, G.; Curry, B.; Broek, A.; Lugtenburg, J.; Mathies, R. *Biochem.* **1982**, *21*, 384. "Assignment and Interpretation of Hydrogen Out-Of-Plane Vibrations in the Resonance Raman Spectra of Rhodopsin and Bathorhodopsin."
Curry, B.; Broek, A.; Lugtenburg, J.; Mathies, R. *J. Am. Chem. Soc.* **1982**, *104*, 5274. "Vibrational Analysis of all-trans Retinal."
Myers, A. B.; Mathies, R. A. *J. Chem. Phys.* **1984**, *81*, 1552. "Excited-State Torsional Dynamics of cis-Stilbene from Resonance Raman Intensities."
Smith, S. O.; Lugtenburg, J.; Mathies, R. A. *J. Memb. Biol.* **1985**, *85*, 95. "Determination of Retinal Chromophore Structure in Bacteriorhodopsin with Resonance Raman Spectroscopy."

Merrill, Robert Perkins (b. 17 Nov 1934)
B.Ch.E. 1960, Cornell.
Sc.D. 1964, MIT, with Baddour on "Semiconductor Catalysis."
On MIT faculty (1964).
Appointed 1964. Research on surface chemistry and physics. Teaching in chemical engineering.
Resigned in 1976 to join Cornell faculty.
Some significant publications:
Masel, R. I.; Merrill, R. P.; Miller, W. H. *J. Chem. Phys.* **1976**, *64*, 45. "A Semiclassical Model for Atomic Scattering from Solid Surfaces - He and Ne Scattering from W(112)."
Purtell, R. J.; Merrill, R. P.; Seabury, C. W.; Rhodin, T. N. *Phys. Rev. Lett.* **1980**, *44*, 1279. "Molecular Adsorbate Structures from Angular-Resolved Photoemission: Ammonia on Ir(III)."
Parham, T. G.; Merrill, R. P. *J. Catal.* **1984**, *85*, 295. "An EXAFS Study of the Structure of Supported Cobalt Molybdate Catalysts as a Function of Sulfiding Temperature."

Misewich, J.; Houston, P. L.; Merrill, R. P. *J. Chem. Phys.* **1985**, *82*, 1577. "Vibrational Relaxation of Carbon Dioxide (101) and Carbon Monoxide (v = 2) During Gas-Surface Collisions."

Miller, William Hughes (b. 16 Mar 1941)
B.S. 1963, Georgia Inst. Tech.
A.M. 1964; Ph.D. 1967, Harvard, with Wilson on "I. Lower Bounds to Eigenvalues. II. Theory of Resonances in Scattering and the Relation to the Decay of a Prepared State."
Junior Fellow, Harvard (1967-69); NATO Postdoctoral Fellow, Freiburg (1968-69).
Appointed 1969. Research on theory of molecular collisions, semiclassical scattering theory, dynamics of chemical reactions, and electronically nonadiabatic effects in molecular collisions. Teaching in physical chemistry.
Some significant publications:
Miller, W. H. *Adv. Chem. Phys.* **1974**, *25*, 69. "Classical-Limit Quantum Mechanics and the Theory of Molecular Collisions."
Miller, W. H. *J. Chem. Phys.* **1974**, *61*, 1823. "Quantum Mechanical Transition State Theory and a New Semiclassical Model for Reaction Rate Constants."
Miller, W. H., Handy, N. C.; Adams, J. E. *J. Chem. Phys.* **1980**, *72*, 99. "Reaction Path Hamiltonian for Polyatomic Molecules."
Miller, W. H. *J. Phys. Chem.* **1983**, *87*, 3811. "Reaction Path Dynamics for Polyatomic Systems."

Moore, (Charles) Bradley (b. 7 Dec 1939)
B.A. 1960, Harvard.
Ph.D. 1963, UC Berkeley, with Pimentel on "Spectroscopic Studies of Ketene and Diazomethane."
Appointed 1963. Research on intra- and intermolecular energy transfer and on reaction kinetics studied by spectroscopic techniques, photochemistry, and isotope separation by lasers. Teaching in physical chemistry.
Some significant publications:
Zittel, P. F.; Moore, C. B. *J. Chem. Phys.* **1973**, *58*, 2004. "Model for V > T, R Relaxation: CH_4 and CD_4 Mixtures."
Leone, S. R.; MacDonald, R. G.; Moore, C. B. *J. Chem. Phys.* **1975**, *63*, 4735. "Vibrational Relaxation and Photochemistry of HCl(v = 1,2) and Br Atoms."
Moore, C. B.; Weisshaar, J. C. *Ann. Rev. Phys. Chem.* **1983**, *34*, 525. "Formaldehyde Photochemistry."
Jasinski, J. M.; Frisoli, J. K.; Moore, C. B. *Faraday Disc. Chem. Soc.* **1983**, *75*, 289. "Unimolecular Reactions Induced by Vibrational Overtone Excitation."

Moretto, Luciano Giuseppe (b. 18 Feb 1940)
B.S. 1959; Ph.D. 1964, Pavia, with Rollier on "Fission Yields in ^{232}Th Fission Induced by Reactor Neutrons."
On Chemistry staff, Pavia (1965; 1968-70); postdoctoral fellow, LBL (1966-68).
Appointed 1971. Research on statistical properties of excited nuclei, nuclear thermodynamics, and the behavior of nuclear matter in heavy ion reactions and fission. Teaching in analytical and nuclear chemistry and statistical mechanics.
Some significant publications:
Moretto, L. G. *Nucl. Phys. A* **1972**, *A185*, 145. "Statistical Description of a Paired Nucleus with the Inclusion of Angular Momentum."
Moretto, L. G.; Sventek, J. S. *Phys. Lett.* **1975**, *58B*, 26. "A Theoretical Approach to the Problem of Partial Equilibration in Heavy Ion Reactions."
Moretto, L. G. *Nucl. Phys. A* **1975**, *A247*, 211. "Statistical Emission of Large Fragments. General Theoretical Approach."
Moretto, L. G.; Schmitt, R. P. *Phys. Rev. C* **1980**, *21*, 204. "Equilibrium Statistical Treatment of Angular Momenta Associated with Collective Modes in Fission and Heavy-Ion Reactions."

Morgan, William Conger (21 Jun 1874 - 9 Feb 1940)
B.S. 1896; Ph.D. 1899, Yale, with Gooch on "The Stereo-Chemistry of Nitrogen."
On faculty of Washburn College, Topeka (1899-1901).
Appointed 1901. Research on stereochemistry of nitrogen and methods of quantitative analysis. Teaching in general chemistry, analytical chemistry, and organic chemistry.
Resigned in 1913 to join faculty of Reed College. Joined faculty of UCLA in 1920.
Some significant publications:
Morgan, W. C. "Qualitative Analysis as a Laboratory Basis for the Study of General Inorganic Chemistry"; Macmillan: New York, 1910.
Morgan, W. C.; Lyman, J. A. "Chemistry, an Elementary Text-Book"; Macmillan: New York, 1913.
Morgan, W. C.; Lyman, J. A. "A Laboratory Manual in Chemistry" Macmillan: New York, 1916.
Morgan, W. C.; Tallmon, M. C. "A Fossil Egg from Arizona"; Bull. Dept. of Geol., UC Publications; Vol 3, No. 19.

Muetterties, Earl Leonard (23 Jun 1927 - 12 Jan 1984)
B.S. 1949, Northwestern.
A.M. 1951; Ph.D. 1952, Harvard, with Rochow on "Complexes of Boron Trifluoride." duPont, Wilmington, Del. (1952-73); Cornell (1973-78).
Appointed 1978. Research on the structure, stereochemistry and reaction mechanisms of inorganic compounds, catalysis, and the coordination

chemistry of metal surfaces and metal clusters. Teaching in inorganic chemistry.

Some significant publications:

Muetterties, E. L.; Phillips, W. D. *Adv. Inorg. Chem. Radiochem.* 1962, *4*, 231. "The Use of Nuclear Magnetic Resonance in Inorganic Chemistry."

Muetterties, E. L.; Knoth, W. H. "Polyhedral Boranes"; Marcel Dekker: New York, 1968.

Muetterties, E. L. *Accts. Chem. Res.* 1970, *3*, 266. "Stereochemically Nonrigid Structures."

Muetterties, E. L.; Wexler, R. M. *Survey Prog. Chem.* 1983, *10*, 62. "Metal Clusters and Metal Surfaces."

Myers, Rollie John   (b. 15 Jul 1924)

B.S. 1947; M.S. 1948, Cal Tech.

Ph.D. 1951, UC Berkeley, with Gwinn on "The Microwave Spectra, Structure and Dipole Moments of Several Isotopic species of Methylene Chloride."

Appointed 1951. Visiting professor, Harvard, Spring 1971. Research on microwave spectroscopy, electron paramagnetic resonance, biophysical chemistry, and nuclear magnetic resonance. Teaching in physical chemistry and general chemistry.

Some significant publications:

Myers, R. J.; Metzler, D. E.; Swift, E. H. *J. Am. Chem. Soc.* 1950, *72*, 3767. "The Distribution of Ferric Iron Between Hydrochloric Acid and Isopropyl Ether Solutions I, II and III."

Blukis, U.; Kasai, P.; Myers, R. J. *J. Chem. Phys.* 1963, *38*, 2753. "Microwave Spectra and Structure of Dimethyl Ether."

Hayes, R. G.; Myers, R. J. *J. Chem. Phys.* 1964, *40*, 877. "Effect of Cl^- and SO_4^{2-} on the Paramagnetic Resonance Linewidth of Mn^{2+} in Aqueous Solution and the Rates of Formation of the Complex Ions."

St. John, M. R.; Myers, R. J. *Phys. Rev. B* 1976, *13*, 1006. "Electron-Paramagnetic-Resonance Spectra of Ions Substituted into Transition-Metal Lattices."

Newman, John Scott   (b. 17 Nov 1938)

B.S. 1960, Northwestern.

M.S. 1962; Ph.D. 1963, UC Berkeley, with Sherman on "Fluid Flow Past a Circular Cylinder at High Reynolds Numbers."

Appointed 1962. Research on design of practical electrochemical systems, fluid flow, electrochemical transport, corrosion processes, transport properties in molten salt solutions, and the analysis of mass-transfer rates and current distribution. Teaching in chemical engineering.

Some significant publications:

Newman, J. *J. Electrochem. Soc.* 1966, *113*, 1235. "Current Distribution on a Rotating Disk Below the Limiting Current."

Newman, J. "Electrochemical Systems"; Prentice-Hall: Englewood

Cliffs, NJ, 1973.

Tiedemann, W.; Newman, J. *AIChE J.* **1975**, *21*, 25. "Porous-Electrode Theory with Battery Applications."

Orazem, M. E.; Newman, J. *J. Electrochem. Soc.* **1984**, *131*, 2582. "Mathematical Modeling of Liquid-Junction Photovoltaic Cells. III. Optimization of Cell Configurations."

Noyce, Donald Sterling   (b. 26 May 1923)

A.B. 1944, Grinnell.

M.A. 1945; Ph.D. 1947, Columbia, with Doering on "Partial Determination of the Structure of Ustin, a Metabolite of Aspergillus ustus."

NIH Fellow, Columbia (1947-48)

Appointed 1948.   Research on the kinetics, mechanisms, and stereochemistry of organic reactions, rearrangements of cyclic compounds, and substituent effects. Teaching in organic chemistry. Retired 1986.

Some significant publications:

Noyce, D. S.; Denney, D. B. *J. Am. Chem. Soc.* **1954**, *76*, 768. "The Direct Chemical Interrelation of the Configuration of Terpenes and Hydroxy Acids."

Noyce, D. S.; Reed, W. L. *J. Am. Chem. Soc.* **1959**, *81*, 624. "Carbonyl Reactions. IX. The Rate and Mechanism of the Base-Catalyzed Condensation of Benzaldehyde and Acetone. Factors Influencing the Structural Course of Condensation of Unsymmetrical Ketones."

Noyce, D. S.; Matesich, M. A.; Schiavelli, M. D.; Peterson, P. E. *J. Am. Chem. Soc.* **1965**, *87*, 2295. "Concerning the Acid-Catalyzed Hydration of Acetylenes."

Noyce, D. S.; Castenson, R. L. *J. Am. Chem. Soc.* **1973**, *95*, 1247. "Participation of Heterocyclic Moieties in the Solvolytic Rearrangement of β-Arylethyl Tosylates."

O'Konski, Chester Thomas   (b. 12 May 1921)

B.S. 1942, Wisconsin.

M.S. 1946; Ph.D. 1948, Northwestern, with Gucker on "Aerosol Studies."

Appointed 1948.   Research on nuclear quadrupole spectroscopy, spectroscopic and electro-optical properties of macromolecules, molecular electronic structure, and hydrogen bonding. Teaching in physical chemistry and biophysical chemistry.

Some significant publications:

O'Konski, C. T.; Haltner, A. J. *J. Am. Chem. Soc.* **1957**, *79*, 5634. "Electric Properties of Macromolecules I.   A Study of Electric Polarization in Polyelectrolyte Solutions by Means of Electric Birefringence."

O'Konski, C. T.; Lehrer, S. S. *J. Chem. Phys.* **1965**, *43*, 1941. "Nuclear Quadropole Resonance and Bonding in Crystalline Ammonia."

O'Konski, C. T.; Shepard, L. S. In "Molecular Electro-Optics, Part 1: Theory and Methods"; O'Konski, C. T., Ed.; Marcel Dekker: New York, 1976; Appendix B. "Inertial Effects in Rotational Diffusion."

O'Konski, C. T.; Jost, J. W. In "Molecular Electro-Optics, Part 2: Applications to Biopolymers"; O'Konski, C. T., Ed.; Marcel Dekker: New York, 1978; Chap. 15. "Electro-Optic Data Acquisition and Processing."

Olander, Donald Raymond (b. 6 Nov 1931)
A.B. 1953; B.S. 1954, Columbia.
Sc.D. 1958, MIT, with Benedict on "Extraction of Nitric Acid by Tributyl Phosphate."
Appointed 1958. Research on materials chemistry of nuclear fuels and on gas-solid chemical reactions by molecular beam techniques. Teaching in chemical engineering and nuclear chemical engineering. Resigned 1961 to join Dept. of Nuclear Engineering.
Some significant publications:
Olander, D. R. *AIChE J.* 1960, *6*, 233. "Simultaneous Mass Transfer and Equilibrium Chemical Reaction."
Olander, D. R. *Adv. Nucl. Sci. Techn.* 1972, *6*, 105. "Technical Basis of the Gas Centrifuge."
Balooch, M.; Olander, D. R. *J. Chem. Phys.* 1975, *63*, 4772. "Reactions of Modulated Molecular Beams with Pyrolytic Graphite. III - Hydrogen."
Olander, D. R. "Fundamental Aspects of Nuclear Reactor Fuel Elements"; U.S. Dept. of Energy, 1976.

Olson, Axel Ragnar (6 Feb 1889 - 22 Dec 1954)
B.S. 1915, Chicago.
Ph.D. 1917, UC Berkeley, with Lewis on "Determination of the Equilibrium between Chlorine, Water, Hydrochloric Acid, and Chloric Acid. The Free Energy of the Chlorate Ion."
Chemical Warfare Service, A.E.F. (1918-19).
Appointed 1919. Research on radiation, the kinetics and mechanisms of reactions, and salt effects on rates and equilibria. Teaching in physical and analytical chemistry. Retired 1954.
Some significant publications:
Olson, A. R.; Goodspeed, T. H. *Proc. Nat. Acad. Sci.* 1928, *14*, 66. "The Production of Variation in Nicotiana Species by X-Ray Treatment of Sex Cells."
Olson, A. R.; Youle, P. V. *J. Am. Chem. Soc.* 1940, *62*, 1027. "The Strength of Carbonic Acid. The Rate of Reaction of Carbon Dioxide with Water and Hydroxyl Ion."
Olson, A. R.; Simonson, T. R. *J. Chem. Phys.* 1949, *17*, 348. "Salt Effects on Ionic Equilibria."
Olson, A. R.; Orlemann, E. F.; Koch, C. W. "Introductory Quantitative Analysis"; Freeman: San Francisco, 1948.

O'Neill, Edmond C. (13 Dec 1858 - 4 Oct 1933)
B.S. 1879, UC Berkeley.
Appointed 1879. Research in biochemistry and analytical chemistry.

Teaching in all aspects of chemistry. Retired 1925.
Some significant publications:
    Stillman, J. M.; O'Neill, E. C. *Am. Chem. J.* **1882**, *4*, 206. "On the
Occurrence of a New Fat Acid in the Nut of the California Bay Tree."
O'Neill, E. C. *J. Ind. Eng. Chem.* **1918**, *10*, 391. "The Dedication of
Gilman Hall, University of California. Introductory Address."
O'Neill, E. C. *Calif. Engineer* **1923**, *2(1)*, 3. "History of the College of
Chemistry."

Orlemann, Edwin Franklyn (19 Jul 1915 - 18 Aug 1985)
B.S. 1936, St. Thomas College (St. Paul, Minn.) 1936.
Ph.D. 1941, Minnesota, with Kolthoff on "Reduction of Iodate and
Bromate Ions, and Theory of Irreversible Reductions at a Dropping
Mercury Electrode."
Appointed 1941. From 1942-45 worked at Chicago and Oak Ridge on the
purification of plutonium and uranium. Research in polarography.
Teaching in quantitative analysis. Retired 1976.
Some significant publications:
    Orlemann, E. F.; Kolthoff, I. M. *J. Am. Chem. Soc.* **1942**, *64*, 833. "The
Anomalous Electroreduction of Water at the Dropping Mercury Electrode
in Relatively Concentrated Salt Solutions."
    Kern, D. M.; Orlemann, E. F. *J. Am. Chem. Soc.* **1949**, *71*, 2102. "The
Potential of the Uranium(V), Uranium(VI) Couple and the Kinetics of
Uranium(V) Disproportionation in Perchlorate Media."
    Sanborn, R. H.; Orlemann, E. F. *J. Am. Chem. Soc.* **1956**, *78*, 4852.
"The Formation of Unipositive Nickel by Electrolysis in Concentrated
Salt Solutions."
    Merideth, C. W.; Mathews, W. D.; Orlemann, E. F. *Inorg. Chem.* **1964**,
3, 320. "The Rate of Aquation of Dichlorotetraaquochromic Ion as a
Function of pH in Chloride Media."

Perlman, Isadore (b. 12 Apr 1915)
B.S. 1936; Ph.D. 1940, UC Berkeley, with Chaikoff on "Studies in the
Phospholipid Metabolism of the Liver Using Radioactive Phosphorus as
an Indicator."
Manhattan Project: Berkeley; Chicago; Oak Ridge, Tenn.; Hanford,
Washington; (1941-45).
Appointed 1946. Research on nuclear chemistry and nuclear
spectroscopy, high energy nuclear reactions, and applications of neutron
activation analysis to chemistry, archaeology, geology and astrochemistry.
Teaching in nuclear chemistry.
Resigned in 1973 to join staff of Weizmann Institute, Rehovoth, Israel.
Some significant publications:
    Perlman, I.; Ruben, S.; Chaikoff, I. L. *J. Biol. Chem.* **1937**, *122*, 169.
"Radioactive Phosphorus as an Indicator of Phospholipid Metabolism. I.
The Rate of Formation and Destruction of Phospholipids in the Fasting
Rat."

Asaro, F.; Perlman, I. *Phys. Rev.* **1952**, *87*, 393. "First Excited States of Even-Even Nuclides in the Heavy Element Region."

Perlman, I.; Asaro, F. *Archaeometry* **1969**, *11*, 21. "Pottery Analysis by Neutron Activation."

Bonen, D.; Perlman, I.; Yellin, J. *Contrib. Mineral. Petrol.* **1980**, *72*, 397. "The Evolution of Trace Element Concentrations in Basic Rocks from Israel, and Their Petrogenesis."

Petersen, Eugene Edward (b. 2 Mar 1924)
B.S. 1949; M.S. 1950, Washington.
Ph.D. 1953, Penn. State, with Wright on "The Effects of Pore Geometry on the Rate of Reaction of Artificial Graphite with Carbon Dioxide."
Appointed 1953. Research on kinetics of heterogeneous reactions, catalysis, reactions of solids, and reaction and reactor engineering. Teaching in chemical engineering.
Some significant publications:
Petersen, E. E. *AIChE J.* **1957**, *3*, 443. "Reaction of Porous Solids."
Petersen, E. E. "Chemical Reaction Analysis"; Prentice-Hall: Englewood Cliffs, NJ, 1965.
Watt, D. M., Jr.; Petersen, E. E. *J. Chem. Phys.* **1969**, *50*, 2196. "Relationship Between the Limiting Pressure and the Solid Temperature for the Deflagration of Ammonium Perchlorate."
Pacheco, M. A.; Petersen, E. E. *J. Catalysis* **1984**, *86*, 75. "On a General Correlation for Catalyst Fouling."

Phillips, Norman Edgar (b. 20 Dec 1928)
B.A. 1949; M.A. 1950, British Columbia.
Ph.D. 1954, Chicago, with Long on "Thermal Conductivity of Indium-thallium Alloys in the Normal and Superconducting States."
NRC Fellow, UC Berkeley (1954-55).
Appointed 1955. Research on low-temperature properties of materials, low-temperature thermometry and calorimetry. Teaching in physical chemistry.
Some significant publications:
Ho, J. C.; Phillips, N. E.; Smith, T. F. *Phys. Rev. Lett.* **1966**, *17*, 694. "Heat Capacity of α-Uranium at a Pressure of 10 kbar, Between 0.3 and 6°K."
Phillips, N. E.; Waterfield, C. G.; Hoffer, J. K. *Phys. Rev. Lett.* **1970**, *25*, 1260. "Calorimetric Evidence for Positive Phonon Dispersion in Liquid Helium-4."
Triplett, B. B.; Phillips, N. E. *Phys. Rev. Lett.* **1971**, *27*, 1001. "Calorimetric Evidence for a Singlet Ground State in CuCr and CuFe."
Fogle, W. E.; Boyer, J. D.; Fisher, R. A.; Phillips, N. E. *Phys. Rev. Lett.* **1983**, *50*, 1815. "Specific Heat Anomaly and Phase Boundary for the Spin-Glass - Paramagnet Transition in CuMn."

Pimentel, George Claude   (b. 2 May 1922)
A.B. 1943, UCLA.
Ph.D. 1949, UC Berkeley, with Pitzer on "(I) Spectroscopic Study of Two Boranes. (II) Thermocouples Involving Superconductors."
Appointed 1949. On leave 1977-80 as Deputy Director, NSF. Research on infrared spectroscopic determination of the molecular structure of molecules that do not satisfy normal bonding rules, matrix isolation study of normally transient molecules, rapid-scan infrared spectroscopic study of transient molecules, infrared spectroscopic study of the atmosphere, surface, and topography of Mars, kinetic data from chemical lasers, chemiluminescence from cryogenic solids, mode selective excitation of bimolecular reactions, and spectroscopic mapping of reaction surfaces that involve electronically excited molecules. Teaching in analytical, general, and physical chemistry.
Some significant publications:
    Whittle, E.; Dows, D. A.; Pimentel, G. C. *J. Chem. Phys.* **1954**, *22*, 1943. "The Matrix Isolation Method for the Experimental Study of Unstable Species."
    Kasper, J. V. V.; Pimentel, G. C. *Phys. Rev. Lett.* **1965**, *14*, 352. "The HCl Chemical Laser."
    Horn, D.; McAfee, J.; Winer, A.; Herr, K.; Pimentel, G. C. *Icarus* **1972**, *16*, 543. "The Composition of the Martian Atmosphere: Minor Constituents."
    Frei, H.; Pimentel, G. C. *J. Chem. Phys.* **1983**, *78*, 3698. "Selective Vibrational Excitation of the Ethylene-Fluorine Reaction in a Nitrogen Matrix. 1."

Pines, Alexander   (b. 22 Jun 1945)
B.S. 1967, Hebrew Univ. of Jerusalem.
Ph.D. 1972, MIT, with Waugh on "High Resolution NMR in Solids."
Appointed 1972. Research on NMR spectroscopy and application to chemistry and materials research, molecular dynamics, optical magnetic double resonance, imaging, liquid crystals. Teaching in freshman and physical chemistry.
Some significant publications:
    Pines, A.; Ruben, D. J.; Allison, S. *Phys. Rev. Lett.* **1974**, *33*, 1002. "Molecular Ordering and Even-Odd Effect in a Homologous Series of Nematic Liquid Crystals."
    Tycko, R.; Pines, A.; Guckenheimer, J. *J. Chem. Phys.* **1985**, *83*, 2775. "Fixed Point Theory of Iterative Excitation Schemes in NMR."
    Zax, D. B.; Bielecki, A; Zilm, K. W.; Pines, A.; Weitekamp, D. P. *J. Chem. Phys.* **1985**, *83*, 4877. "Zero Field NMR and NQR."
    Munowitz, M.; Pines, A. *Adv. Chem. Phys.* **1986**, *64*. "Principles and Applications of Multiple Quantum Spectroscopy."

Pitzer, Kenneth Sanborn   (b. 6 Jan 1914)
B.S. 1935, Cal Tech.

Ph.D. 1937, UC Berkeley, with Latimer on "Theoretical Calculations and Experimental Determinations of Entropies and Related Thermodynamic Quantities."
Appointed 1937. On leave as Technical Director, Maryland Res. Lab. (1943-44); Director of Research, AEC (1949-51). Resigned to become President, Rice Univ. (1961-68); president, Stanford Univ. (1968-71). Returned to UC Berkeley 1971. Research on the thermodynamics of molecules with internal rotation, strain energies and pseudorotation in cyclic hydrocarbons, the corresponding state theory and the acentric factor theory for fluids, intramolecular repulsive forces, relativistic effects in chemistry, and the thermodynamics of electrolytic solutions. Teaching in physical chemistry.
Some significant publications:
Pitzer, K. S.; Gwinn, W. D. *J. Chem. Phys.* 1942, 10, 428. "Energy Levels and Thermodynamic Functions for Molecules with Internal Rotation. I. Rigid Frame with Attached Tops."
Pitzer, K. S. *Science* 1945, *101*, 672. "Strain Energies of Cyclic Hydrocarbons."
Pitzer, K. S. *J. Phys. Chem.* 1973, *77*, 268. "Thermodynamics of Electrolytes. I. Theoretical Basis and General Equations."
Pitzer, K. S. *Int. J. Quantum Chem.* 1984, *25*, 131. "Relativistic Calculations of Dissociation Energies and Related Properties."

Porter, Charles Walter (16 May 1880 - 1971)
B.S. 1905, Utah Agr. College.
A.M. 1909, Harvard.
Ph.D. 1915, UC Berkeley, with Biddle on "Temperature Coefficients and the Effects of Acids, Bases and Salts on Reaction Velocities of the Triphenylmethane Dyes."
Appointed 1918. Research on molecular rearrangements, dipole moments of organic compounds, stereochemistry of compounds containing deuterium, and induction of organic reactions by ultrasonic waves. Teaching in organic chemistry. Retired 1946.
Some significant publications:
Porter, C. W. "The Carbon Compounds"; Ginn: Boston, 1924.
Porter, C. W. "Molecular Rearrangements"; Chemical Catalog: New York, 1928.
Kumler, W. D.; Porter, C. W. *J. Am. Chem. Soc.* 1934, 56, 2549. "Dipole Moments and Molecular Structure of Amides."
Young, L. E.; Porter, C. W. *J. Am. Chem. Soc.* 1937, *59*, 328. "Stereochemistry of Deuterium Compounds. I. Optical Rotation of Methylhexyldeuterocarbinol."

Powell, Richard Edward (20 Dec 1917 - 6 Apr 1979)
B.S. 1939, UC Berkeley.
Ph.D. 1943, Princeton, with Eyring on "Theory of Flow Processes."
Instructor, Princeton (1943-46).

Appointed 1946. Research on the kinetics and mechanisms of the reactions of inorganic compounds (especially nonmetal compounds) in aqueous solution. Teaching in inorganic chemistry.
Some significant publications:
    Dusenbury, J. H.; Powell, R. E. *J. Am. Chem. Soc.* 1951, *73*, 3266. "Reactions of Nitrous Acid. I. Ammonium Nitrite Decomposition."
    Cahn, J. W.; Powell, R. E. *J. Am. Chem. Soc.* 1954, *76*, 2565. "The Raschig Synthesis of Hydrazine."
    Powell, R. E. *J. Phys. Chem.* 1954, *58*, 528. "The Entropies of Aqueous Ions."
    Powell, R. E. *J. Chem. Educ.* 1968, *45*, 558. "Relativistic Quantum Chemistry. The Electrons and the Nodes."

Prausnitz, John Michael (b. 7 Jan 1928)
B.Ch.E. 1950, Cornell.
M.S. 1951, Rochester.
Ph.D. 1955, Princeton, with Wilhelm on "Turbulent Diffusion and Rapid Chemical Reaction in Packed Bed."
Appointed 1955. Research on the thermodynamic properties of fluid mixtures and molecular thermodynamics for computer-aided chemical process design. Teaching in chemical engineering.
Some significant publications:
    Prausnitz, J. M. "Properties of Gases and Liquids," 3rd ed.; McGraw-Hill: New York, 1977.
    Prausnitz, J. M. *Science* 1979, *205*, 759. "Molecular Thermodynamics for Chemical process Design."
    Prausnitz, J. M. "Computer Calculations for Multicomponent Vapor-Liquid and Liquid-Liquid Equilibria"; Prentice-Hall: Englewood Cliffs, NJ, 1980.
    Prausnitz, J. M. "Molecular Thermodynamics of Fluid-Phase Equilibria," 2nd ed.; Prentice-Hall: Englewood Cliffs, NJ, 1985.

Radke, Clayton John (b. 3 Aug 1944)
B.S. 1966, Washington.
Ph.D. 1971, UC Berkeley, with Prausnitz on "Thermodynamics of Adsorption from Dilute Liquid Solution."
NSF Postdoctoral, Bristol (1972-73); Faculty, Penn. State (1973-76).
Appointed 1976. Research on surface and colloid science technology, equili-bria and dynamics of adsorption from solution, colloid stability and rheology, chromatography, two-phase and dispersed phase flow in porous media, electro-kinetics, enhanced oil recovery, nuclear waste storage, and processing of ceramics. Teaching in chemical engineering.
Some significant publications:
    Bisio, P. D.; Cartledge, J. G.; Keesom, W. H.; Radke, C. J. *J. Colloid Int. Sci.* 1980, *78*, 225. "Molecular Orientation of Aqueous Surfactants on a Hydrophobic Solid."
    Bunge, A. L.; Radke, C. J. *Soc. Pet. Eng. J.* 1982, *22*, 998. "Migration

of Alkaline Pulses in Reservoir Sands."
deZabala, E. F.; J. M. Vislocky; Rubin, E.; Radke, C. J. *Soc. Pet. Eng. J.* **1982**, *22*, 245. "A Chemical Theory for Linear Alkaline Flooding."
Soo, H.; Radke, C. J. *J. Coll. Int. Sci.* **1984**, *102*, 462. "Velocity Effects in Emulsion Flow Through Porous Media."

Randall, Merle (29 Jan 1888 - 17 Mar 1950)
B.S. 1907; M.A. 1909, Missouri.
Ph.D. 1912, MIT, with Lewis on "Studies in Free Energy."
Research Asst., UC Berkeley (1912-17)
Appointed 1917. Research and teaching in thermodynamics. Retired 1944.
Some significant publications:
Lewis, G. N.; Randall, M. "Thermodynamics and the Free Energy of Chemical Substances"; McGraw-Hill: New York, 1923.
Randall, M.; Farley, C. F. *Chem. Revs.* **1927**, *4*, 285. "The Activity Coefficient of Non-Electrolytes in Aqueous Salt Solutions from Solubility Measurements. The Salting-Out Order of the Ions."
Ruben, S.; Randall, M.; Kamen, M.; Hyde, J. L. *J. Am. Chem. Soc.* **1941**, *63*, 877. "Oxygen-18 as a Tracer in the Study of Photosynthesis."
Randall, M.; Young, L. E. "Elementary Physical Chemistry"; Randall & Sons: Berkeley, 1942.

Rapoport, Henry (b. 16 Nov 1918)
B.S. 1940; Ph.D. 1943, MIT, with Morton on "Studies in the Indole Synthesis. Synthesis of Physostigmine Intermediates."
Position at Heyden Corporation (1943-45); Research Fellow, US Public Health Service (1945-46).
Appointed 1946. Research on the structure and synthesis of natural products, including alkaloids, pigments, porphyrins, toxins, mutagens, and oligonucleotides. Teaching in organic chemistry.
Some significant publications:
Rapoport, H.; Holden, K. *J. Am. Chem. Soc.* **1962**, *84*, 635. "The Synthesis of Prodigiosin."
Bhalerao, U. T.; Plattner, J. J.; Rapoport, H. *J. Am. Chem. Soc.* **1970**, *92*, 3429. "Synthesis of dl-Sirenin and dl-Isosirenin."
Moos, W. H.; Gless, R. D.; Rapoport, H. *J. Org. Chem.* **1983**, *48*, 227. "Codeine Analogues. Synthesis of 4a-Aryldecahydroisoquinolines Containing Nitrogen Ring Functionality and of Octahydro-1H-indeno[1,2,3-ef]isoquinolines. A Total Synthesis of Codeine.
Koskinen, A. M. P.; Rapoport, H. *J. Med. Chem.* **1985**, *28*, 1301. "Synthetic and Conformational Studies on Anatoxin-a: A Potent Acetylcholine Agonist."

Rasmussen, John Oscar, Jr. (b. 8 Aug 1926)
B.S. 1948, Cal Tech.

Ph.D. 1952, UC Berkeley, with Seaborg on "Alpha Radioactivity of Nuclides with Atomic Numbers Less than 83." **Appointed 1952.** Research Associate, Res. Inst. Physics, Stockholm (1953). Resigned 1969 to join Chem. Dept. and Heavy Ion Accelerator Laboratory, Yale. Reappointed 1972. Research on radioactive decay schemes, alpha decay and the Bohr-Mottelson unified nuclear model, in-beam heavy-ion reaction studies, angle-dependent nuclear reaction theory of deformed nuclei, and semi-classical trajectory methods for deformed nuclei. Teaching in nuclear and physical chemistry.
Some significant publications:
> Rasmussen, J. O., Jr.; Thompson, S. G.; Ghiorso, A. *Phys. Rev.* 1953, *89*, 33. "Alpha Radioactivity in the 82-Neutron Region."
> Mang, H. J.; Rasmussen, J. O., Jr. *Mat. Fys. Skr. Dan. Vid. Selsk.* 1962, *2*, 3. "Shell-Model Calculations of Alpha Decay Rates of Even-even Spheroidal Nuclei."
> Rasmussen, J. O. In "Alpha-, Beta-, and Gamma-Spectroscopy"; Siegbahn, K., Ed.; North-Holland: Amsterdam, 1964; Chap. XI. "Alpha Decay."
> Massmann, H.; Rasmussen, J. O. *Nucl. Phys.* 1975, *A243*, 155. "Uniform Semiclassical Orbital Calculations of Heavy Ion Coulomb Excitation."

Raymond, Kenneth Norman (b. 7 Jan 1942)
B.A. 1964, Reed.
Ph.D. 1968, Northwestern, with Basolo on "5 Coordination in d^8 and d^9 Transition Metal Complexes." **Appointed 1968.** Research on the coordination chemistry and mechanisms of biological iron transport, the synthesis of metal-ion-specific complexing agents, and the structure and bonding of coordination compounds. Teaching in inorganic chemistry.
Some significant publications:
> Baker, E. C.; Halstead, G. W.; Raymond, K. N. *Struct. Bonding* 1976, *25*, 23. "The Structure and Bonding of 4f and 5f Series Organometallic Compounds."
> Raymond, K. N.; Carrano, C. J. *Acc. Chem. Res.* 1979, *12*, 183. "Coordination Chemistry and Microbial Iron Transport."
> Raymond, K. N.; Freeman, G. E.; Kappel, M. J. *Inorg. Chim. Acta* 1984, *94*, 193. "Actinide-Specific Complexing Agents: Their Structural and Solution Chemistry."
> Raymond, K. N.; Mueller, G.; Matzanke, B. F. *Topics Curr. Chem.* 1984, *123*, 49. "Complexation of Iron by Siderophores. A Review of Their Solution and Structural Chemistry and Biological Function."

Rising, Willard Bradley (26 Sep. 1839 - 9 Feb 1910)
A.B. 1864; M.A. 1867, Hamilton College.
Ph.D. 1871, Heidelberg, with Bunsen.

Appointed 1872. Research and teaching in analytical chemistry. Retired 1909.
Some significant publications:
Rising, W. B. "Methods of Detecting Adulterants in Olive Oil"; Berkeley, Calif.
Rising, W. B. In UC Archives, "The Biology of Ferments."
LeConte, J.; Rising, W. B. *Am. J. Sci.* **1882**, *24*, 23. "The Phenomena of Metalliferous Vein-Formation Now in Progress at Sulphur Bank, California."
Rising, W. B.; Lenher, V. *J. Am. Chem. Soc.* **1896**, *18*, 96. "An Electrolytic Method for the Determination of Mercury in Cinnabar."

Rollefson, Gerhard Krohn (12 Jan 1900 - 15 Nov 1955)
A.B. 1920; A.M. 1921, Wisconsin.
Ph.D. 1923, UC Berkeley, with Lewis on "Spectral Series in the Soft X-Ray Region."
Appointed 1923. Research on photochemistry, quenching of fluorescence, kinetic isotope effects, x-ray studies, and interionic effects on reaction rates in solution. Teaching in physical chemistry.
Some significant publications:
Rollefson, G. K. *J. Chem. Phys.* **1934**, *2*, 144. "The Relative Reactivities of the Hydrogen Isotopes with Chlorine."
Rollefson, G. K.; Burton, M. "Photochemistry and the Mechanism of Chemical Reactions"; Prentice-Hall: New York, 1939.
Curme, H. G.; Rollefson, G. K. *J. Am. Chem. Soc.* **1952**, *74*, 3766. "Experimental Measurement of the Effect of a Solvent on the Rate of a Very Fast Bimolecular Reaction."
Rollefson, G. K. *Ann. Rev. Phys. Chem.* **1952**, *3*, 199. "Photochemistry."

Ruben, Samuel (8 Nov 1913 - 28 Sep 1943)
B.S. 1935; Ph.D. 1938, UC Berkeley, with Latimer and Libby on "Studies in Artificial Radioactivity."
Appointed 1939. Research on the use of carbon-11 and carbon-14 in the study of photosynthesis. Teaching in organic chemistry.
Some significant publications:
Ruben, S.; Kamen, M. D. *Phys. Rev.* **1941**, *59*, 349. "Long-Lived Radioactive Carbon: C^{14}."
Ruben, S.; Randall, M.; Kamen, M.; Hyde, J. L. *J. Am. Chem. Soc.* **1941**, *63*, 877. "Heavy Oxygen (O^{18}) as a Tracer in the Study of Photosynthesis."
Ruben, S.; Kamen, M. D.; Allen, M. B.; Nahinsky, P. *J. Am. Chem. Soc.* **1942**, *64*, 2297. "Some Exchange Experiments with Radioactive Tracers."
Ruben, S. *J. Am. Chem. Soc.* **1943**, *65*, 279. "Photosynthesis and Phosphorylation."

Sauer, Kenneth (b. 19 Jun 1931)
A.B. 1953, Oberlin.
M.S. 1954; Ph.D. 1958, Harvard, with Kistiakowsky on "The Photolysis of Ketene."
On staff of American Univ. of Beirut (1957-60); Postdoctoral Fellow, UC Berkeley (1960-63).
Appointed 1963. Research on photosynthesis, biomolecular spectroscopy, EPR, picosecond kinetics, structure of chlorophyll proteins and photosynthetic membranes, and the mechanism of photosynthetic oxygen evolution. Teaching in biophysical chemistry and general chemistry.
Some significant publications:
Sauer, K.; Dratz, E. A.; Coyne, L. *Proc. Natl. Acad. Sci.* USA **1968**, *61*, 17. "Circular Dichroism Spectra and the Molecular Arrangement of Bacteriochlorophylls in the Reaction Centers of Photosynthetic Bacteria."
Sauer, K.; Mathis, P.; Acker, S.; Van Best, J. A. *Biochim. Biophys. Acta* **1978**, *503*, 120. "Electron Acceptors Associated with P-700 in Triton Solubilized Photosystem I Particles from Spinach Chloroplasts."
Sauer, K. *Acc. Chem. Res.* **1980**, *13*, 249. "A Role for Manganese in Oxygen Evolution in Photosynthesis."
Haehnel, W.; Nairn, J. A.; Reisberg, P.; Sauer, K. *Biochim. Biophys. Acta* **1982**, *680*, 161. "Picosecond Fluorescence Kinetics and Energy Transfer in Chloroplasts and Algae."

Saykally, Richard James (b. 10 Sep 1947)
B.S. 1970, Wisconsin/Eau Claire.
Ph.D. 1977, Wisconsin/Madison, with Woods on "Microwave Spectroscopy of Transient Molecular Species in Glow Discharges."
NRC Postdoctoral Fellow, Natl. Bur. Stds., Boulder, CO, (1977-79).
Appointed 1979. Research on laser spectroscopy of molecular ions, plasma dynamics, surface-plasma interactions, and metal clusters. Teaching in physical chemistry.
Some significant publications:
Gudemann, C. S.; Saykally, R. J. *Ann. Rev. Phys. Chem.* **1984**, *35*, 387. "Velocity Modulation Infrared Laser Spectroscopy of Molecular Ions."
Saykally, R. J. *Chem. Britain* **1985**, Feb. issue. "Laser Magnetic Resonance Rotational Spectroscopy."
Begemann, M. H.; Saykally, R. J. *J. Chem. Phys.* **1985**, *82*, 3570. "A Study of the Structure and Dynamics of the Hydronium Ion by High-Resolution Infrared Laser Spectroscopy, I. The υ_3 Band of $H_3^{16}O^+$."
Owrutsky, J. C.; Rosenbaum, N. H.; Tack, L. M.; Saykally, R. J. *J. Chem. Phys.* **1985**, *83*, 5338. "The Vibration-Rotation Spectrum of the Hydroxide Anion (OH-)."

Schaefer, (Henry) Frederick, III (b. 8 Jun 1944)
B.S. 1966, MIT.
Ph.D. 1969, Stanford, with Harris on "Configuration Interaction Wave Functions and the Properties of Atoms and Diatomic Molecules."

Appointed 1969. Research on quantum mechanics and molecular electronic structure, theoretical methods for the description of correlation effects, the prediction of molecular properties, the structures of excited electronic states, and chemisorption. Teaching in physical chemistry and general chemistry.
On faculty of University of Texas, Austin, 1979-80.
Some significant publications:
Schaefer, H. F. "The Electronic Structure of Atoms and Molecules: A Survey of Rigorous Quantum Mechanical Results"; Addison-Wesley: Reading, MA, 1972.
Schaefer, H. F. *Ann. Rev. Phys. Chem.* **1976**, *27*, 261. "Molecular Electronic Structure Theory."
Schaefer, H. F., Ed. "Modern Theoretical Chemistry"; Plenum: New York, 1977; Vols. 3 and 4,
Schaefer, H. F. "Quantum Chemistry: The Development of Ab Initio Methods in Molecular Electronic Structure Theory"; Clarendon Press: Oxford, 1984.

Schutz, Philip William (23 Aug 1908 - 7 Mar 1947)
B.S. 1929; M.S. 1931, Washington Univ., St. Louis.
Ph.D. 1933, UC Berkeley, with Latimer on "The Entropies of Aqueous Ions with Special Reference to Oxalate, Chlorate and Mercurous Ions."
Appointed 1933. Resigned to join Shell Oil Co., Martinez, Calif. (1934-35). Research Assoc. to G. N. Lewis (1935-37). On staff of State Coll. Washington, Pullman (1937-40); Columbia (1940-46).
Returned to UC Berkeley as professor, 1946.
Research on ionic entropies, the properties of deuterated compounds, equilibria in binary liquid systems, and dielectric heating. Teaching in chemical engineering.
Some significant publications:
Latimer, W. M.; Hicks, J. F. G., Jr.; Schutz, P. W. *J. Chem. Phys.* **1934**, *2*, 82. "A Summary of the Entropies of Aqueous Ions."
Lewis, G. N.; Schutz, P. W. *J. Am. Chem. Soc.* **1934**, *56*, 493. "Some Properties of Pure Deutacetic Acid."
Redlich, O.; Schutz, P. W. *J. Am. Chem. Soc.* **1944**, *66*, 1007. "On the Thermodynamics of Azeotropic Solutions. I. Shift of Equilibrium in Binary Systems."
McMahon, E. K.; Schutz, P. W. *Ind. Eng. Chem.* **1946**, *38*, 179. "The Dielectric Heating of Granular Materials. Aluminum and Silicon Oxides."

Seaborg, Glenn Theodore (b. 19 Apr 1912)
A.B. 1934, UCLA.
Ph.D. 1937, UC Berkeley, with Gibson on "The Interaction of Fast Neutrons with Lead."
Research Asst., UC Berkeley (1937-39).
Appointed 1939. Worked on Manhattan Project 1942-46. Chairman AEC

1961-71. Research on the discovery of new transuranium isotopes, the chemistry of the actinides, and heavy ion reactions.
Some significant publications:
Seaborg, G. T. "The Transuranium Elements"; Yale Univ. Press: New Haven, 1958.
Seaborg, G. T., Ed. "The Transuranium Elements - Products of Modern Alchemy"; Dowden, Hutchinson, Ross: Stroudsberg, PA, 1978.
Seaborg, G. T.; Loveland, W., Eds. "Nuclear Chemistry"; Hutchinson, Ross: Stroudsberg, PA 1982.
Katz, J. J.; Seaborg, G. T.; Morss, L., Eds. "Chemistry of the Actinide Elements," 2nd ed.; Wiley: New York, 1986.

Sharwood, William John (1867-?)
Associate 1887, Roy. School of Mines, London.
Ph.D. 1903, UC Berkeley, on "A Study of the Double Salts of Zinc with Potassium and with Sodium."
Appointed 1892.
Montana Mining Co., Maryville, MT (1898-1904). Returned to UC Berkeley, 1904-05. Left in 1905 to become Chemist and Asst. Metallurgist, Homestake Mining Co., Lead, SD.
Some significant publications:
Sharwood, W. J. "Outline of a Short Course in Qualitative Chemical Analysis Arranged for Students in the Colleges of Science of the University of California"; Students' Cooperative Assn.: Berkeley, 1894, 1898.
Sharwood, W. J. *J. Am. Chem. Soc.* 1897, *19*, 400. "Notes on the Estimation of Cyanogen by Silver Nitrate, Using Potassium Iodide and Ammonia as Indicators."
Sharwood, W. J. *J. Am. Chem. Soc.* 1903, *25*, 570. "A Study of the Double Cyanides of Zinc with Potassium and with Sodium."
Fulton, C. H.; Sharwood, W. J. "A Manual of Fire Assaying"; McGraw-Hill: New York, 1929.

Shen, Mitchel Ming-Chi (1 Sep 1938 - 7 Aug 1979)
B.S. 1959, St. Francis College
M.A. 1962; Ph.D. 1963, Princeton, with Tobolsky on "The Viscoelastic Properties of Hydrogen Bonding and Preswollen Polymer Networks."
Postdoctoral Fellow, Princeton (1964); on staff of North American Rockwell Science Center (1965-69).
Appointed 1969. Research on polymer viscoelasticity, polymerization in gaseous plasmas, and mechanical and dielectric relaxation in polymers. Teaching in chemical engineering.
Some significant publications:
Wu, C. K.; Shen, M. *J. Macromol. Sci. Part B: Phys.* 1973, *B7*, 559. "Pressure Effects on the Vibrational Spectra of Amorphous Polystyrene. II. Grueneisen Parameters."
Shen, M. In "Science and Technology of Rubber," Eirich and Roland,

Eds.; Academic Press: New York, 1978; Chapter 4. "The Molecular and Phenomenological Basis of Rubberlike Elasticity."
Hashimoto, T.; Fujimura, M.; Saijo, K.; Kawai, H.; Diamant, J.; Shen, M. *Adv. Chem. Ser.*, 1979, *176*, 257. "Strain-Induced Plastic-to-Rubber Transition of a SBS Block Copolymer and Its Blend with PS."
Shen, M.; Bell, A. T. *Adv. Chem. Ser.* 1979, *108*, 1. "A Review of Recent Advances in Plasma Polymerization."

Shirley, David Arthur (b. 30 Mar 1934)
B.S. 1955, Maine.
Ph.D. 1959, UC Berkeley, with Giauque on "The Heat Capacities and Entropies of Iodine and Lithium Chloride from 15 to 325 Degrees Kelvin."
Lecturer, UC Berkeley (1959-60).
Appointed 1960. Research on nuclear alignment, Moessbauer spectroscopy, synchrotron radiation, electron spectroscopy, and surface science. Teaching in physical chemistry.
Some significant publications:
Shirley, D. A. *Phys. Rev.* 1961, *124*, 354. "Interpretation of the Isomeric Chemical Shifts in Au[197]."
Fadley, C. S.; Shirley, D. A.; Freeman, A. J.; Bagus, P. S.; Mallow, J. V. *Phys. Rev. Lett.* 1969, *23*, 1397. "Multiplet Splitting of Core-Electron Binding Energies in Transition-Metal Ions."
Shirley, D. A. *Chem. Phys. Lett.* 1972, *16*, 220. "The Effect of Atomic and Extra-Atomic Relaxation on Atomic Binding Energies."
Barton, J. J.; Bahr, C. C.; Hussain, Z.; Robey, S. W.; Tobin, J. G.; Klebanoff, L. E.; Shirley, D. A. *Phys. Rev. Lett.* 1983, *51*, 272. "Direct Surface Structure Determination with Photoelectron Diffraction."

Somorjai, Gabor Arpad (b. 4 May 1935)
B.S. 1956, Univ. of Tech. Sci., Budapest.
Ph.D. 1960, UC Berkeley, with Powell on "Small Angle X-ray Scattering of Catalyzed Particles."
Research staff, IBM, Yorktown Heights (1960-64).
Appointed 1964. Research on structure of clean crystal surfaces, catalytic reactions on single crystal surfaces, and reactions of excited state molecules. Teaching in physical chemistry.
Some significant publications:
Somorjai, G. A. "Chemistry in Two Dimensions: Surfaces"; Cornell Univ. Press: Ithaca, NY, 1981.
Somorjai, G. A.; Davis, S. M.; Zaera, F. *J. Catal.* 1982, *77*, 439. "The Reactivity and Composition of Strongly Adsorbed Carbonaceous Deposits on Platinum. Model of the Working Hydrocarbon Conversion Catalyst."
Somorjai, G. A. *Chem. Soc. Rev.* 1984, *13*, 321. "Molecular Ingredients of Heterogeneous Catalysis."
Somorjai, G. A. *Science* 1985, *227*, 902. "Surface Science and Catalysis."

Soong, David Syhlih (b. 22 Aug 1951)
B.S. 1973, Taiwan.
M.S. 1977; Ph.D. 1978, UC Berkeley, with Shen on "Viscoelastic Properties of Bulk Polymers."
Postdoctoral, Lawrence Berkeley Lab. (1978-79).
Appointed 1979. Research on polymer rheology and viscoelasticity, polymerization reaction engineering, membrane technology, and polymer applications in microelectronics and microsensors. Teaching in chemical engineering.
Some significant publications:
Chiu, W. Y.; Carratt, G. M.; Soong, D. S. *Macromol.* **1983**, *16*, 348. "A Molecular Model for the Gel Effect in Free-Radical Polymerization."
Tsai, A. T.; Soong, D. S. *J. Rheol.* **1985**, *29*, 1. "Measurement of Fast Transient and Steady State Responses of Viscoelastic Fluids with a Sliding Cylinder Rheometer Executing Coaxial Displacements."
Soong, D. S. *SPIE Proc.* **1985**, *539*, 2. "Dissolution Kinetics of E-Beam Resists."
Caneba, G. T.; Soong, D. S. *Macromol.* **1985**, *18*, 2538, 2545. "Polymer Membrane Formation through the Thermal Inversion Process, I. Experimental Study of Membrane Structure Formation, II. Mathematical Modeling of Membrane Structure Formation."

Stewart, (Thomas) Dale (14 Aug 1890 - 6 Feb 1958)
B.S. 1913; M.S. 1914; Ph.D. 1916, UC Berkeley with Tolman on "The Electromotive Force Produced by the Acceleration of Metals."
Research Assoc., Chicago (1916-17).
Appointed 1918. Research on acid-base equilibria of organic nitrogen compounds, mechanisms and kinetics of halogenation reactions, aldehydebisulfite reactions, reactions of amines with halides, and alkylation of olefins. Teaching in organic chemistry. Retired 1957.
Some significant publications:
Stewart, T. D.; Aston, J. G. *J. Am. Chem. Soc.* **1926**, *48*, 1642. "The Base Strength of Alpha-Alkoxyl Amines. The Effect of Oxygen on the Basicity of Amines."
Stewart, T. D.; Donnally, L. H. *J. Am. Chem. Soc.* **1932**, *54*, 2333. "The Aldehyde Bisulfite Compounds. I. The Rate of Dissociation of Benzaldehyde Sodium Bisulfite as measured by its First Order Reaction with Iodine."
Stewart, T. D.; Weidenbaum, B. *J. Am. Chem. Soc.* **1935**, *57*, 2036. "The Reaction Between Ethylene and Chlorine in the Presence of Chlorine Acceptors. The Photochlorination of Ethylene."
Stewart, T. D.; Harman, D. *J. Am. Chem. Soc.* **1946**, *68*, 1135. "The Exchange of Hydrogen and Tritium Ions During Alkylation Catalyzed by Tritium Sulfuric Acid."

Stillman, John Maxson (14 Apr 1852 - 13 Dec 1923)
B.S. 1874; Ph.D. 1885, UC Berkeley, on studies of certain resins and the

ethereal oil of the California bay tree.
Appointed 1876. Research on analytical and biochemistry.
Resigned in 1882 to join sugar company; in 1891 became head of Chem.
Dept., Stanford.
Some significant publications:
Stillman, J. M. *Am. J. Sci., Ser. 3* 1879, *18*, 57. "Bernardinite: a New
Mineral Resin from San Bernardino County, California."
Stillman, J. M. *Am. Chem. J.* 1880, *2*, 38. "Ethereal Oil of California
Bay Tree."
Stillman, J. M. "Theophrastus Bombastus von Hohenheim called
Paracelsus"; Open Court: Chicago, 1920.
Stillman, J. M. "The Story of Early Chemistry"; Appleton: New York,
1924.

Strauss, Herbert Leopold (b. 26 Mar 1936)
B.A. 1957; M.A. 1958; Ph.D. 1960, Columbia, with Fraenkel on "Studies of
Paramagnetic Resonance Spectra of Some negative Ions in Solution."
Fellow, Oxford (1960-61).
Appointed 1961. Research on vibrational spectroscopy, large-amplitude
molecular motion, phase transitions of liquids, solids and biological
assemblies. Teaching in physical chemistry.
Visiting Prof., Indian Inst. Technology, Kampur (1968-69).
Some significant publications:
Strauss, H. L. "Quantum Mechanics: An Introduction"; Prentice-Hall:
Englewood Cliffs, NJ, 1968.
Strauss, H. L. *Ann. Rev. Phys. Chem.* 1983, *34*, 301. "Pseudorotation: A
Large Amplitude Molecular Motion."
Strauss, H. L. *J. Mol. Struct.* 1985, *126*, 177. "The Dynamics of
Rotational Isomerism in Crystals as Studied by Vibrational Spectroscopy."
MacPhail, R. A.; Strauss, H. L. *J. Chem. Phys.* 1985, *82*, 1156. "Can
the Bloch Equations Describe the Vibrational Spectra of a Rotating
Molecule?"

Street, Kenneth, Jr. (b. 30 Jan 1920)
B.A. 1943; Ph.D. 1949, UC Berkeley, with Seaborg on "Isotopes of
Americium and Curium."
Appointed 1949. Department Head, Associate Director, Deputy Director,
Livermore Radiation Laboratory (1952-59).
Returned to Chem. Dept. 1959. Research in molecular beam electric-
resonance spectroscopy, nuclear chemistry, and nuclear reactions.
Teaching in physical and nuclear chemistry.
Resigned in 1974 to rejoin the Lawrence Livermore Laboratory.
Some significant publications:
Thompson, S. G.; Street, K.; Giorso, A.; Seaborg, G. T. *Phys. Rev.* 1950,
80, 790. "The New Element Californium (Atomic Number 98)."
Street, K., Jr.; Thompson, S. G.; Seaborg, G. T. *J. Am. Chem. Soc.* 1950,

72, 4832. "Chemical Properties of Californium."
Perlman, I.; Street, K., Jr. In NNES, PPR; McGraw-Hill: New York, 1954; Vol. 14A, Chap. 14. "The Actinide Elements."
Hollowell, C. D.; Hebert, A. J.; Street, K., Jr. *J. Chem. Phys.* 1964, *41*, 3540. "Radio-frequency and Microwave Spectra of NaF by the Molecular-Beam Electric-Resonance Method."

Streitwieser, Andrew, Jr. (b. 23 Jun 1927)
A.B. 1949; M.S. 1950; Ph.D. 1952, Columbia, with Doering on "A Stereochemical Study of the Solvolysis of Hydrogen-2,4-Dimethylhexyl-4-Phthalate."
AEC Postdoctoral Fellow, MIT (1951-52).
Appointed 1952. Research on displacement reactions, hydrogen-deuterium asymmetry, reaction mechanisms, isotope effects, MO theory, carbon acidity, structure-reactivity relationships, and organolanthanide and organoactinide chemistry. Teaching in organic chemistry.
Some significant publications:
Streitwieser, A., Jr. *Chem. Revs.* 1956, *56*, 571. "Solvolytic Displacement Reactions at Saturated Carbon Atoms."
Streitwieser, A., Jr. "Molecular Orbital Theory for Organic Chemists," Wiley: New York, 1961.
Streitwieser, A., Jr.; Mueller-Westerhoff, U. *J. Am. Chem. Soc.* 1968, *90*, 7364. "Bis-(Cyclooctatetraenyl)uranium (Uranocene). A New Class of Sandwich Complexes That Utilize Atomic f Orbitals."
Streitwieser, A., Jr. *Acc. Chem. Res.* 1984, *10*, 353. "Carbanion Ion Pairs and Triplets."

Templeton, David Henry (b. 2 Mar 1920)
B.S. 1941, Louisiana Polytechnic Inst.
M.A. 1943, Texas.
Ph.D. 1947, UC Berkeley, with Perlman on "Artificial Radioactive Isotopes of Polonium, Bismuth, and Lead."
Appointed 1947. Research on nuclear transmutations, methods of x-ray crystallography, structures of complex salts, salt hydrates, and molecular crystals, x-ray dichroism, and anomolous scattering of x-rays. Teaching in physical chemistry.
Some significant publications:
Douthett, E. M.; Templeton, D. H. *Phys. Rev.* 1954, *94*, 128. "The Ranges of Fragments from High-Energy Fission of Uranium."
Templeton, D. H. *Acta Cryst.* 1955, *8*, 842. "X-ray Dispersion Effects in Crystal-Structure Determinations."
Zalkin, A.; Forrester, J. D.; Templeton, D. H. *J. Chem. Phys.* 1963, *39*, 2881. "Crystal Structure of Cerium Magnesium Nitrate Hydrate."
Templeton, D. H.; Templeton, L. K. *Acta Cryst.* 1985, *A41*, 133. "Tensor X-ray Optical Properties of the Bromate Ion."

Tinoco, Ignacio, Jr. (b. 22 Nov 1930)
B.S. 1951, New Mexico.
Ph.D. 1954, Wisconsin, with Ferry on "Some Physical Chemical Studies of Fibrinogen."
Postdoctoral Fellow, Yale (1954-56).
Appointed 1956. Research on structures and functions of nucleic acids, NMR, circular dichroism, and differential scattering of circularly polarized light. Teaching in physical chemistry.
Some significant publications:
DeVoe, H.; Tinoco, I., Jr. *J. Mol. Biol.* 1962, *4*, 500. "The Stability of Helical Polynucleotides: Base Contributions."
Tinoco, I., Jr. *Adv. Chem. Phys.* 1962, *4*, 113. "Theoretical Aspects of Optical Activity. Part Two: Polymers."
Tinoco, I., Jr.; Borer, P. N.; Dengler, B.; Levine, M. D.; Uhlenbeck, O. C.; Crothers, D. M.; Gralla, J. *Nature New Biol.* 1973, *246*, 40. "Improved Estimation of Secondary Structure in Ribonucleic Acids."
Hall, K.; Cruz, P.; Tinoco, I., Jr.; Jovin, T. M.; van de Sande, J. H. *Nature* 1984, *311*, 584. "Z-RNA--A Left-Handed RNA Double Helix."

Tobias, Charles William (b. 2 Nov 1920)
Dipl. Ch.E. 1942; Ph.D. 1946, Univ. Tech. Sci. Budapest, with Nary-Szabo on "Crystal Structure of Boron Prepared by Thermal Dissociation."
Appointed 1947. Research on mass transport and current distribution in electrode systems, the study of boundary layers, porous electrodes, electromachining, electrolytic gas evolution, and electrode processes in nonaqueous media. Teaching in chemical engineering.
Some significant publications:
Eisenberg, M.; Tobias, C. W.; Wilke, C. R. *J. Electrochem. Soc.* 1954, *101*, 306. "Ionic Mass Transfer and Concentration Polarization at Rotating Electrodes."
Newman, J.; Tobias, C. W. *J. Electrochem. Soc.* 1962, *109*, 1183. "Theoretical Analysis of Current Distribution in Porous Electrodes."
McLarnon, F. R.; Muller, R. H.; Tobias, C. W. *I&EC Fund.* 1979, *18*, 97. "Interferometric Study of Forced Convection Mass Transfer Boundary Layers in Laminar Channel Flow."
Foller, P. C.; Tobias, C. W. *J. Electrochem. Soc.* 1982, *129*, 567. "Mechanism of the Disintegration of Lead Dioxide Anodes under Conditions of Ozone Evolution in Strong Acid Electrolytes."

Tolman, Richard Chace (4 Mar 1881 - 5 Sep 1948)
B.S.Ch.E. 1903; Ph.D. 1910, MIT, with Noyes on "The Electromotive Force Produced in Solutions by Centrifugal Action."
On staff at MIT (1910-12).
Appointed 1912. Research on statistical mechanics, relativity, chemical physics, thermodynamics, kinetics, and cosmology. Teaching in physical chemistry and chemical physics.
Resigned 1916 to join faculty at Illinois. Govt. service for 4 years. In

1922 joined faculty at Cal Tech.
Some significant publications:
Tolman, R. C. *Proc. Am. Acad. Arts Sci.* 1910, *46*, 109. "The Electromotive Force Produced in Solutions by Centrifugal Action."
Tolman, R. C.; Stewart, T. D. *Phys. Rev.* 1917, *9*, 164. "The Mass of the Electric Carrier in Copper, Silver and Aluminum."
Tolman, R. C.; Ramsperger, H. C.; Nordberg, M. E. *Proc. Nat. Acad. Sci.* 1929, *15*, 453. "The Rate of Decomposition of Nitrogen Pentoxide at Moderately Low Pressures."
Tolman, R. C.; Brass, P. D. *J. Am. Chem. Soc.* 1932, *54*, 1003. "Experiments on the Rate of Dissociation of Nitrogen Tetroxide."

Vermeulen, Theodore (7 May 1916 - 20 Oct 1983)
B.S. 1936; M.S. 1937, Cal. Tech.
Ph.D. 1942, UCLA, with Coryell on "The Structural Chemistry of Ferri-Hemoglobin and Color Theory."
Shell Development Co., 1942-47.
Appointed 1947. Research on ion exchange, adsorption and electrochromatography, chemical kinetics, mass transfer, and homogeneous catalytic hydrogenation. Teaching in chemical engineering.
Some significant publications:
Hiester, N. K.; Vermeulen, T. *Chem. Eng. Prog.* 1952, *48*, 505. "Saturation Performance of Ion-Exchange and Adsorption Columns."
Vermeulen, T,; Miyauchi, T. *I&EC Fund.* 1963, *2*, 113. "Longitudinal Dispersion in Two-Phase Continuous-Flow Operations."
Vermeulen, T.; LeVan, M. D.; Hiester, N. K.; Klein, G. In "Chemical Engineers' Handbook," 5th ed.; Perry, R. H.; Chilton, C. H., Eds.; McGraw-Hill: New York, 1973. "Adsorption and Ion Exchange."
Grens, E. A.; Hershkowitz, F.; Holten, R. R.; Shinn, J. H.; Vermeulen, T. *I&EC Proc. Des. and Devel.* 1980, *19*, 396. "Coal Liquefaction Catalysis by Zinc Chloride Melts in Combination with Organic Solvents."

Vollhardt, (Kurt) Peter Christian (b. 7 Mar 1946)
Vor dipl. 1967, Munich.
Ph.D. 1972, Univ. Coll. London, with Garratt on "The Synthesis of Polycyclic Nonbenzenoid Aromatic Hydrocarbons Containing Four-Membered Rings."
Appointed 1974. Research on synthetic and mechanistic organic and organometallic chemistry. Teaching in organic chemistry.
Some significant publications:
Vollhardt, K. P. C. *Pure Appl. Chem.* 1980, *52*, 1645. "Physical, Chemical, and Some Biological Properties of Strained Ring Hydrocarbons."
Dower, W. V.; Vollhardt, K. P. C. *J. Am. Chem. Soc.* 1982, *104*, 6878. "Mechanism of the Isomerization of 1,5,9-Cyclododecatriyne to Hexaradialene: 1,2:3,4:5,6-Tricyclobutabenzene is Not an Intermediate."
Allison, N. T.; Fritch, J. R.; Vollhardt, K. P. C.; Walborsky, E. C. *J. Am. Chem. Soc.* 1983, *105*, 1384. "An Unprecedented Bis(carbyne) Cluster

Rearrangement Involving Simultaneous Coupling and Decoupling of Carbyne Fragments: A New Homogeneous Model for C-C Bond Forming and Bond Breaking on Surfaces."
Vollhardt, K. P. C. *Angew. Chem., Intl. Ed. Engl.* 1984, *23*, 539.
"Cobalt-Mediated [2+2+2]Cycloadditions: A Maturing Synthetic Strategy."

Wang, James C. (b. 18 Nov 1936)
B.S. 1959, Engineering, Natl. Taiwan Univ.
M.A. 1961, Chemistry, South Dakota
Ph.D. 1964, Missouri, with Bauman on "Calorimetric Studies on Some Metal Ion Complexes."
Research Fellow, Cal Tech (1964-66).
Appointed 1966. Research on physico-chemical studies of DNA and its interactions with other molecules. Teaching in physical chemistry and biophysical chemistry.
Resigned 1977 to join Dept. of Biochemistry, Harvard.
Some significant publications:
Wang, J. C. *J. Mol. Biol.* 1971, *55*, 523. "Interaction Between DNA and an Escherichia coli Protein I."
Wang, J. C. *J. Mol. Biol.* 1974, *89*, 783. "The Degree of Unwinding of the DNA Helix by Ethidium. I. Titration of Twisted PM2 DNA Molecules in Alkaline Cesium Chloride Density Gradients."
Wang, J. C. *Proc. Natl. Acad. Sci.* 1979, *76*, 200. "Helical Repeat of DNA in Solution."
Wang, J. C. *Ann. Rev. Biochem.* 1985, *54*, 665. "DNA Topoisomerases."

Wilke, Charles Robert (b. 4 Feb 1917)
B.S. 1940, Dayton
M.S. 1942, Wash. State.
Ph.D. 1944, Wisconsin, with Hougen on "Falling Rate Period in Through-Circulation Drying."
Union Oil Co., Rodeo, Calif. (1944-45); State College of Washington faculty, (1945-46).
Appointed 1946. Research on biochemical engineering, enzymatic processes, gas-liquid mass transfer. Teaching in chemical engineering.
Some significant publications:
Crawford, J. W.; Wilke, C. R. *Chem. Eng. Prog.* 1951, *47*, 423. "Limiting Flows in Packed Extraction Columns. Correlation for Large Packings."
Wilke, C. R.; Chang, P. *AIChE J.* 1955, *1*, 264. "Correlation of Diffusion Coefficients in Dilute Solutions."
Wasan, D. T.; Wilke, C. R. *AIChE J.* 1968, *14*, 577. "Role of the Concentration Level of the Nondiffusing Species in Turbulent Gas Phase Mass Transfer at Ordinary Mass Transfer Rates."
Wilke, C. R.; Yang, R. D.; Sciamanna, A. F.; Freitas, R. P. *Biotech. Bioeng.* 1981, *23*, 163. "Raw Materials Evaluation and Process Development Studies for Conversion of Biomass to Sugars and Ethanol."

Williams, (Ford) Campbell (b. 28 Dec 1921)
B.A.Sc. 1943; M.A.Sc. 1946, U.B.C.
Ph.D. 1948, Iowa, with Osborne on "Vapor Liquid Equilibria of Fatty Acids and Vacuum Distillation."
Appointed 1948. Research on vapor-liquid equilibria, catalytic cracking and catalytic reforming. Teaching in chemical engineering. Resigned in 1952 to become consultant, Conselho Nacional de Petroleo, Brasil (1952-55), Petroleo Brasileiro, Brasil (1955-67). In 1967 founded NATRON - Consultoria e Projetos S.A., Brasil.
Some significant publications:
Otsuki, H.; Williams, F. C. *Chem. Eng. Prog. Symp. Series No. 6* 1953, *49*, 55. "Effect of Pressure on Vapor-Liquid Equilibria for the System Ethyl Alcohol-Water."
Williams, F. C. and staff "Optimization of Catalytic Cracking Process to Maximize Production of LPG," Internal publication of Petrobras - Petroleo: Brasileiro S.A.
Williams, F. C. "Double Absorption Sulfuric Acid Process," "Sulfur from Gypsum," and "Utilization of Babassu Coconut as Energy Source"; Internal reports and patents for NATRON.

Williams, Michael Charles (b. 11 Jun 1937)
B.S. 1959; M.S. 1960; Ph.D. 1964, Wisconsin, with Bird on "Normal Stresses and Related Viscoelastic Phenomena in Polymer Solutions."
Postdoctoral Fellow, Oregon (1964-65).
Appointed 1965. Research on rheology and viscoelasticity, polymer dynamics, fluid mechanics, block copolymers, and hemolysis. Teaching in chemical engineering.
Some significant publications:
Bazua, E. R.; Williams, M. C. *J. Polym. Sci. (Physics)* 1974, *12*, 825. "Rheological Properties of Internal Viscosity Models with Stress Symmetry."
Offerman, R. D.; Williams, M. C. *Biomat., Med. Dev., Art. Organs* 1979, *7*, 393. "Observations on Shear-Induced Hemolysis."
Diamant, J.; Soong, D. S.; Williams, M. C. *Contemp. Topics Polym. Sci.* 1984, *4*, 599. "Modeling the Viscoelastic Behavior of SBS Block Copolymer Solids."
Wildemuth, C. R.; Williams, M. C. *Rheol. Acta* 1985, *24*, 75. "A New Interpretation of Viscosity and Yield Stress in Dense Slurries: Coal and Other Irregular Particles."

Zimm, Bruno Hasbrouck (b. 31 Oct. 1920)
A.B. 1941; M.S. 1943; Ph.D. 1944, Columbia, with Mayer on "Vapor Pressures, Heats of Vaporization, and Entropies of Some Alkali Halides."
Research Assistant, Columbia University (1944); Research Associate and Instructor, Polytechnic Institute of Brooklyn, (1944-46).
Appointed 1946. On leave, 1950-52. Resigned 1952 to join General Electric Co., Appointed to Chemistry Dept., UC San Diego, 1960.

Research on experimental and theoretical aspects of macromolecules, especially DNA, statistical mechanics and Brownian-motion theory of macromolecular solutions, relaxation processes in macromolecules. Teaching in physical and biophysical chemistry.

Some significant publications:

Zimm, B. H. *J. Chem. Phys.* **1948**, *16*, 1099. "Apparatus and Methods for Measurement and Interpretation of the Angular Variation of Light Scattering; Preliminary Results on Polystyrene Solutions."

Zimm, B. H. *J. Chem. Phys.* **1956**, *24*, 269. "Dynamics of Polymer Molecules in Dilute Solution: Viscoelasticity, Flow Birefringence and Dielectric Loss."

Kavenoff, R.; Zimm, B. H. *Chromosoma* **1973**, *41*, 1. "Chromosome-Sized DNA Molecules from Drosophila."

Lumpkin, O. J.; Dejardin, P.; Zimm, B. H. *Biopolymers* **1985**, *24*, 1573. "Theory of Gel Electrophoresis of DNA."

APPENDIX 3

Chronological List of Untenured Faculty

Name	First date of appointment or first date in catalog*	Date of departure or last date in catalog in Chem.	Highest rank
Jackson, Abraham Wendell, Jr.	1874	1875	Prof. of Mineralogy
Barbour, W. A.	1875	1875	Instructor
Hilgard, Eugene W.	1875	1878	Prof. Ag., Bot.
Slate, Frederick, Jr.	1875	1876	Professor of Physics
Harding, August	1876	1880	Ass't. in Chem.
Willcutt, George B.	1880	1881	Ass't. Inst.
Jaffa, Myer E.	1881	1881	Ass't. in Ag. Chem.
Wenzell, William T.	1881	1882	Prof., Coll. of Pharm.
Atkinson, John W.	1882	1883	Ass't. Inst.
Gehring, George	1882	1882	Ass't. in Chem.
Morse, Frederick W.	1882	1882	Ass't. in Ag. Chem.
Gehring, Gustave	1883	1883	Ass't. in Chem.
Dunn, James P. H.	1884	1887	Ass't. in Chem.
Sommer, Adolph	1884	1885	Ass't. in Chem.
Harding, Mr.	1887	1887	
Chestnut, V. K.	1891	1894	Ass't. in Chem.
Lengfeld, Felix	1891	1891	Instructor
Wright, F. W.	1891	1891	Ass't. in Chem.
Norris, R. S.	1893	1899	Instructor
Lenher, Victor	1894	1895	Ass't. in Chem.
Rogers, R. R.	1897	1898	Ass't. in Chem.
Allen, I. C.	1898	1900	Ass't. in Chem.
Beattie, G. W.	1898	1900	Reader in Chem.
Pearce, J. A.	1898	1900	Ass't. in Chem.
Daniels, R. C.	1899	1899	Ass't. in Chem.
Christensen, J. C.	1900	1900	Ass't. in Chem.
Collins, R. H.	1900	1900	Ass't. in Chem.
Cuttle, Frederick	1900	1900	Ass't. in Chem.
Laist, Frederick	1900	1900	Ass't. in Chem.
Myers, H. C.	1900	1900	Hon. Fellow in Chem.

Gilman, Charles	1901	1901	Ass't. in Chem.
McCharles, Carl H.	1909	1909	Ass't. in Chem.
Pracy, Edna	1909	1910	Ass't. in Chem.
Alderman, Ernest S.	1910	1910	Ass't. in Chem.
Brauer, Oscar L.	1910	1910	Ass't. in Chem.
Edwards, Vance P.	1910	1910	Ass't. in Chem.
Riddell, Wallace C.	1910	1910	Ass't. in Chem.
Welch, Harry V.	1910	1910	Ass't. in Chem.
Winkler, J. F.	1910	1910	Ass't. in Chem.
Burke, Charles E.	1912	1914	Instructor
Morse, Harry Wheeler	1912	1912	Lecturer
Rosenstein, Ludwig	1912	1931	Lecturer
Adams, Elliot Quincy	1915	1916	Instructor
Argo, William Lind	1915	1918	Instructor
Schmidt, Carl Louis August	1918	1946	Prof. Biochem.
Newton, Roy F.	1920	1922	Instructor
Noyes, William A., Jr.	1921	1921	Instructor
Taylor, Nelson Woodsworth	1923	1924	Instructor
Cornish, Robert Edwin	1926	1926	Instructor
Lachman, Arthur	1926	1926	Lecturer
Livingston, Robert Stanley	1926	1926	Instructor
Ramsperger, Herman Carl	1926	1926	Instructor
Frank, Henry Sorg	1927	1944	Instructor
Frank, James	1927	1927	Lecturer (visiting)
Freed, Simon	1927	1929	Instructor
Liebhafsky, Herman Alfred	1929	1933	Instructor
Stern, Otto	1929	1929	Lecturer (visiting)
Fowler, Robert Dudley	1930	1935	Instructor
Kramers, H. A.	1930	1930	Lecturer (visiting)
Pauling, Linus C.	1930	1932	Lecturer
Badger, Richard M.	1931	1931	Visiting
Koenig, Frederick Otto	1931	1931	Instructor
Simon, Franz	1931	1931	Visiting
Fowler, Ralph H.	1932	1932	Lecturer (visiting)
Makower, Benjamin	1932	1932	Instructor
Meads, Philip Francis	1932	1932	Instructor
Spedding, Frank Harold	1932	1932	Instructor
Yabroff, David Louis	1932	1932	Instructor
Young, Herbert Alexander	1932	1932	Instructor
MacDougall, Duncan Peck	1933	1933	Instructor

Nixon, Alan Charles	1934	1936	Instructor
Nutting, George Cook	1934	1936	Instructor
Long, Franklin Asbury	1935	1936	Instructor
Voge, Hervey Harper	1936	1937	Instructor
Meehan, Edward Joseph	1937	1938	Instructor
Grahame, David Caldwell	1938	1938	Instructor (visiting)
Halford, Ralph Stanley	1939	1939	Instructor
Kennedy, Joseph William	1939	1945	Instructor
Lingane, James J.	1939	1941	Instructor
Barieau, Robert E.	1940	1940	Instructor
Taube, Henry	1940	1941	Instructor
Keefer, Raymond Marsh**	1941	-	Prof., UC Davis
Benson, A. A.	1942	1942	Instructor
Campbell, J. Arthur	1942	1943	Instructor
Heldman, Julius	1943	1944	Instructor
Leitz, Mr.	1943	1943	Instructor
Norris, Thomas Hughes	1943	1945	Instructor
Wilmarth, Wayne Keith	1943	1945	Instructor
Andrews, Lawrence J.**	1945	1958	Prof., UC Davis
English, Spofford G.	1946	1946	Ass't. Prof.
Koch, Charles W.	1946	1974	Lecturer
Petersen, Jack W.	1946	1947	Instructor
Shand, William, Jr.	1946	1946	Instructor
Cronyn, Marshall W.	1947	1951	Ass't. Prof.
Simonson, Thomas R.	1947	1948	Instructor
Guffy, Joseph C.	1948	1950	Instructor
McClure, Donald S.	1948	1956	Ass't. Prof.
Walsh, Arthur D.	1950	1950	Visiting Prof., fall
Hugus, Z Zimmerman	1951	1951	Instructor
Alder, Berni J.	1952	1953	Instructor
Dickey, Frank H.	1952	1952	Instructor
Gordon, Kenneth F.	1952	1952	Inst. in Ch. Eng.
Hollander, Jack M.	1952	1952	Instructor
Scott, Earle S.	1952	1954	Instructor
Allen, Charles F.	1953	1953	Instructor
Bradley, Dan F.	1953	1954	Instructor
McGarvey, Bruce R.	1953	1956	Ass't. Prof.
Hadley, Wayne B.	1954	1955	Instructor

Payot, Pierre H.	1954	1955	Instructor
Bergman, Elliott	1955	1955	Instructor
Freeman, Mark P.	1956	1957	Instructor
Harris, Frank E., Jr.	1956	1957	Ass't. Prof.
Wassmundt, Frederick W.	1956	1957	Instructor
Urry, Wilbert H.	1957	1957	Lecturer
Bassham, James A.	1958	1958	Lecturer
James, Philip N.	1958	1958	Instructor
Oldershaw, Charles F.	1958	1976	Lecturer
Sherwood, Thomas K.	1958	1975	Visiting Prof.
Thomas, Thomas Darrah	1958	1959	Ass't. Prof.
Thompson, Warren E.	1958	1958	Instructor
Applequist, Jon B.	1959	1960	Ass't. Prof.
Blue, E. Morse	1959	-	Lecturer
Chilton, Thomas H.	1959	1959	Regents' Prof.
Schaefer, John P.	1959	1959	Ass't. Prof.
Sederholm, Charles H.	1959	1964	Ass't. Prof.
Wilde, Douglass J.	1959	1959	Instructor
Wiley, George P.	1959	1959	Ass't. Prof.
Agosta, William C.	1960	1960	Ass't. Prof.
Barltrop, John A.	1960	1960	Visiting Prof.
Eaton, Philip E.	1960	1962	Ass't. Prof.
Fackler, John P.	1960	1961	Ass't. Prof.
Howe, John A.	1960	1961	Ass't. Prof.
Prosen, Edward J.	1960	1960	Lecturer
Brieger, Gottfried	1961	1962	Ass't. Prof.
Johnson, Alan W.	1961	1961	Visiting Prof., s1962
Rickborn, Bruce F.	1961	1961	Ass't. Prof.
Wenhert, Ernest	1961	1961	Visiting Prof., f1961
Williamson, Stanley M.	1961	1964	Ass't. Prof.
Harvey, Bernard G.	1962	1972	Lecturer
Redlich, Otto	1962	1978	Lecturer
Griffin, Rodger, W.	1963	1964	Ass't. Prof.
Kirtman, Bernard G.	1963	1964	Ass't. Prof.
Scherer, Kirby V.	1963	1966	Ass't. Prof.
Wallace, Richard A.	1963	1964	Ass't. Prof.
Wrathall, Jay W.	1963	1963	Ass't. Prof.
Ayen, Richard J.	1964	1967	Ass't. Prof.
Burlingame, Alma L.	1964	1967	Ass't. Prof.
Jorgenson, Margaret J.	1964	1968	Lecturer
Interrante, Leonard V.	1965	1966	Ass't. Prof.
Herm, Ronald R.	1966	1973	Ass't. Prof.
Pigford, Robert	1966	1975	Visiting Prof.
Sternlicht, Himan	1966	1969	Ass't. Prof.

Timms, Peter L.	1966	1969	Ass't. Prof.
Klein, Gerhard	1967	1985	Lecturer
Muller, Rolf H.	1967	-	Lecturer
Frosch, R. Peter	1968	1970	Ass't. Prof.
Kenyon, George L.	1968	1972	Ass't. Prof.
McClain, W. Martin	1968	1972	Ass't. Prof.
Browne, Douglas T.	1969	1973	Ass't. Prof.
Fuerstenau, Douglas, W.	1969	-	Prof. of Metall.
Heck, Henry d'A.	1969	1972	Ass't. Prof.
Struble, Gordon L.	1969	1970	Ass't. Prof.
Donaghey, Lee F.	1970	1976	Ass't. Prof.
Morgan, Arthur I., Jr.	1970	1984	Lecturer
Gelbart, William M.	1972	1975	Ass't. Prof.
Modrich, Paul L.	1974	1975	Ass't. Prof.
Smart, James C.	1974	1977	Ass't. Prof.
Washburn, William N.	1974	1979	Ass't. Prof.
Michaels, Alan S.	1975	1979	Lecturer
Valle-Riestra, J. Frank	1975	-	Lecturer
Winn, John S.	1976	1982	Ass't. Prof.
Hill, Craig L.	1977	1981	Ass't. Prof.
Brown, Steven D.	1979	1980	Ass't. Prof.
Clark, John H.	1979	1984	Ass't. Prof.
Pratt, Lawrence R.	1979	1984	Ass't. Prof.
Quady, David E.	1979	-	Lecturer
Aalbersberg, William G. L.	1980	1981	Lecturer
Falick, Arnold M.	1980	1984	Lecturer
Faltens, Marjorie O.	1980	-	Lecturer
Heinemann, Heinz	1980	-	Lecturer
Kayalar, Celik	1980	1986	Ass't. Prof.
McGahey, Lawrence F.	1980	1983	Lecturer
Reiff, Edward K.	1980	1981	Ass't. Prof.
Richardson, Thomas J.	1980	1981	Lecturer
Schroeder, Albert H.	1980	1980	Ass't. Prof.
Armentrout, Peter B.	1981	1987	Ass't. Prof.
Benjamin, William J.	1981	1983	Lecturer
Davis, Hubert G.	1981	1984	Lecturer
Maier, Wilhelm F.	1981	1987	Ass't. Prof.
Majda, Marcin M.	1982	-	Ass't. Prof.
Sullivan, Ralda R.	1982	-	Lecturer
Haymet, Anthony D. J.	1983	-	Ass't. Prof.
Hillard, Russell L.	1983	1983	Lecturer
Michaels, James N.	1983	-	Ass't. Prof.

Reimer, Jeffrey A.	1983	-	Ass't. Prof.
Stacy, Angelica M.	1983	-	Ass't. Prof.
Myers, Arlyn M.	1984	-	Lecturer
Schultz, Peter G.	1984	-	Ass't. Prof.
Vorhis, Fred H.	1984	-	Lecturer
Armstrong, William H.	1985	-	Ass't. Prof.
Graves, David B.	1985	-	Ass't. Prof.
Gulari, Erdogan	1985	1985	Visit. Assoc. Prof.
Joseph, Babu	1985	1985	Visit. Assoc. Prof.
Pedersen, Steven F.	1985	-	Ass't. Prof.
Wemmer, David E.	1985	-	Ass't. Prof.
Whaley, K. Birgitta	1985	-	Ass't. Prof.
Clark, Douglas S.	1986	-	Ass't. Prof.
Neumark, Daniel M.	1986	-	Ass't. Prof.
Porter, John D.	1986	-	Ass't. Prof.
Theodorou, Doros N.	1986	-	Ass't. Prof.

* Before 1912, in any rank. In 1912 and thereafter, as lecturer or higher rank (summer school ignored).
** Faculty of other departments or campuses who were Ph.D. thesis advisors of students in the Berkeley College of Chemistry.

APPENDIX 4

Alphabetical List of Untenured Faculty
with date of first appointment

Aalbersberg, William G. L.	1980	Falick, Arnold M.	1980
Adams, Elliot Quincy	1915	Faltens, Marjorie O.	1980
Agosta, William C.	1960	Fowler, Ralph H.	1932
Alder, Berni J.	1952	Fowler, Robert Dudley	1930
Alderman, Ernest S.	1910	Frank, Henry Sorg	1927
Allen, Charles F.	1953	Frank, James	1927
Allen, I. C.	1898	Freed, Simon	1927
Andrews, Lawrence J.	1945	Freeman, Mark P.	1956
Applequist, Jon B.	1959	Frosch, R. Peter	1968
Argo, William Lind	1915	Fuerstenau, Douglas W.	1969
Armentrout, Peter B.	1982	Gehring, George	1882
Armstrong, William H.	1985	Gehring, Gustave	1883
Atkinson, John W.	1882	Gelbart, William M.	1972
Ayen, Richard J.	1964	Gilman, Charles	1901
Badger, Richard M.	1931	Gordon, Kenneth F.	1952
Barbour, W. A.	1875	Grahame, David Caldwell	1938
Barieau, Robert E.	1940	Graves, David B.	1985
Barltrop, John A.	1960	Rodger, W.	1963
Bassham, James A.	1958	Guffy, Joseph C.	1948
Beattie, G. W.	1898	Gulari, Erdogan	1985
Benjamin, William J.	1981	Hadley, Wayne B.	1954
Benson, A. A.	1942	Halford, Ralph Stanley	1939
Bergman, Elliott	1955	Harding, August	1876
Blue, E. Morse	1959	Harding, Mr.	1887
Bradley, Dan F.	1953	Harris, Frank E., Jr.	1956
Brauer, Oscar L.	1910	Harvey, Bernard G.	1962
Brieger, Gottfried	1961	Haymet, Anthony D. J.	1983
Brown, Steven D.	1979	Heck, Henry d'A.	1969
Browne, Douglas T.	1969	Heinemann, Heinz	1980
Burke, Charles E.	1912	Heldman, Julius	1943
Burlingame, Alma L.	1964	Herm, Ronald R.	1966
Campbell, J. Arthur	1942	Hilgard, Eugene W.	1875
Chestnut, V. K.	1891	Hill, Craig L.	1977
Chilton, Thomas H.	1959	Hillard, Russell L.	1983
Christensen, J. C.	1900	Hollander, Jack M.	1952
Clark, Douglas S.	1986	Howe, John A.	1960
Clark, John H.	1979	Hugus, Z Zimmerman	1951
Collins, R. H.	1900	Interrante, Leonard V.	1965
Cornish, Robert Edwin	1926	Jackson, Abraham W., Jr.	1874
Cronyn, Marshall W.	1947	Jaffa, Myer E.	1881
Cuttle, Frederick	1900	James, Philip N.	1958
Daniels, R. C.	1899	Johnson, Alan W.	1961
Davis, Hubert G.	1981	Jorgenson, Margaret J.	1964
Dickey, Frank H.	1952	Joseph, Babu	1985
Donaghey, Lee F.	1970	Kayalar, Celik	1980
Dunn, James P. H.	1884	Keefer, Raymond Marsh	1941
Eaton, Philip E.	1960	Kennedy, Joseph William	1939
Edwards, Vance P.	1910	Kenyon, George L.	1968
English, Spofford G.	1946	Kirtman, Bernard G.	1963
Fackler, John P.	1960	Klein, Gerhard	1967

Koch, Charles W.	1946	Reimer, Jeffrey A.	1983
Koenig, Frederick Otto	1931	Richardson, Thomas J.	1980
Kramers, H. A.	1930	Rickborn, Bruce F.	1961
Lachman, Arthur	1926	Riddell, Wallace C.	1910
Laist, Frederick	1900	Rogers, R. R.	1897
Leitz, Mr.	1943	Rosenstein, Ludwig	1912
Lengfeld, Felix	1891	Schaefer, John P.	1959
Lenher, Victor	1894	Scherer, Kirby V.	1963
Liebhafsky, Herman A.	1929	Schmidt, Carl Louis August	1918
Lingane, James J.	1939	Schroeder, Albert H.	1980
Livingston, Robert Stanley	1926	Schultz, Peter G.	1984
Long, Franklin Asbury	1935	Scott, Earle S.	1952
MacDougall, Duncan Peck	1933	Sederholm, Charles H.	1959
Maier, Wilhelm F.	1982	Shand, William, Jr.	1946
Majda, Marcin M.	1982	Sherwood, Thomas K.	1958
Makower, Benjamin	1932	Simon, Franz	1931
McCharles, Carl H.	1909	Simonson, Thomas R.	1947
McClain, W. Martin	1968	Slate, F., Jr.	1875
McClure, Donald S.	1948	Smart, James C.	1974
McGahey, Lawrence F.	1980	Sommer, Adolph	1884
McGarvey, Bruce R.	1953	Spedding, Frank Harold	1932
Meads, Philip Francis	1932	Stacy, Angelica M.	1983
Meehan, Edward Joseph	1937	Stern, Otto	1929
Michaels, Alan S.	1975	Sternlicht, Himan	1966
Michaels, James N.	1983	Struble, Gordon L.	1969
Modrich, Paul L.	1974	Sullivan, Ralda R.	1982
Morgan, Arthur I., Jr.	1970	Taube, Henry	1940
Morse, Frederick W.	1882	Taylor, Nelson Woodsworth	1923
Morse, Harry Wheeler	1912	Theodorou, Doros N.	1986
Muller, Rolf H.	1967	Thomas, Thomas Darrah	1958
Myers, Arlyn M.	1984	Thompson, Warren E.	1958
Myers, H. C.	1900	Timms, Peter L.	1966
Neumark, Daniel M.	1986	Urry, Wilbert H.	1957
Newton, Roy F.	1920	Valle-Riestra, J. Frank	1975
Nixon, Alan Charles	1934	Voge, Hervey Harper	1936
Norris, R. S.	1893	Vorhis, Fred H.	1984
Norris, Thomas Hughes	1943	Wallace, Richard A.	1963
Nutting, George Cook	1934	Walsh, Arthur D.	1950
Oldershaw, Charles F.	1958	Washburn, William N.	1974
Painter, Edgar P.	1946	Wassmundt, Frederick W.	1956
Pauling, Linus C.	1930	Welch, Harry V.	1910
Payot, Pierre H.	1954	Wemmer, David E.	1985
Pearce, J. A.	1898	Wenhert, Ernest	1961
Pedersen, Steven F.	1985	Wenzell, William T.	1881
Petersen, Jack W.	1946	Whaley, K. Birgitta	1986
Pigford, Robert	1966	Wilde, Douglass J.	1959
Polissar, Milton Joseph	1929	Wiley, George P.	1959
Porter, John B.	1986	Willcutt, George B.	1880
Pracy, Edna	1909	Williamson, Stanley M.	1961
Pratt, Lawrence R.	1979	Wilmarth, Wayne Keith	1943
Prosen, Edward J.	1960	Winkler, J. F.	1910
Quady, David E.	1979	Winn, John S.	1976
Ramsperger, Herman Carl	1926	Wrathall, Jay W.	1963
Redlich, Otto	1962	Wright, F. W.	1891
Reiff, Edward K.	1980	Yabroff, David Louis	1932
		Young, Herbert Alexander	1932

APPENDIX 5

Deans of the College of Chemistry

Irving Stringham	1886-1896
Willard B. Rising	1896-1901
Edmond C. O'Neill	1901-1912
Gilbert N. Lewis	1912-1918
Edmond C. O'Neill	1918-1919
Gilbert N. Lewis	1919-1923
Charles W. Porter	July-Dec. 1923
Gilbert N. Lewis	1924-1941
Wendell M. Latimer	1941-1949
Joel H. Hildebrand	1949-1951
Kenneth S. Pitzer	1951-1955
James Cason	1955-1956
Kenneth S. Pitzer	1956-1960
Robert E. Connick	1960-1965
Richard E. Powell	Aug. 1965-Jan. 1966
Harold S. Johnston	1966-1970
David H. Templeton	1970-1975
Norman E. Phillips	1975-Nov. 1977
Charles W. Tobias	Dec. 1977-July 1978
Norman E. Phillips	Aug. 1978-1981
C. Judson King	1981-

APPENDIX 6

Chairmen of the Department of Chemistry
(Dean same as Chairman until 1941)

Joel H. Hildebrand	1941-1943
William C. Bray	1943-1945
Wendell M. Latimer	1945-1949
Joel H. Hildebrand	1949-1951
Kenneth S. Pitzer	1951-1955
James Cason	1955-1956
Isadore Perlman	1957-1958
Robert E. Connick	1958-1959
Rollie J. Myers	Feb.-Sept. 1959
Robert E. Connick	1959-1960
Richard E. Powell	1960-1966
George C. Pimentel	1966-1968
Bruce H. Mahan	1968-1971
David A. Shirley	1971-1975
Joseph Cerny	1975-1979
Ignacio Tinoco, Jr.	1979-1982
C. Bradley Moore	1982-1986
Clayton H. Heathcock	1986-

APPENDIX **7**

Chairmen of the Department of Chemical Engineering

W. Schutz (Division Head)	Fall 1946
Theodore Vermeulen (Division Head)	1947-1953
Charles W. Wilke (Division Head)	1953-1956
Charles W. Wilke	1957-1959
Leroy A. Bromley	Jan.-June 1960
Charles W. Wilke	1960-1963
Donald N. Hanson	1963-1966
Charles W. Tobias	1966-1972
C. Judson King	1972-1981
Alexis T. Bell	1981-

APPENDIX **8**

Nobel Prize Winners from the College of Chemistry

1934: Harold C. Urey (Berkeley Ph.D. 1923), for his discovery of heavy hydrogen.

1949: William F. Giauque (Berkeley Ph.D. 1922), for his contributions in the field of chemical thermodynamics, particularly concerning the behavior of substances at extremely low temperatures.

1951: Glenn T. Seaborg (Berkeley Ph.D. 1937), for his discoveries (with McMillan) in the chemistry of the transuranium elements.

1960: Willard F. Libby (Berkeley Ph.D. 1933), for his method to use carbon-14 for age determination in archaeology, geology, geophysics, and other branches of science.

1961: Melvin Calvin (UC Berkeley staff appointment 1937), for his research on the carbon dioxide assimilation in plants.

1983: Henry Taube (Berkeley Ph.D. 1940), for his studies of the mechanisms of oxidation-reduction reactions of metal complexes.

1986: Dudley R. Herschbach (UC Berkeley staff 1959-1963) and Yuan T. Lee (Berkeley Ph.D. 1965), for their studies, with John C. Polanyi, of elementary chemical reactions.

Name Index

**Gives chapter numbers (e.g. 5), appendix numbers (e.g. A2),
and references to photograph collection (ph).
Bold-faced** chapter numbers refer to relatively extensive discussions.

McCullom, Art, ph
McCullom, Ross, ph
McGahey, Lawrence F., A3, A4
McGarvey, Bruce R., A3, A4
McGee, John M., ph
McKenzie, Kenneth R., 34
McMillan, Edwin M., 35, ph
McNamara, Robert, ph
Meads, Philip F., A3, A4
Meehan, Edward J., A3, A4
Meitner, L., 35
Mendeleev, Dmitri I., 4
Merrill, Robert P., A1, A2
Michaels, Alan S., A3, A4
Michaels, James N., A3, A4
Miller, Harry E., 5, 6
Miller, William H., A1, A2
Miller, W. Lash, 18
Mitchell, John T., 40
Modrich, Paul L., A3, A4
Moe, Lawrence H., 5, ph
Moeller, Therald, 48
Mohr, Arthur, ph
Moore, C. Bradley, A1, A2
Moore, E. H., 40
Moore, T. S., 25
Moretto, Luciano G., A1, A2
Morgan, Arthur I., Jr., A3, A4
Morgan, William C., 10, A1, A2
Morse, Frederick W., A3, A4
Morse, Harry W., 10, A3, A4
Mueller, W., 27
Muetterties, Earl L., A1, A2
Muller, Rolf H., 43, A3, A4
Mulliken, Robert S., 31
Myers, Arlyn M. A3, A4
Myers, H. C. A3, A4
Myers, Rollie J. A1, A2
Nernst, Walther H., 9, 15, 21
Neumark, Daniel M., A3, A4
Newman, John S., 43
Newton, Amos, 3
Newton, Roy F., A3, A4
Nixon, Alan C., A3, A4
Noble, Haymond W., 24
Norris, R. S., A3, A4
Norris, Thomas H., 27, A3, A4
Northrop, John H., ph
Noyce, Donald S., 46, A1, A2, ph
Noyes, Arthur A., 9, 13, 18, 19, 33, ph
Noyes, William A., Jr., 11, A3, A4
Nutting, Bill, ph
Nutting, George C., 35, A3, A4
Nutting, Willard H., 24
O'Brien, Morrough, 47

O'Konski, Chester T., 49, A1, A2, ph
Olander, Donald R., A1, A2
Oldershaw, Charles F., A3, A4
Olson, Axel R., 27, 35, 38, 46, A1, A2, ph
O'Neill, Edmond C., 4, 5, 6, 8, 10, 14, 17, 24, 47, A1, A2, ph
O'Neill, Mrs. E., 5
Oppenheimer, J. Robert, 3, 28, 35
Orlemann, Edwin F., 3, A1, A2, ph
Ostwald, Wilhelm, 6, 7, 9, 15, 18
Painter, Edgar P., A3, A4
Pardee, George C., 5
Parker, Earl, 47
Parks, George S., 20, ph
Partington, J. R., 15
Pauling, Linus, 13, 31, 33, 38, A3, A4
Pavliger, Joseph, 24
Payot, Pierre H., A3, A4
Pearce, J. A., A3, A4
Pedersen, Steven F., A3, A4
Perlman, Isadore, 35, A1, A2
Petersen, Eugene E., A1, A2
Petersen, Jack W., A3, A4
Phillips, Norman E., A1, A2
Phipps, Thomas E., 20
Pierce, Orestes, 5
Pigford, Robert, A3, A4
Pimentel, George C., 26, 45, 50, A1, A2, ph
Pimentel, Jose, 45
Pines, Alexander, A1, A2
Pitzer, Kenneth S., 3, 14, 16, 23, 27, 28, 33, 42, 45, 48, A1, A2, ph
Pitzer, Russell, 33
Plato, 21
Pokrovskii, G. I., 29
Polanyi, Michael, 32
Polissar, Milton J., A3, A4
Pontecorvo, Bruno, 35
Porter, C. Walter, 14, 37, 46, A1, A2, ph
Porter, John D., A3, A4
Powell, Mary Ellen, 40
Powell, Richard E., 13, 40, 48, A1, A2, ph
Pracy, Edna, A3, A4
Pratt, Lawrence R., A3, A4
Prausnitz, John M. A1, A2
Prosen, Edward J., A3, A4
Quady, David E., A3, A4
Radke, Clayton J., A1, A2
Ramage, William D., ph